MW00610048

Following in Their Footsteps

Following in Their Footsteps
Land Surveying in North Carolina

OTIS A. JONES, PLS, DEDICATES HIS EFFORTS
AS EXECUTIVE COORDINATOR TO THE PAST AND
FUTURE SURVEYORS OF NORTH CAROLINA.

CHAPEL HILL
PRESS, INC.

Photographs—North Carolina beach, ocean, and Pilot Mountain on back cover of book contributed by Natalie J. Foster. Used by permission. Western North Carolina mountain picture on back cover contributed by Kenneth T. Mills, PLS. Used by permission. Joint artwork for book cover sketched by Elinor C. Jones and Hal T. Siler. Enhanced and finished by Elinor C. Jones. Used by permission.

ISBN 1-59715-006-1
Library of Congress Catalog Number 2005929034

Printed in the United States of America
First Printing

NCSS MAPS, INC.
(NCSS Museum Of Archives And Preservation Of Surveying, Inc.)

2005 Board of Directors

NORTH CAROLINA SOCIETY OF SURVEYORS, INC
(NCSS, INC.)

2005 Officers/Directors

2005 Chapter Presidents/Directors

Albemarle Chapter	Katherine C. Marchello
Cape Fear Chapter	Ronald D. Plummer
Central Chapter	Ronald O. Graham
Coastal Chapter	Donald C. Clements, Jr.
Dan River Basin Chapter	Jesse B. Irving
Eastern Chapter	E. Hugh Clark
Foothills Chapter	James D. Ferguson
Guilford Chapter	Brent R. Weston
Johnston County Chapter	T. Lester Stancil
Lake Norman Chapter	Jimmy N. Faires
Mecklenburg Chapter	Charles J. Dunbar
Nantahala Chapter	Clark S. Lipkin
NE Piedmont Chapter	Nathan R. Hymiller, Jr.
Northwest Chapter	C. Neal Bare
NW Triangle Chapter	Steve F. Yuhasz
Piedmont Chapter	T. David Whitt
Southeastern Chapter	Hoyt S. Bradshaw
Southwest Piedmont Chapter	E. Steve Smith
Triangle Chapter	Donald T. Israel
Western Chapter	Kristopher M. Kline
Yadkin Valley Chapter	James E. Craddock

Historical Committee

Otis A. Jones, Co-Chairman
Robert M. Stalls, Co-Chairman
Michael D. Barr
Martin L. Barrow
Richard P. Bennett
Michael J. Evans
R. Larry Greene
Joseph F. Hardee
Kenneth T. Mills
John Y. Phelps
John Randall Puckett
Sherrill Styers
Jonathan C. Witherspoon

Contents

Foreword ix

Acknowledgements xi

Introduction xiii

PART I—COMPASS/TRANSIT ERA—EARLY YEARS

Land Grants and the North Carolina Surveyor ~ Walter G. Robillard, Esq., RLS 3

Compass/Transit Era ~ Otis A. Jones, PLS 17

Wachovia, North Carolina: The First Settlements ~ Silvio A. Bedini 23

William Churton (fl. 1749–1767) North Carolina Cartographer ~ Silvio A. Bedini 27

John Vogler 1783–1881: Silversmith of Old Salem ~ Silvio A. Bedini 33

PART II—TRANSIT/ELECTRONIC ERA—TRANSITION PERIOD

Surveying on the Outer Banks ~ Henry C. Cuningham, PLS 39

Outdoor Hardships Retold by a Surveyor's Son ~ Hank Cuningham 41

Moving a Piece of History: Robotics and common sense kept the Cape Hatteras Lighthouse standing tall ~ Vicki Speed 43

Redrawing the Line ~ Lieca N. Brown 51

Surveying In the Coastal Plains ~ John W. Parker, PLS 59

Trying To Remember: (Stories, Humor, etc) ~ A. J. "Jimmie" Davis III, PLS 77

Early North Carolina Land Surveyors ~ A.J. "Jimmie" Davis III, PLS 83

175 Years of Surveying and Engineering: 1812–1987—The Ward and Blanchard Family Heritage ~ Tom Boney 93

Surveying in the Piedmont ~ Michael J. Evans, Sr., PLS 101

Surveying in the Mountains of Western North Carolina ~ Kenneth T. Mills, PLS 109

Woodrow Wilson Bedsaul (1912–1998)—Compass-Transit-Electronic Surveyor in North Carolina in the Twentieth Century ~ Carolyn M. Huskey 119

North Carolina Society of Surveyors, Inc. History—Part I (1939–1956)—The Early Years ~ Otis A. Jones, PLS 129

North Carolina Society of Surveyors, Inc. History—Part II (1957–2003) ~ R. Larry Greene, PLS 147

North Carolina Society of Surveyors Institute: "A Unique Experience in Continuing Education" ~ Otis A. Jones 177

North Carolina Board of Examiners for Engineers and Surveyors—Years 1921–2003 ~ R. Larry Greene, PLS 181

PART III—ELECTRONIC AGE OF SURVEYING

North Carolina Geodetic Survey: The First State Agency Dedicated to the Coordinate System ~ Gary W. Thompson, PLS 197

North Carolina Geodetic Survey—1959–2002 ~ Curt D. Johnson, NCGS Technicial Writer 201

The Electronic Age of Surveying ~ C. Phil Wagoner, PLS 219

Permissions 241

APPENDIX

In Honor of Those Who Brought Us to the Future—NCSS Past Presidents 244

NCSS Institute Graduates 1989–2004 245

NCSS Surveyor of the Year 247

North Carolina Society of Surveyors Membership Listing 248

North Carolina Board of Examiners for Engineers and Surveyors Member Listing 250

North Carolina State Board of Registration for Professional Engineers and Land Surveyors: 1960 Manual of Practice for Land Surveying (Historical Document) 251

Foreword

In 1998, the directors of the North Carolina Society of Surveyors Museum of Archives and Preservation of Surveying, Inc. (NCSS Maps, Inc.) embarked on a goal to put together a book on the History of Land Surveying in North Carolina. Otis A. Jones, president of NCSS Maps, Inc., was asked to head this project. Under his leadership, a number of land surveyors throughout the state volunteered to help with deciding on and organizing of the topics, writing the chapters, and designing the layout of the book.

The idea was not to present a book full of technical information or to cover every second of time from the first land grant to today. Nor, for that matter, was the idea to cover every surveyor of importance who ever worked and lived, or who still works and lives in North Carolina. The idea was to take a snapshot look at different areas, different equipment, different types of surveying, different organizations affecting surveying, and some of the individuals who contributed to the profession.

We wanted to produce a book you could sit back and relax with, a book in which you could read some interesting facts about the history of surveying and how it is interwoven with the growth of North Carolina. Land surveyors who used the equipment or researched the use of the older instruments added their information. The people who crawled through the swamps and climbed over the mountains wrote about the difficulties in surveying the land. Surveyors who developed different types and techniques of surveys and kept up with the rapid changes of technology also added to the book.

Following in Their Footsteps: Land Surveying in North Carolina is not a learned treatise just for surveyors only. It is a wonderful source of information for the general public. Set aside some time to enjoy this wonderful adventure.

Kenneth T. Mills, PLS
Past Chairman
Member Board of Directors
NCSS Maps, Inc.

Acknowledgements

This book is possible only because so many writers wanted to share their expertise and knowledge of surveying with you, the reader. Others gave their permission to use previous writings of interest, and still others made sure that this book became a reality.

The following individuals were willing to take the time and effort to write of their experiences while enlightening you in the profession of land surveying and, occasionally, providing a good laugh. Our heartfelt thanks go to the following writers for their participation: William W. Blanchard, PE, PLS; Henry C. Cuningham, PLS; Hank Cuningham; A. J. "Jimmie" Davis, III, PLS; Michael J. Evans, Sr., PLS; R. Larry Greene, PLS; Carolyn M. Huskey; Curt D. Johnson, PLS; Otis A. Jones, PLS; Kenneth T. Mills, PLS; John W. Parker, PLS; Walter G. Robillard, RLS, Esq.; Gary W. Thompson, PLS; and C. Phil Wagoner, PLS.

Others gave permission and approval to use previous writings and photographs in our publication: Lieca N. Brown, editor, *POB (Point of Beginning) Magazine;* Donna E. Kelly, administrator, Historical Publications section of the North Carolina Department of Cultural Resources; John G. Wolfe, III, attorney, Wolfe and Associates; Tom Boney, Jr., publisher of *The Alamance News;* Jennifer B. Bower, manager of Photographic Resources, Old Salem, Inc.; Angie Crum, administrator, *Professional Surveyor Magazine (GITC America);* Andrew Ritter of the North Carolina Board of Examiners for Engineers and Surveyors; Ann Hawks, daughter of Woodrow Wilson Bedsaul; Natalie J. Foster; Hal T. Siler for assisting with the book cover; Sherrill H. Styers, PLS and Joseph E. Hardee, PLS-PE for reading through the text and giving their valuable opinions.

The friendly and helpful staff of the Chapel Hill Press, Inc. contributed in making this publication a reality and a success.

There were those who contributed in other ways. Darline H. Johnson, past executive director of the North Carolina Society of Surveyors who was instrumental in the launching of this book; Carolyn M. Huskey, who spent many hours on the computer assisting with the organizing of this book; Patti J. Varner, who came to our rescue when the computers crashed; Celia H. Miles, Ph.D. and my wife, Elinor C. Jones, editing; also, Elinor assisted with the writing, the cover, and did the inside artwork, she encouraged and worked with me throughout the process.

A special thanks and gratitude to Milton Denny, PLS, for his sound advice and inspiration.

Heartfelt thanks go to all!

Introduction

The North Carolina Board of Examiners for Engineers and Surveyors 2004 Yearbook defines surveying as:

> "Providing professional services such as consultation, investigation, testimony, evaluation, planning, mapping, assembling, and interpreting reliable scientific measurements and information relative to the location, size, shape, and physical features of the earth, improvements on the earth, the space above the earth, or any part of the earth, whether the gathering of information for the providing of these services is accomplished by conventional ground measurements, by aerial photography, by global positioning via satellites, or by a combination of any of these methods, and the utilization and development of these facts and interpretations into an orderly survey map, plan, report, description, or project."

Surveying is one of the world's oldest and most honored professions. From the ancient Egyptians, Greeks, and Romans, to the discoverers of the New World, to our country's founding fathers and explorers, surveyors have literally led the way throughout history. The professional surveyor, using today's changing technology, will continue to lead as we face the challenges of the twenty-first century.

A progressive North Carolina Board of Registration for Professional Engineers and Land Surveyors (now the Board of Examiners), organized in 1921, and the North Carolina Society of Surveyors, Inc., organized in 1939, worked together to mold our profession into what it is today. Since that time, many surveyors have worked long and hard to build and move our profession into the mainstream to serve the people of our state and to enhance the environment for all.

For the past six years, the NCSS Historical Committee/NCSS Maps, Inc. has diligently worked on three goals: (1) archiving survey maps of deceased and retired surveyors—more than 27,000 maps have been microfilmed and archived in the North Carolina Division of Archives and History, (2) collecting surveying equipment, books, ancient maps, and other artifacts of the profession, and (3) writing this book, *Following in their Footsteps, Land Surveying in North Carolina.*

The archiving of maps has exceeded our wildest dreams and will continue as funds and maps become available. The collection of prized artifacts has moved beyond our expectations and will be placed in the future museum of surveying in Raleigh, North Carolina. To make this book, *Following in their Footsteps, Land Surveying in North Carolina* a reality, many fine surveyors have shared their experiences while surveying in all regions of North Carolina. They have given generously of their time and money. We are proud to present you with a look into surveying in North Carolina.

Otis A. Jones, PLS,
Executive Coordinator

PART I

Compass/Transit Era—Early Years

Land Grants and the North Carolina Surveyor

Walter G. Robillard, Esq., RLS

Very few modern land surveyors ever have an opportunity to retrace all of the lines of an original land grant or even a single line of such a grant. The thrill and the beauty of attempting to step back in time to retrace or find the footsteps or evidence of surveyors who have been dead for perhaps three hundred years should start the adrenaline running through the young modern surveyor. Yet today, even with the advent of new technology, few surveyors realize that from the basis of the title and from descriptions, for the most part, land grants either originated from a sovereign king or from the state of North Carolina. Some surveyors will practice their entire career and not be required either to understand or to locate an original land grant on the ground from original documents.

Today, because the nature of our society is creating smaller and smaller parcels of land on which to build homes, surveyors tend to survey and retrace smaller and smaller parcels. The average surveyor never has had an opportunity to retrace large areas of land. Yet, now and again, a few fortunate individuals will focus their careers on specializing in locating these boundaries of grants that were originally created as early as the 17th century in what was called "The Carolinas."

In examining grants in North Carolina, one will find three specific types of grants as follows:

1. Those made by the king of England to the proprietors that created the exterior boundaries of the original colony.
2. Those made by the king of England or the proprietors after the colony boundaries had been determined.
3. Those made after the War of Independence by the state of North Carolina to individuals and others.

In the early stages of the colonization of America, and especially in the Carolinas, North Carolina and South Carolina were considered a single colony, (a portion of the original Virginia grant by England). Spanish colonists also considered this area to be part of the original grants made to them by the king of Spain.

The Spanish attempted the first colonization as early as 1526, when 500 settlers were brought over from Spain and established a colony at the mouth of the Pee Dee River.

Disease and Indian attacks decimated the colony, and it ultimately was abandoned after a few months. In 1562, a number of French Huguenots settled at Port Royal, but soon returned to France. Then in 1585 and 1587, the British landed two groups of settlers, which ultimately became the "lost colony" of Sir Walter Raleigh. No more attempts were made to colonize the area until 1629.

Since this area was originally considered as a portion of Virginia, the name "Carolina" was not used until 1629 when a grant was made by Charles I to Sir Robert Heath, who failed to foster any settlement of lands in the "New World." Then in 1660, three years after he assumed the throne, Charles II granted the territory of Carolina to eight proprietors.

These proprietors had full and complete authority to govern the colony, but failed to show any propensity to do so. They were incapable of dealing with governing the colony, yet they commenced to grant out large areas of land to friends and others. Dissatisfaction rose to a point where the colonists deposed the governors. One of the main contentions was the confusing terms of land ownership that was granted to them. The proprietors were instructed to have the land divided into rectangular parcels. However, these instructions were disregarded, as a means to quickly convey lands to individuals. Originally, the proprietors were to recognize the degrees of nobility: barons, caciques, and landgraves, with baronies receiving 12,000 acres, caciques receiving 24,000 acres, and landgraves receiving 48,000 acres.

There were other disturbing problems: some lands were described without the benefit of a survey, some were surveyed and the notes and plats were subsequently lost, and some individuals moved onto the land as squatters. A continuing problem, the boundary between North and South Carolina was in dispute, as was the boundary between the two colonies Virginia and Carolina. This boundary was bitterly disputed for over one-hundred years before it was finally resolved in 1728.

For over 50 years, during the proprietors' control, Carolina was administered as one colony, administered alternately from Albemarle and then from Charleston. It was ultimately divided in 1712. The division did little to improve conditions, and the settlers complained about the quitrents that had to be paid. They expelled the agents of the proprietors and petitioned the king to convert the Carolinas into royal colonies. The king consented, but it took eight years to do so. They required the king to liquidate the claims of the proprietors, which he did, and the Carolinas once again became a royal colony.

This one act assured a freer land policy for the settlers, and development progressed, with smaller and smaller tracts, described by metes and bounds. This permitted the colonists to progress from the coastal plain to piedmont areas.

This one fact changed the composition and produced regional distinctions in social conditions, settlement patterns, and land distribution. On the coastal plain where settlement started, large estates, with small holdings of private ownership, were the norm. For the most part, they were along the major rivers and these became the boundaries of the lands conveyed, with large areas omitted that were not "fit for cultivation." In the Piedmont, the pattern of land distribution was quite different. The settlements were mainly small farms of family groups.

As with all of the other colonies, the land ownership was poorly defined, and most parcels were described by metes and bounds surveys, and deeds or grants were executed without attempting to identify or to correlate surveys, boundaries, or previous grants for conflicts.

Then it happened!!! 1776.

With the advent of the cession of hostilities and the Revolutionary War, all lands that had not been granted by the previous kings became the sole and exclusive ownership of the respective colonies. These original grants carried claim of ownership from the Atlantic Ocean to the "South Sea," or the Pacific Ocean. The Treaty of Paris then limited the claim to terminate at the Mississippi River.

The respective states then started a concentrated effort to foster settlements by awarding land grants to these formerly free lands, and in some cases, to lands that had already been granted.

These are the lands that today's surveyor may be asked to locate. In a few instances, a modern surveyor will be asked to identify or retrace the line of a sovereign English grant. However, it will be the state grants that will interest most surveyors. The records for these grants are located in the Department of Archives in Raleigh and are filed under various categories.

Grants may be filed under number, name, entry, watershed, county, and a number of various other categories. Most of the grants that are filed under a specific name are in the name of the male family member. In working in the archives for over ten years, this author found not a single grant made in the name of a female. Many of the grants were made in the following manner.

The state of North Carolina grants to Eligh Howe and Company. After considerable research and consultation with legal counsel, it was determined that this grant was not to a company or a corporation. Rather, this was an antiquated method of conveying to one's heirs.

The descriptions of many of these grants are quite abbreviated, in that they failed to mention the type of corner monument, if any, that was established at the time of the survey. In attempting to retrace and to locate these grants on the ground, a modern surveyor must resort to all forms and types of extrinsic evidence.

If the surveyor is lucky and the grant number is known, the grant can be located by the grant number. However, in many instances, it may not be all that easy, in that dates become critical. Certain information may be lacking on a particular card. In any grant that was made by the state of North Carolina, certain elements must be considered. The majority of grants issued by the state may be identified by a number of elements:

Grant Name
Grant Number
Entry Number
Date
Survey Date

In considering land grants in North Carolina, the practicing surveyor has to consider two elements: one is primarily a legal consideration based on the written record and the second is a survey consideration. First is the determination of the validity of the document that contains the description as described in the written record (the land grant). The second is locating the written record, recovering the land(s) that are described in the written record, and then identifying the lands described in the written record.

In most instances, a surveyor is not involved in the validation of the written title or the written record that reflects the description of the lands that the surveyor may be asked to locate and survey.

The first phase of the surveyor's responsibility is to identify, based on the written record, that unique parcel that must be located.

Addressing the first element may have involved visits to the courthouse in the respective county in which the land is located, as well as a visit to the state archives to research grant data. Many of the county courthouses may have land grant data on record, but to be completely certain as to the exact nature of the grant(s) that may cover the parcel being surveyed, the surveyor should check the records in the State Archives in Raleigh. Even at that office, the visit may take research based on the manner in which the records are maintained, one will have to become accustomed to being a "record detective."

There is absolute certainty that questions of law will have to be addressed in researching the grant records and, in all probability, the results will not be clean-cut for application. As far as the surveyor is concerned, the question will be "Is the grant capable of being retraced on the ground?"

Yet the attorney may have to address legal questions relative to determining, in the case of multiple or even contiguous grants, "which is senior?"

The usual practice for grants was as follows:

> 1. The landowner made an application or entry.
>
> 2. Then a survey was conducted in which lines were run and corners were established. The usual practice was to either mark trees that were in close proximity to the corner, and in many instances, to set posts of local wood for the corner. Where no tree was called for, the usual practice was to call for either a "post" or a "stake." In many instances, when the grant was surveyed, the beginning corner was identified as a tree, and all other corners were identified as stakes. When a single corner was identified as being corner 1 of Grant 628, if a subsequent grant tied into Grant 628, the subsequent grant MAY, or MAY NOT, have called for the Grant 628 corner. If, in reality, the corners are common but the subsequent grant does not call for the common corner, then it becomes a matter of expert testimony to piece the grants together.

Then a survey was conducted to identify the lines and the corners; based on that description, a grant was then made, finalizing the process. Unfortunately, that is the ideal situation, if all went according to the law.

In many instances, we find sequential grants as follows:

	Senior Grant	Junior Grant
Entry Number	2150	2152
Grant Number	628	630
Date of Survey	October 12, 1864	September 17, 1864

If the senior grant is the junior survey, what controls? We accept the fact that a survey that is senior controls a junior survey. Thus the September survey is senior to the October survey, but the October Grant, 628, is senior to the October Grant, 630, which is the senior survey. This works out fine, but in many instances, contiguous grants MAY NOT have been called for. When the lines are surveyed on the ground, an overlap may occur. What controls then? Or even if the grant lines are called for, it is a well-established surveying principle that the junior survey yields to the senior survey, but that is still a legal question that must be addressed by the courts. The surveyor's responsibility is to report the facts and let the courts determine the results.

Situations may be presented, in the case of multiple grants, such as follows:

Grant 628 Entry 2180 Surveyed June 9, 1850 Date of Grant October 17, 1850
Grant 629 Entry 2178 Surveyed June 5, 1850 Date of Grant October 16, 1850
Grant 630 Entry 2181 Surveyed June 11, 1850 Date of Grant October 17, 1850

In this instance, Grant 630 is junior in number and in survey, but senior in patenting. The responsibility of the surveyor is to REPORT THE FACTS and let the attorneys argue the legalities. The presumption is that the grant with the lower number is the senior; that may be so, BUT, what controls if the senior grant is the junior survey? Is the senior survey principle disregarded? Is preference given to the junior survey over the senior survey?

If a grant fails to call for or identify an adjoining or contiguous grant, then the surveyor "gets to play detective."

For instance: Two grants, 640 and 641, fail to call for adjoining grants. They read as follows:

Grant 640 to Elihue Barnes dated November 12, 1869
Grant 641 to Elihue Barnes dated November 14, 1869
Both grants are identified as being in Swain County.
Grant 640 reads as follows:
East 40 poles to a cedar
South 45 poles to a spruce pine
South 34 degrees west 122 poles to a black gum and a birch, etc.
Grant 641 reads as follows:
East 40 poles to a cedar

South 45 poles to a spruce pine
South 34 degrees West 122 poles to a black gum and a birch, etc.

It would be hard to say that Grant 641 is not contiguous to Grant 640 in that specific area. This problem now becomes a matter for the attorney to argue and the surveyor to convince through testimony. A knowledge of probability and statistics is a must.

In retracing old grants, the surveyor must, of necessity, rely on circumstantial evidence in attempting to retrace old boundaries.

In some instances, a surveyor who is given the responsibility of retracing a line of a grant may determine that the lines identified do not meet, that is, there is a gap (a gore) between two grants that has not been granted from the state to an individual. Having retraced over 200 grants within North Carolina, this author ascertained several gaps or gores.

The surveyor will encounter numerous instances where grants have been made to a grantee identified as follows:

"To Elihue Barnes & Company." Under the concept of early English law, this was not a grant to a company as we recognize it today, which would have different implications for legal succession. It has been ascertained that the "& Company" was an old world method of saying "to his heirs."

There are no fixed rules or principles. This situation was addressed in a classic North Carolina decision in 1819. Having to address a situation as to what are the controlling elements in a description contained in a grant, the North Carolina Supreme Court in the decision of Cherry v. Slade's Administrator, from Martin, wrote guidelines to attorneys and surveyors. For further detail research this case.

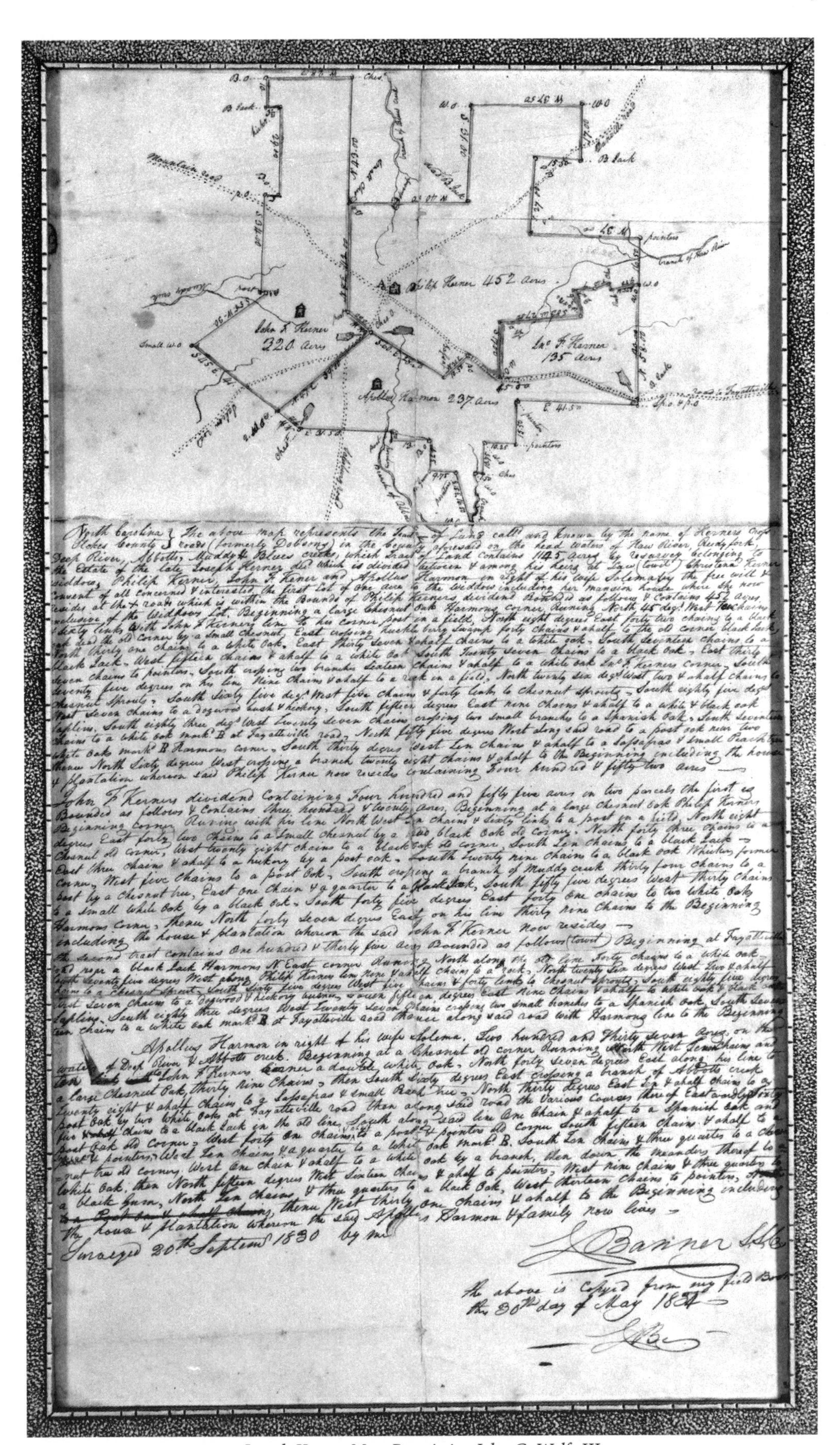

Philip Kerner 452 Acres

John F. Kerner 320 Acres

Jno F. Kerner 135 Acres

Apollus Harmon 237 Acres

North Carolina } The above map represents the Tract of Land call^d and known by the name of Kerners Cross
Stokes County } roads (formerly Dobsons) in the County afforesaid on the head waters of Haw River, Reedy fork, Deep River, Abbotts, Muddy & Blues creeks, which Tract of Land contains 1145 acres by resurvey belonging to the Estate of the late Joseph Kerner dec^d which is divided between & among his heirs at Law (towit) Christena Kerner widdow, Philip Kerner, John F. Kerner and Apollus Harmon in right of his wife Solema by the free will & consent of all concerned & interested the first Lot of one acre to the widdow including her mansion house where she now resides at the + roads which is within the Bounds of Philip Kerners divident Bounded as follows & contains 452 acres exclusive of the widdows Lot. Beginning a large Chesnut Oak Harmons corner, Running North 45 deg^s West [illegible] chains & sixty links with John F. Kerners line to his corner post on a field, North eight degrees East forty two chains to a black oak dead the old corner by a small Chesnut, East crossing huckleberry swamp forty chains & ahalf to the old corner black Jack, North thirty one chains to a White Oak, East thirty seven & ahalf chains to a white oak, South seventeen chains to a black Jack, West fifteen chains & ahalf to a white oak South twenty seven chains to a black oak, East thirty seven chains to pointers, South crossing two branches Sixteen chains & ahalf to a white oak Jno F. Kerners corner, South seventy five degrees on his line Nine chains & ahalf to a rock in a field, North twenty six deg^s West two & ahalf chains to chesnut sprouts, South sixty five deg^s West five chains & forty links to chesnut sprouts, South eighty five deg^s West seven chains to a dogwood bush & hickory, South fifteen degrees East nine chains & ahalf to a white & black oak saplins, South eighty three deg^s West twenty seven chains crossing two small branches to a Spanish Oak, South seventeen chains to a white oak mark^d B at Fayatteville road, North fifty five degrees West along said road to a post oak near two white oaks mark^d B Harmons corner, South thirty degrees West ten chains & ahalf to a Sassafras & small Peach tree thence North sixty degrees West crossing a branch twenty eight chains & ahalf to the Beginning including the house & plantation whereon said Philip Kerner now resides containing Four hundred & fifty two acres —

John F. Kerners divident containing Four hundred and fifty five acres on two parcels the first is Bounded as follows & contains three hundred & twenty acres, Beginning at a large Chesnut Oak Philip Kerners Beginning corner, Runing with his line North West [illegible] chains & sixty links to a post on a field, North eight degrees East forty two chains to a small Chesnut by a dead black Oak old corner, North forty three chains to a Chesnut old corner, West twenty eight chains to a black oak old corner, South ten chains to a black Jack — East three chains & ahalf to a hickory by a post oak. South twenty nine chains to a black oak Whickers former corner, West five chains to a post Oak, South crossing a branch of Muddy creek thirty four chains to a post by a Chesnut tree, East one chain & a quarter to a black Jack, South fifty five degrees West thirty chains to a small White Oak by a black oak. South forty five degrees East forty one chains to two White Oaks Harmons corner, thence North forty seven degrees East on his line thirty nine chains to the Beginning including the house & plantation whereon the said John F. Kerner now resides —

the second tract contains One hundred & Thirty five acres Bounded as follows (towit) Beginning at Fayatteville road near a black Jack Harmons N East corner Running North along the old line Forty chains to a white oak South seventy five degrees West along Philip Kerners line nine & ahalf chains to a rock, North twenty six degrees West two & ahalf down to a Chesnut Sprout, South sixty five degrees West five chains & forty links to chesnut sprouts, South eighty five degrees West seven chains to a dogwood & hickory bushes, South fifteen degrees East nine chains & ahalf to white oak & black oak sapling, South eighty three degrees West twenty seven chains crossing two small branches to a Spanish oak, South seventeen chains to a white oak mark^d B at Fayatteville road thence along said road with Harmons line to the Beginning

Apollus Harmon in right of his wife Solema. Two hundred and Thirty seven acres, on the waters of Deep River & Abbotts creek. Beginning at a Chesnut old corner Running North West seven chains and [illegible] John F. Kerners corner a double white oak, North forty seven degrees East along his line to a large Chesnut Oak, thirty nine chains, then South sixty degrees East crossing a branch of Abbotts creek twenty eight & ahalf chains, to a Sassafras & small Peach tree, North thirty degrees East six & ahalf chains to a post oak by two white oaks at Fayatteville road then along said road the various courses thereof East and [illegible] sixty five chains to a black Jack in the old line, South along said line one chain & ahalf to a Spanish oak and post oak old corner, West forty one chains to a post & pointers old corner South fifteen chains & ahalf to a [illegible] & pointers, West ten chains & a quarter to a white oak mark^d B. South ten chains & three quarters to a chesnut tree old corner, West one chain & ahalf to a white oak by a branch, then down the meanders thereof to a white oak, then North fifteen degrees West sixteen chains & ahalf to pointers, West nine chains & three quarters to a black gum, North ten chains & three quarters to a black Oak, West thirteen chains to pointers, [illegible] ~~[illegible]~~, thence West thirty one chains & ahalf to the Beginning including the house & plantation whereon the said Apollus Harmon & family now lives —

Surveyed 20th Septemb^r 1830 by me

J. Banner [illegible]

The above is Copyed from my field Book the 30th day of May 1834

J. B.

Joseph Kerner Map. Permission John G. Wolfe III

V I R
T E N N E S S E E
S O U T H C A R O L I N A
TO
David Stone and Peter Brown Esqrs
THIS FIRST ACTUAL SURVEY
OF THE
State of North Carolina
Taken by the Subscribers
is respectfully dedicated
By their humble Servants
Jon. Price
John Strother
1808

W. P. Cumming, *North Carolina in Maps* (Raleigh: State Department of Archives and History, 1966), Plate IX.

Pric

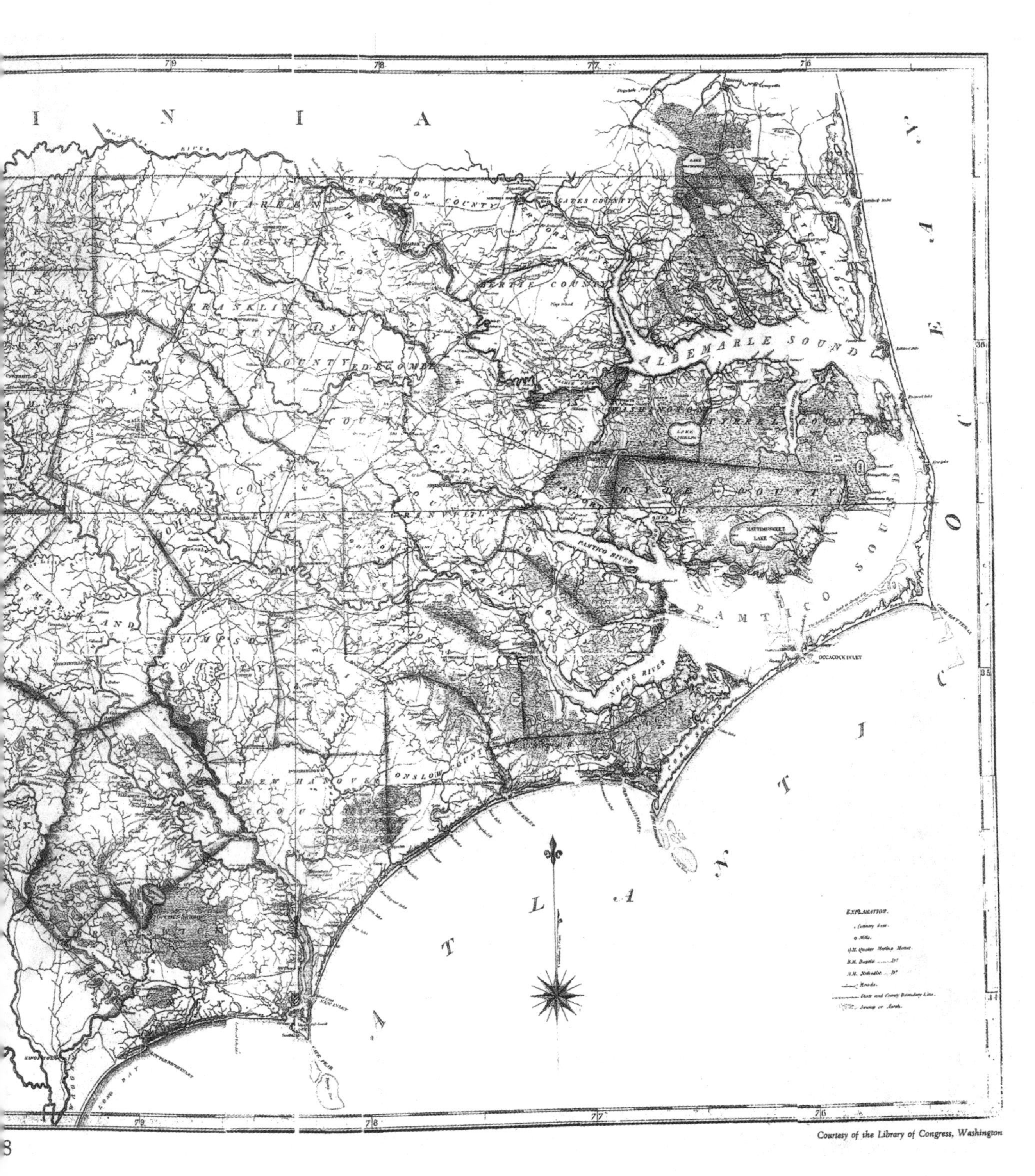

Courtesy of the Library of Congress, Washington

The first actual Survey of the State of North Carolina, Price—Strother, 1808.

[See page xxix]

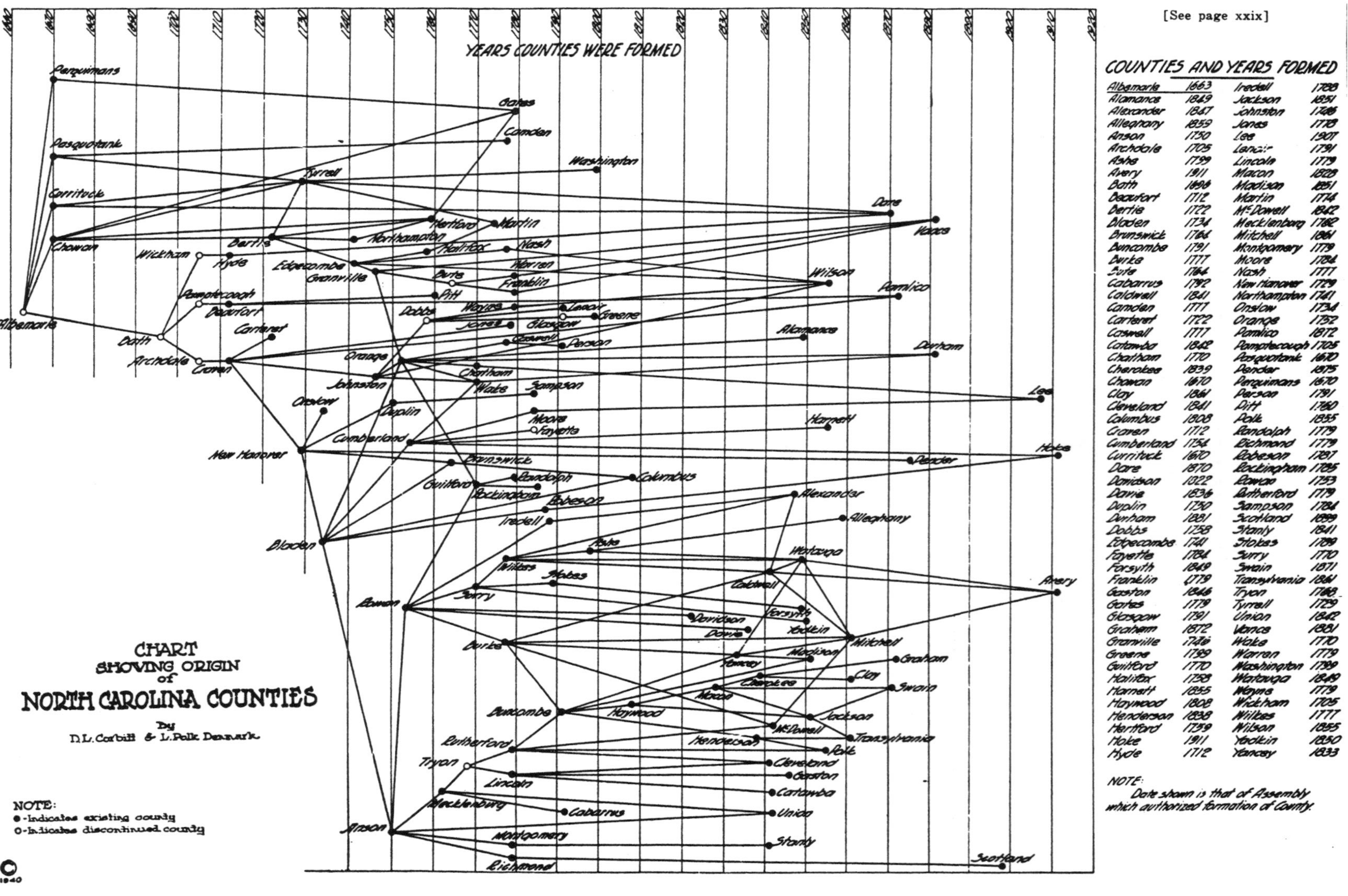

COUNTIES AND YEARS FORMED

Albemarle	1663	Iredell	1788
Alamance	1849	Jackson	1851
Alexander	1847	Johnston	1746
Alleghany	1859	Jones	1778
Anson	1750	Lee	1907
Archdale	1705	Lenoir	1791
Ashe	1799	Lincoln	1779
Avery	1911	Macon	1828
Bath	1696	Madison	1851
Beaufort	1712	Martin	1774
Bertie	1722	McDowell	1842
Bladen	1734	Mecklenburg	1762
Brunswick	1764	Mitchell	1861
Buncombe	1791	Montgomery	1779
Burke	1777	Moore	1784
Bute	1764	Nash	1777
Cabarrus	1792	New Hanover	1729
Caldwell	1841	Northampton	1741
Camden	1777	Onslow	1734
Carteret	1722	Orange	1752
Caswell	1777	Pamlico	1872
Catawba	1842	Pamptecough	1705
Chatham	1770	Pasquotank	1670
Cherokee	1839	Pender	1875
Chowan	1670	Perquimans	1670
Clay	1861	Person	1791
Cleveland	1841	Pitt	1760
Columbus	1808	Polk	1855
Craven	1712	Randolph	1779
Cumberland	1754	Richmond	1779
Currituck	1670	Robeson	1787
Dare	1870	Rockingham	1785
Davidson	1822	Rowan	1753
Davie	1836	Rutherford	1779
Duplin	1750	Sampson	1784
Durham	1881	Scotland	1899
Dobbs	1758	Stanly	1841
Edgecombe	1741	Stokes	1789
Fayette	1784	Surry	1770
Forsyth	1849	Swain	1871
Franklin	1779	Transylvania	1861
Gaston	1846	Tryon	1768
Gates	1779	Tyrrell	1729
Glasgow	1791	Union	1842
Graham	1872	Vance	1881
Granville	1746	Wake	1770
Greene	1799	Warren	1779
Guilford	1770	Washington	1799
Halifax	1758	Watauga	1849
Harnett	1855	Wayne	1779
Haywood	1808	Wickham	1705
Henderson	1838	Wilkes	1777
Hertford	1759	Wilson	1855
Hoke	1911	Yadkin	1850
Hyde	1712	Yancey	1833

NOTE:
Date shown is that of Assembly which authorized formation of County.

To determine the origin of any desired county:—(1) Locate from the above list the date the county was formed. (2) Find this date on the line at the top of the chart. (3) Follow down from this point until the county is located. (4) The lines connecting the counties to the left indicate the origin of the county. Seven Tennessee counties which were created by North Carolina are not included in this chart.

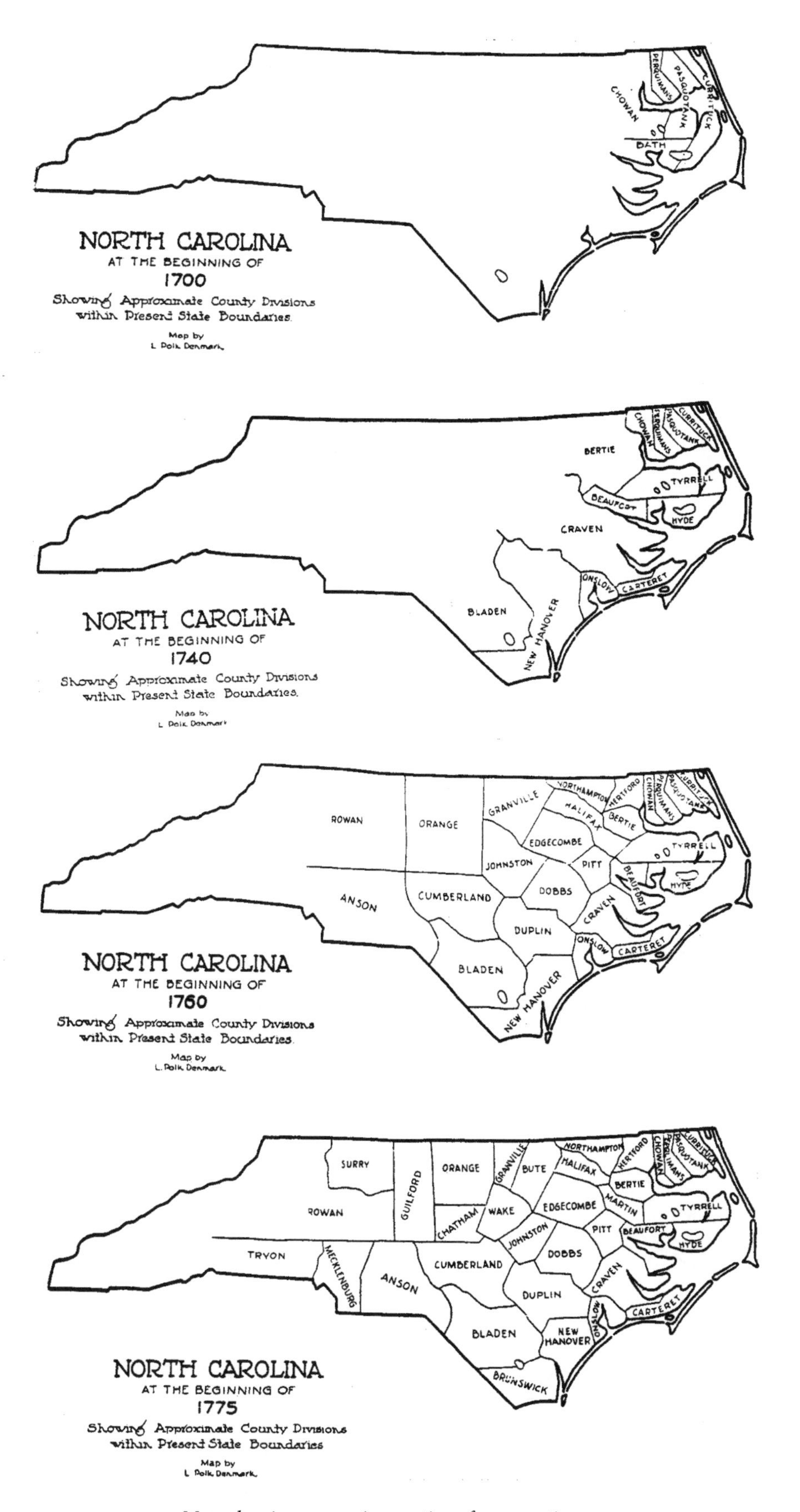

12 Maps showing progressive creation of 100 counties—1700–1912.

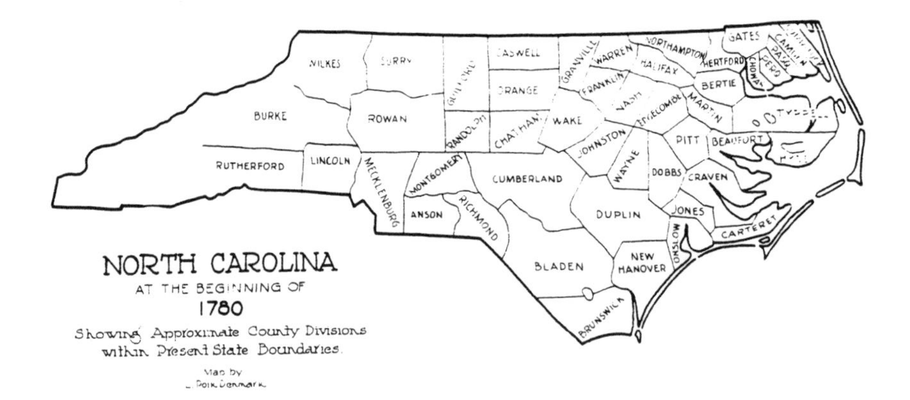

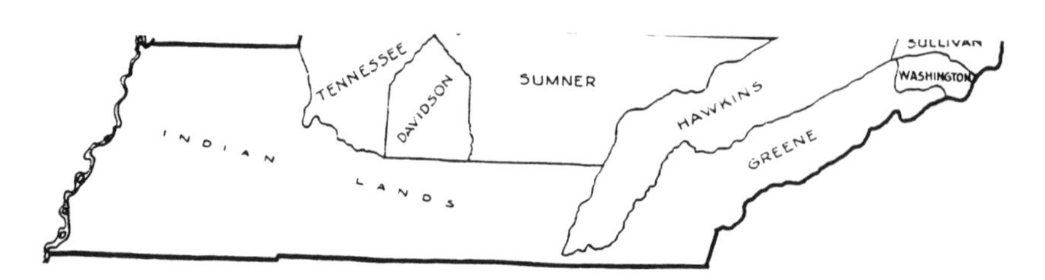

TENNESSEE
AT THE BEGINNING OF
1790
Showing Approximate County Divisions
within Present State Boundaries
Map by
L. Polk Denmark

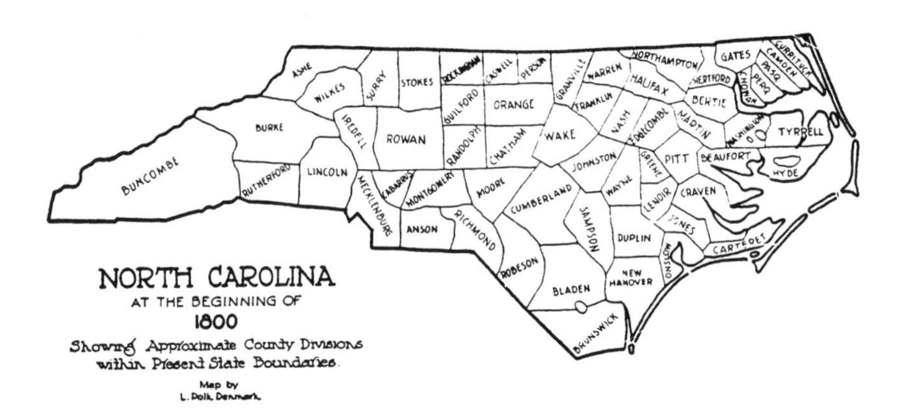

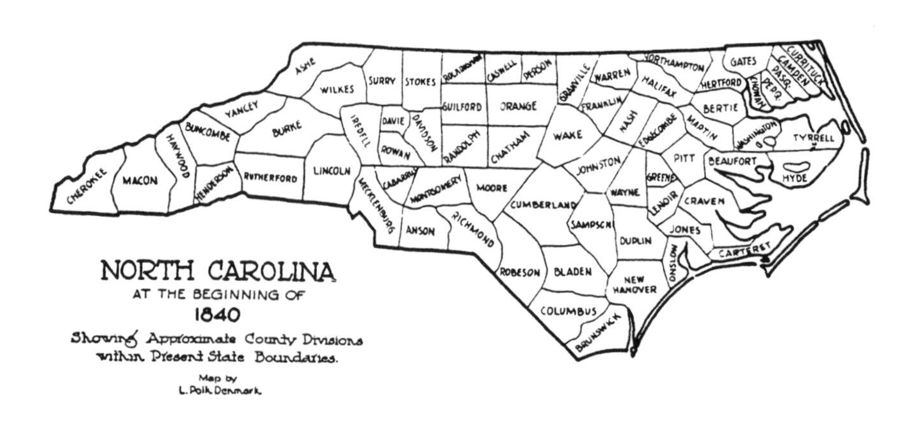

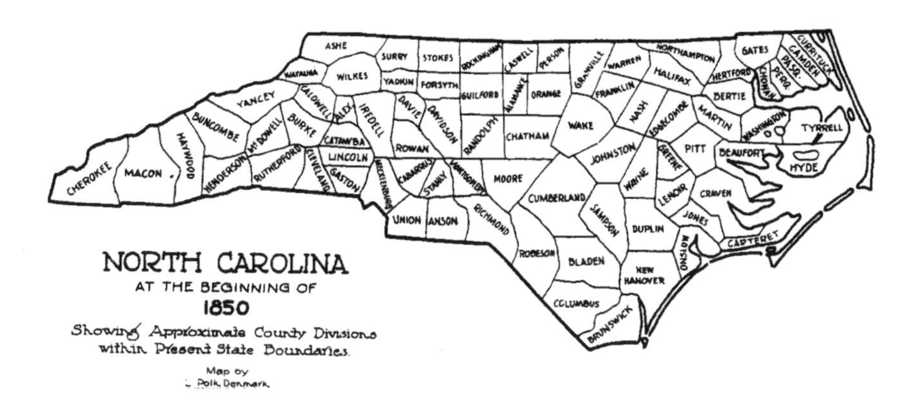
NORTH CAROLINA
AT THE BEGINNING OF
1850
Showing Approximate County Divisions
within Present State Boundaries.
Map by
L. Polk Denmark

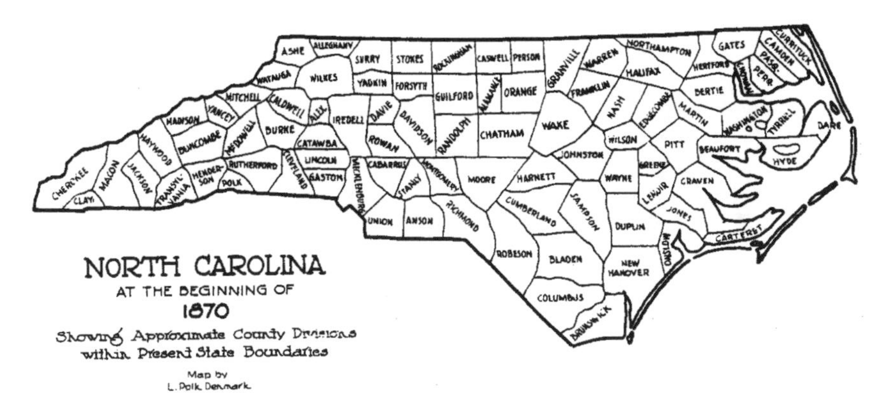
NORTH CAROLINA
AT THE BEGINNING OF
1870
Showing Approximate County Divisions
within Present State Boundaries
Map by
L. Polk Denmark

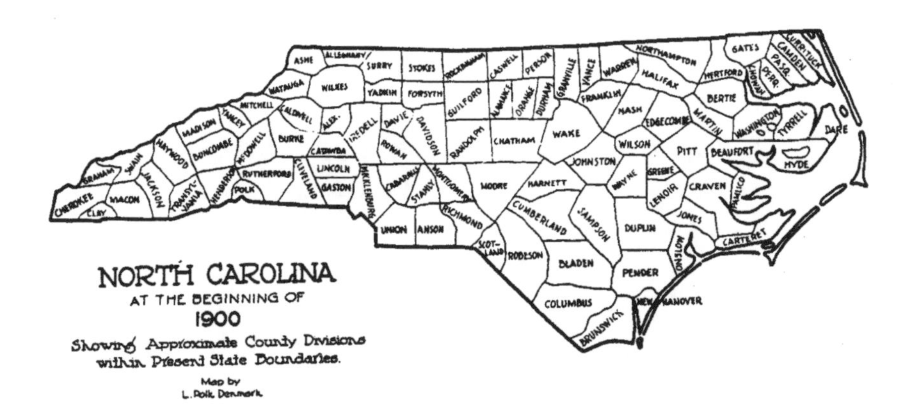
NORTH CAROLINA
AT THE BEGINNING OF
1900
Showing Approximate County Divisions
within Present State Boundaries.
Map by
L. Polk Denmark

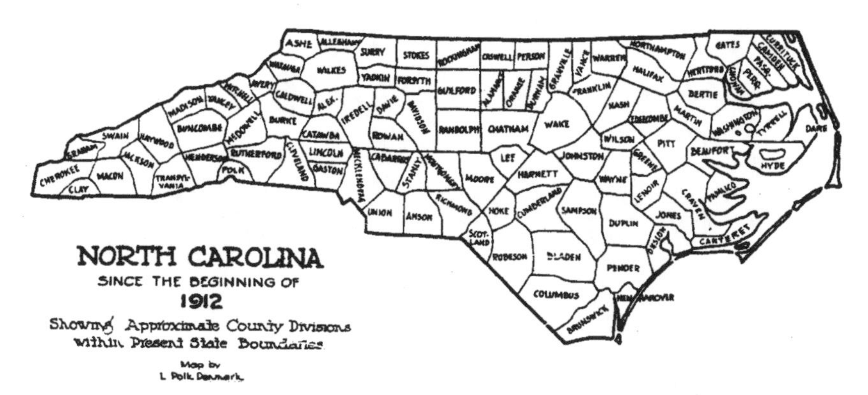
NORTH CAROLINA
SINCE THE BEGINNING OF
1912
Showing Approximate County Divisions
within Present State Boundaries
Map by
L. Polk Denmark

Map of the first acutal survey of the state of North Carolina and twelve maps, showing the progressive creation of 100 counties, including a chart showing the origin of the counties. Reproduced by permission of the North Carolina Department of Cultural Resources Office of Archives and History, Raleigh, NC.

First Recorded Land Deed in North Carolina

First land transaction recorded between white man (George Durant) and Indian Chief (Kilcocanen) in which the Indian was paid for his land — March 1, 1661

PERQUIMANS COUNTY COURT HOUSE

HERTFORD, NORTH CAROLINA

CHIEF KILCOCANEN DEED TO GEORGE DURANT 1661

Know all men by these presents that I, Kilcocanen, King of Yeopim have for a valuable consideration of satisfaction received with ye consent of my people sold and made over & delivered to George Durant a parcell of land lying & being on Roanoke Sound & on a River called by ye name of Perquimans which issueth out of the north side of the aforesaid sound which land at present bears ye name of Wicocomicke, beginning at a marked oak tree which divided this land from ye land I formerly sold to Sam: Pricklove and extending westerly up ye said sound to a point, point or turning of ye aforesaid Perquimans iver and so up the eastward side of ye said river to a creek called by ye name of Owoseake to wit all ye land betwixt ye aforesaid bounds of Samuel Pricklove & the said creek thence to ye head thereof and thence through ye woods to ye first bounds to have and to hold ye quiet possession of ye same to him & his heirs forever, with all rights and privileges thereto forever from me or any person or persons whatsoever as witness my hand this first day of March 1661

Test Tho. Weamouth
Caleb Calleway

ye ♁ marke of
Kilcocanen
or Kirtotanew.

This is a true copie examined word by word out of ye original by me Edward Remington

Witness
Will: Lloyd
Thomas Havett

Registered the 24th of Oct. 1716
John Stepney, Register

First Recorded Land Deed in North Carolina, Perquimans County.

Compass/Transit Era

Otis A. Jones, PLS

Following in Their Footsteps: Land Surveying in North Carolina is an orderly retracement of surveying in the past. One must gain knowledge of the tools, methods, and practices used in the initial survey to determine its retracement from early times to the present.

In the history of mankind, there has been little change in the quantity of land on earth. Surveying is as old as civilization and had a portion of its beginning in Egypt. In addition to surveying, the Egyptians were the first to introduce algebra and geometry to the Old World. It is thought that they used knotted rope or string to survey the pyramids with a great deal of accuracy.

It is unknown when the division of land actually had its beginning. Historical records, such as the Old Testament (King James Version), refer to the division of land and landmarks.

> DEUTERONOMY 19:14: *Thou shall not remove thy neighbour's landmark, which they of old time have set in thine inheritance, which thou shalt inherit in the land that the Lord thy God giveth thee to possess it.*
> DEUTERONOMY 27:17: *Cursed be he that removeth his neighbour's landmark.*
> JOSHUA 18:8: *And the men arose, and went away: and Joshua charged them that went to describe the land, saying, Go and walk through the land and describe it, and come again to me, that I may here cast lots for you before the Lord in Shiloh.*
> JOB 24:2: *Some remove the landmarks; they violently take away flocks, and feed thereof.*
> PROVERBS 22:28: *Remove not the ancient landmark, which thy fathers have set.*

The survey system in North Carolina is based on English measurements and methods. Early measurements were made using the chain, pole, rod or perch. Also, North Carolina is one of the original thirteen colonies that uses the metes and bounds system to describe property boundaries. The rectangular system is commonly used in other states in the nation.

In the early 1600s, Edmund Gunter invented the surveyor's chain, which was 66.00 feet in length. The chain was constructed with one hundred connected wire links, each being

0.66 feet long. Eighty chains are equal to one mile, ten square chains are equal to 1.00 acre, and one pole, rod or perch is equal to 16.50 feet.

A surveyor's plain compass attached to the Jacob's staff, had no telescope. It was designed with two sight vanes and two spirit levels located at right angles to each other, which were used to level the plate in all directions. It had a round glass-covered box that contained the banded balanced magnetic needle (a bar of magnetic steel) and a graduated circle vernier. The vernier was graduated from 0 degrees to 90 degrees, with 0 degrees being at the north and south and 90 degrees being at the east and west. The magnetic compass needle points to the north magnetic pole. The surveyor would always take into consideration the variation or *declination* of the magnetic needle, which does not remain constant throughout the day. In order to obtain a correct reading, he also had to make sure that all metals that would cause a disturbance in the magnetic field were avoided.

The surveyor's compass and chain have a romantic history, which is associated with the early settlement of our country. They were widely used in North Carolina for about 225 years.

Until the early 1900s, most of the land surveyed in rural North Carolina was done using a magnetic compass for direction, and the chain, pole, rod or perch were used for measurements.

The recorded evidence of this method of surveying can be found in deeds, and some maps, in the offices of the Register of Deeds in each of the one hundred counties in North Carolina. A large majority of maps containing past surveys were not recorded, and in times past, many have been lost.

Research of the public records in the Register of Deeds and Clerk of Court's offices will reveal the results of the compass, chain, pole, rod or perch surveys in recorded deeds, wills, and maps. It was also necessary to research the adjoiners' records. Upon completion of the

Compass, Courtesy Elinor C. Jones

research procedure, a retracement field survey would be made. To follow in the footsteps of the original surveyor, it would help to find at least two corners of the tract. From this data, you would determine the magnetic bearing difference of the original property lines, *then and now.* The method of measuring distances of the lines was determined by checking the distance between the original corners. This would reflect either ground contour or level measurements. To retrace the property lines, you would use the same methods that the original surveyor used.

The dawning of the twentieth century brought about more changes than any in previous history. The mode of transportation changed with the coming of the automobile and the Wright Brothers' first powered aircraft flight at Kitty Hawk, North Carolina. Locomotive trains had been on the scene for about seventy years, and progress along them continued by the building of a vast network of rails and stations across the nation. These changes reflected our way of life in many ways.

At the turn of the century, surveying was moving into a transition period. Graduate engineers began to make engineering and surveying their career, which started a trend in surveying using the engineer's transit and steel tape. Even though the transit had been around since the 1830s, it was used mostly for survey work that required much more precision than the compass and chain was ever capable of acquiring. The transit had similarities to the surveyor's compass, in that it would lend itself to the retracement of the multitude of compass and chain surveys. Sometimes these surveys would need to be retraced; due to the transit's versatility, however, a surveyor could accomplish much more.

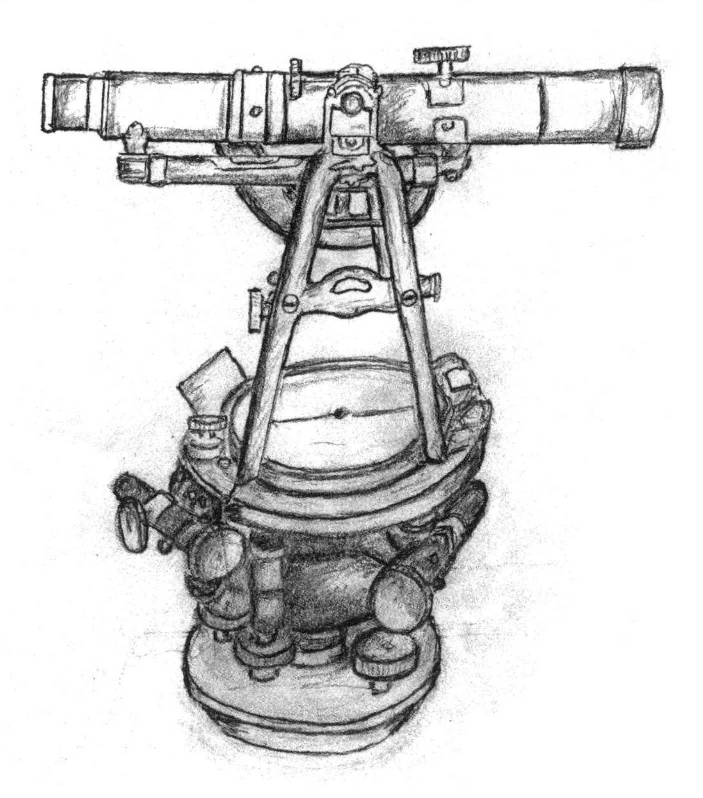

Transit, Courtesy Elinor C. Jones

The transit had the capability of reading the following functions: horizontal angles, vertical angles, and magnetic bearings. It also had the ability to determine relationships to the North Star, or true north. In fact, the transit was used for alignment purposes in most everything involving civil engineering and surveying.

Many auxiliary items were used with the transit. A brass plumb bob, weighing 6–14 ounces, was suspended by a strong string on a hook located in the bottom center of the transit, to 0.02' above a point of reference (such as a nail, stone, metal corner material, or a concrete monument, etc). Other items included a steel tape for making all horizontal measurements, a Locke level, and brass plumb bobs, which were needed to keep the tape on a level plane. To accomplish the survey work, a two-or three-man crew was needed.

Even with the advent of the transit and with engineers who were making engineering and surveying their career, much of their professional work was done in and around small and large municipalities, involving government and commercial properties, residential subdivisions, and schools, with some of the same in rural areas across the state. Early in the twentieth century, many surveyors across North Carolina were using transits and accomplishing some of this professional work, especially for residential subdivisions. In addition to land subdivision design and development, surveyors have continued in their practice of compiling boundary and topographical surveys. Surveyors have kept pace with changes and improvements in equipment for field surveying, mapping, and computing. They have worked to raise their educational standards and broaden their experiences to make themselves true professionals in every sense of the word. Surveyors, as a whole, are givers and not takers. Their willingness to share their knowledge unselfishly with others, and to train others to follow in their footsteps is the strength and backbone of the profession. The following story is an amazing example of an individual who lived and practiced this philosophy.

Guy F. Hinshaw, Civil Engineer-Land Surveyor
1880–1977

Mr. Hinshaw lived his entire life in Forsyth County, North Carolina, except for while serving his country during World War II in Washington, D.C. and Richmond, Virginia, and while attending college at A & M College (now North Carolina State University). In 1907, he received his B. S. degree in civil engineering. He then joined the city of Winston's engineering department. Then in 1915, he opened a private practice in civil engineering and land surveying. He worked on thousands of surveying and engineering projects. All of his office work was done with a small mechanical calculator, and his maps were drawn using a drafting machine. His curves were drawn with a grooved, transparent, plastic spline with cast iron weight and drafting pens and ink. All of his work was done with the greatest degree of pride and accuracy. His life's work will "stand the test of time," the same yesterday, today, and forever. He was dedicated to his family and his profession. In addition to educating his children, he constantly had some young men "under his wing," instilling in them the knowledge of land surveying, while creating in them a desire to be the best in all aspects of the profession. Because of this, he was affectionately known as "Hinshaw's College of Surveying." He retired in 1969, near the end of the transit era and the beginning of the electronics era.

I consider myself fortunate that I was one of those young men that received his training, and that he was my mentor. On October 18, 1984, I had the honor of presenting a plaque from the Piedmont Chapter of the North Carolina Society of Surveyors to Eunice Ayers, Register of Deeds of Forsyth County, to be placed in the Register of Deeds office. The plaque reads:

In Memory
Of
Guy F. Hinshaw
Civil Engineer-Land Surveyor
In Recognition of His Outstanding
And Professional Service To The
People of Winston-Salem and Forsyth County
His Standard of Excellence
A Worthy Example for Engineers and Surveyors
Placed in His Honor
By
Piedmont Chapter
North Carolina Society of Surveyors

One of his four sons, Lee M. Hinshaw (1915–2003), followed in his footsteps. In 1937, Lee graduated from North Carolina State College (now North Carolina State University), and received his B. S. degree in mechanical engineering. For the next ten years, he worked for various companies and also served in the United States Air Force during World War II. After the war, he continued to serve in the reserves, retiring in 1965. He was employed by the North Carolina Department of Transportation from 1949–1950 and Joyce Mapping Company in 1951. In 1952, he opened his own business, Hinshaw Engineers, and specialized in engineering and surveying. He retired in 1980.

In the twentieth century, there were many experienced surveyors across our state, who unselfishly shared their experience and taught the next generation the art of land surveying.

With the advent of the community college system in North Carolina in 1963, which benefited many in their thirst for knowledge, associate degrees in surveying were offered. Many of today's professional surveyors have been awarded these degrees. With a two-year associate degree and the required experience, an individual can sit for the examination given by the North Carolina Board of Examiners for Engineers and Surveyors. Upon completion and passing of the examination, he or she becomes a professional surveyor.

Many thousands of maps have been produced during the compass/transit era. Behind those maps are the men responsible for them—the surveyors and engineers who worked long, hard hours to make the maps become a reality. Those maps are our heritage in our history.

North Carolina Society of Surveyors, Inc., Historical Committee has archived approximately 27,000 surveying maps from the compass/transit era in the North Carolina Department of Cultural Resources of Archives and History in Raleigh, North Carolina. This is only a small portion of the maps that were produced by those hard-working surveyors and engineers of days gone by. The maps that were archived thus far were prepared by six prominent surveyors and engineers (now deceased) from across the state. They were:

Woodrow W. Bedsaul, RLS
J.E Ellerbe, P.E.
Philip R. Inscoe, RLS
Guy F. Hinshaw, P.E.
Lee M. Hinshaw, P.E., RLS
John Morgan, RLS

With the appearance of the electronic age, compass/transit surveying has slipped into history…

Wachovia, North Carolina: The First Settlements

Silvio A. Bedini

The area of Wachovia in Forsyth County, North Carolina, includes the community of Winston-Salem and contained several towns founded in the mid-eighteenth century as religious, cultural, and trade communities of the German pietistic sect known as the *Unitas Fratrum.* The Brethren, as they came to be called, was organized by followers of the Czechoslovakian religious reformer Jan Huss; after seceding from the Church of Rome, they elected their own ministers.

Following years of persecution, the Moravians, as they later came to be known, fled from Moravia and Bohemia and found protection under the Austrian aristocrat Count Nicholas Ludwig von Zinzendorf on his estate in Saxony. From there they embarked on missionary activities that led to the establishment of settlements in Europe, the British Isles, North America, the Caribbean and Africa. With English guarantees of religious freedom, the Moravians made their first settlement in North America in 1741 in Bethlehem, Pennsylvania. From this base they continued to seek land on which they could establish communities. When they learned of land that was being offered for sale by Lord Granville, their leaders turned their attention to North Carolina.

Guides and Chainmen

In December 1751, the Moravian bishop, August Gottlieb Spangenberg, set forth from Bethlehem to explore the Granville holdings in search of a suitable tract. Eventually, he selected one that became the future region known as Wachovia. Accompanying the bishop's group on horseback were two hunters who doubled as guides—and who worked as chain men during the survey—and the professional surveyor, William Churton. Hoping to find a suitable area along the Yadkin River, Spangenberg and his exploring party traveled across North Carolina from Edenton to the Blue Ridge Mountains and over the mountains at Blowing Rock, returning down the Yadkin River valley. They surveyed small tracts as they traversed the region across North Carolina from east to west, but during this travel, they did not succeed in finding an area suitable for the major settlement the bishop visualized.

On the west side of the Blue Ridge Mountains they became lost because one of the hunters, who had previously traveled the wilderness route to the Yadkin River, missed the trail and led the party into the mountains instead. Enduring extreme hardship and illness, several months passed since they had seen a living soul.

Best Land in North Carolina

In January 1753, the Spangenberg party camped at "the three forks of Muddy Creek" and there decided to make their settlement. After having made their way back from the mountains into the Yadkin drainage, the bishop wrote about the region: "Towards the end of the year we came into this neighborhood, and found 'a body of land' which is probably the best left in North Carolina. If we had a true account of this in the beginning, perhaps we would not have gone to the Catawba nor beyond the Blue Mountains to the New River...." He selected the tract of land that encompassed the entire drainage of Muddy Creek or Carguels Creek because, he wrote:

"This tract lies particularly well. It has countless springs, and numerous fine creeks; as many mills as may be desired can be built. There is good pastureage (sic) for cattle, and the canes growing along the creeks will help out for a couple of years until the meadows are in shape. There is also much lowland which is suitable for raising corn, etc."

Arriving at a broad plateau that divided the Yadkin and Dan River valleys, the Spangenberg expedition made camp. Churton surveyed a tract that Spangenberg named "Wachau" after the ancestral estate in Saxony of their patron, Count Zinzendorf. In time, the name was anglicized to "Wachovia." Considered to be the best land still unsettled in North Carolina at that time, it lay about twenty miles south of the Virginia border and conveniently on the road to Pennsylvania. After the tract had been surveyed and laid out during the winter months, Spangenberg proceeded to make plans for settlement. In August 1753, the *Unitas Fratrum* purchased from Lord Granville 98,985 acres of the surveyed tract. A land company was organized to finance the settlement, each stockholder of which received 2,000 shares and agreed to bear the proportionate share of the cost of colonization.

On October 8, 1753, a group of fifteen unmarried Moravian men set out on foot from Bethlehem, Pennsylvania, bringing with them a wagonload of supplies, and arriving at the Wachovia tract on November 17th. Twelve of the men, chosen for their skills useful in a pioneer community, were to remain as settlers. They took possession of a cabin near a meadow that had been abandoned by a hunter named Wagner, and there they held their first fellowship meeting. As wolves howled in the forest all about them, they set about to erect their settlement, and within a year the advance group of men had completed construction of a carpenter shop, a tannery, blacksmith shop, a flour mill, a pottery, a cooperage, and a shoe shop and had them operating to serve the settlers who soon followed. This became the first of the Moravian towns founded in the region; it was situated some three and a half miles from the present Winston-Salem, and they named it Bethabara, or "House of Passage."

The first to settle in Bethabara received a goodly number of visitors during the first several years, many of whom came for trade, some for medical attention, and others seeking refuge during the unrest caused by the French and Indian War, which was just beginning. It was not long before the settlement had become a developing center that served the dispersed population living throughout the surrounding countryside. Despite the alarms and reports of bloodshed as a result of French and Indian activity in the region, the Moravians held to their agenda for developing Wachovia, following instructions that came from Pennsylvania and Europe.

Founding of Salem in 1766

The development of Bethabara in 1753 was followed by the founding of Bethania in 1759 and of Salem in 1766. In these new communities, the Moravians were able to preserve their own religious, social, and economic customs, and they tended to segregate themselves from other settlements. They believed in common ownership of property and community cooperation, and it was not until 1849, almost a century later, that the congregation abandoned its supervision of business, and in 1856, its lease system.

Several surveyors had been involved in the laying out and development of the early towns in the Wachovia region. The first, as noted, was William Churton, who accompanied Bishop Spangenberg on his initial venture into North Carolina. Later, Philip Christian Gottlieb Reuter was sent to initiate a program of mapping the entire Wachovia tract and planning its development. He was assigned to work with the church leadership in selecting the site for a town that would become the center and dominant community. Reuter drew up plans for it, laying out a 2,000-acre lot in the traditional form of a German or linear village, the homes for residents concentrated along the main street while farming and tending the

Sea Quandrant or Astroscope invented by Caleb Smith and made byThomas Heath of London, with optical element made by James Mann, 1734. "Collection of the Wachovia History Society" courtesy of Old Salem, Inc.—Used by permission.

outlots. Within a few months, in 1759 the new community, which was named Bethania, was settled. A surveyor of a later period was Carl Ludwig Meinung (1743–1817), a native of Salem. He worked also as bookkeeper and held several other responsibilities.

A number of surveying instruments used by the early Wachovia surveyors have survived, preserved in the Museum of the Boys School in Old Salem, Inc. Included is a particularly rare instrument named the Sea Quadrant designed "*for taking Altitudes of the Sun, Sea and Stars, from the middle Horizon,...whereby the Latitude at Sea may be obtained with greater Certainty, and more frequently, than by any other Instrument commonly used for that purpose.*" Invented by Caleb Smith, it was first produced by the prominent London instrument maker, Thomas Heath, in 1734, with the optical element made by James Mann. Formerly, the property of the Moravian Land Office, it was probably used by early Wachovia surveyors and later by Ludwig Meinung of Salem. Regrettably, the telescope tube is presently lacking.

Silvio Bedini *is a historian emeritus with the Smithsonian Institution in Washington, D.C. and a contributing editor for the magazine.*

Reproduced by permission of GITC America, Inc. The Professional Surveyor Magazine (March, 1996) pages 61,62. Wachovia, North Carolina, The First Settlements

William Churton (fl. 1749–1767) North Carolina Cartographer

Silvio A. Bedini

PART 1

Although William Churton (fl. 1749–1767) was a major contributor to several of the most important colonial American maps, his contributions were not acknowledged, and his name has been virtually lost to history. Born in England, virtually nothing is known of his background and early history, except that he probably was a native of London with family roots in Gloucestershire. He arrived in the American colonies in the 1740s as a trained surveyor attached to the Granville Land Office in Edenton. In addition to pioneering as a surveyor and cartographer for the Granville District, he served as a colonial official of Orange County and Childsburgh, which later was renamed Hillsborough in honor of the Earl of Hillsborough, and he was also member for Orange County in the colonial legislature of North Carolina.

No Acknowledgement of Churton's Contribution

Daniel Weldon, a Crown lawyer, and William Churton were appointed in 1749 as its two commissioners for North Carolina. Together with Virginia's commissioners Joshua Fry and Peter Jefferson, who had been appointed by Acting Governor Lewis Burwell, they extended the existing Virginia-North Carolina boundary line 90 miles westward beyond the Blue Ridge Mountains, as far as Steep Rock Creek. It was probably during this period that Churton supplied the topographical information relating to the Granville District to Fry and Jefferson, which they later included in their map in 1751. The second edition of the Fry and Jefferson map, published in 1755, contained significant additions in detail, particularly in the vast area of the survey of which Churton had just surveyed for the Moravians. However, no acknowledgment of Churton's contribution was made in either edition.

Between August 1752 and January 1753, Churton accompanied Bishop August Gottlieb Spangenburg and a party of five Moravians from Bethlehem, Pennsylvania, in another arduous expedition to the mountainous western lands in the "Blue Mountains" to the east coast of North Carolina to survey tracts that totaled 98,925 acres, which the Moravians purchased from Lord Granville. Bishop Spangenburg (1704–1792) was a son of George Spangenburg, Lutheran pastor of Klettenberg-Hohenstein, Germany. He emigrated to the

American colonies in 1735, with Swiss colonists and as head of the American branch of the *Unitas Fratrum,* subsequently became the driving force for the Moravians in America. Churton was mentioned frequently in the *Spangenburg Diary* and other Moravian records, in which he is characterized as a surveyor who was "*certainly a reasonable man,*" and "*excessively scrupulous.*" The tract was named *Wachau* or *Wachovia,* for the ancestral home of the Zinzendorf family of their early church leader near the Wach River. The first settlers came from Pennsylvania and arrived in November 1753, consisting of eleven single men selected to provide the skills necessary to establish a new community. Four others who had accompanied them on their journey returned to Pennsylvania soon after. Additional settlers began to arrive in 1754 and 1755, including the first women.

Diary Excerpt

A particularly interesting entry in the *Diary* of Bishop Spangenburg related to Moravian settlements in North Carolina:

> *It is important that I should mention certain things about surveying in North Carolina which will affect all the tracts we may take up.*
>
> *The surveyors have strict orders from Lord Granville's agent to run lines only north and south, east and west. The agent may have reasons for this which seem to him sufficiently important, and it may be practicable in the eastern counties where there are no hills, or only very small ones, but here it is quite different, and often inconvenient. If a strip of land lies north-west and south-east I have to include corners of land to finish out the north and south lines, even when the land is not worth a heller* [a small German coin worth one half cent]. *I have spoken much about this to the surveyor, Mr. William Churton, an otherwise tractable man, but he insists that these are his orders and that he dare not disobey them. The only thing he will do is to make offsets in the lines where too much barren land would be included.*
>
> *When the* [Moravian] *Brethren come they would find it useful to employ the hunters, whom we have with us to carry the chains and to furnish us with game. These men could conduct them to this and other tracts, and show them where our land lies....*
>
> *In the third place, I would mention that ordinarily our surveyor measures and marks only three sides of a tract. He considers it unnecessary to run the fourth side, and says it is here a lawful survey when only three sides have been measured. That the Brethren who come here may understand this, and not give themselves useless trouble seeking the unmarked trees, I will report for each tract which side is not marked, and indicate it on the map.*
>
> *In the fourth place, I would say that our surveyor has been very unwilling to measure out small pieces of land for us... In the Warrant from Lord*

Granville it is stated that we are to pay £3 Sterling for the survey of each 5000 acres. He interprets that to mean that we must take tracts of that size… We would be only too glad if that were possible, but here at the edge of the mountains we could only do it by including many, and often barren, hills…

Although Churton had been appointed in 1752 as the first public register of Orange County, he did not actually qualify until the 12 June court, because he had been absent so much of the time on surveying expeditions. In 1753, Churton and Richard Vigers were

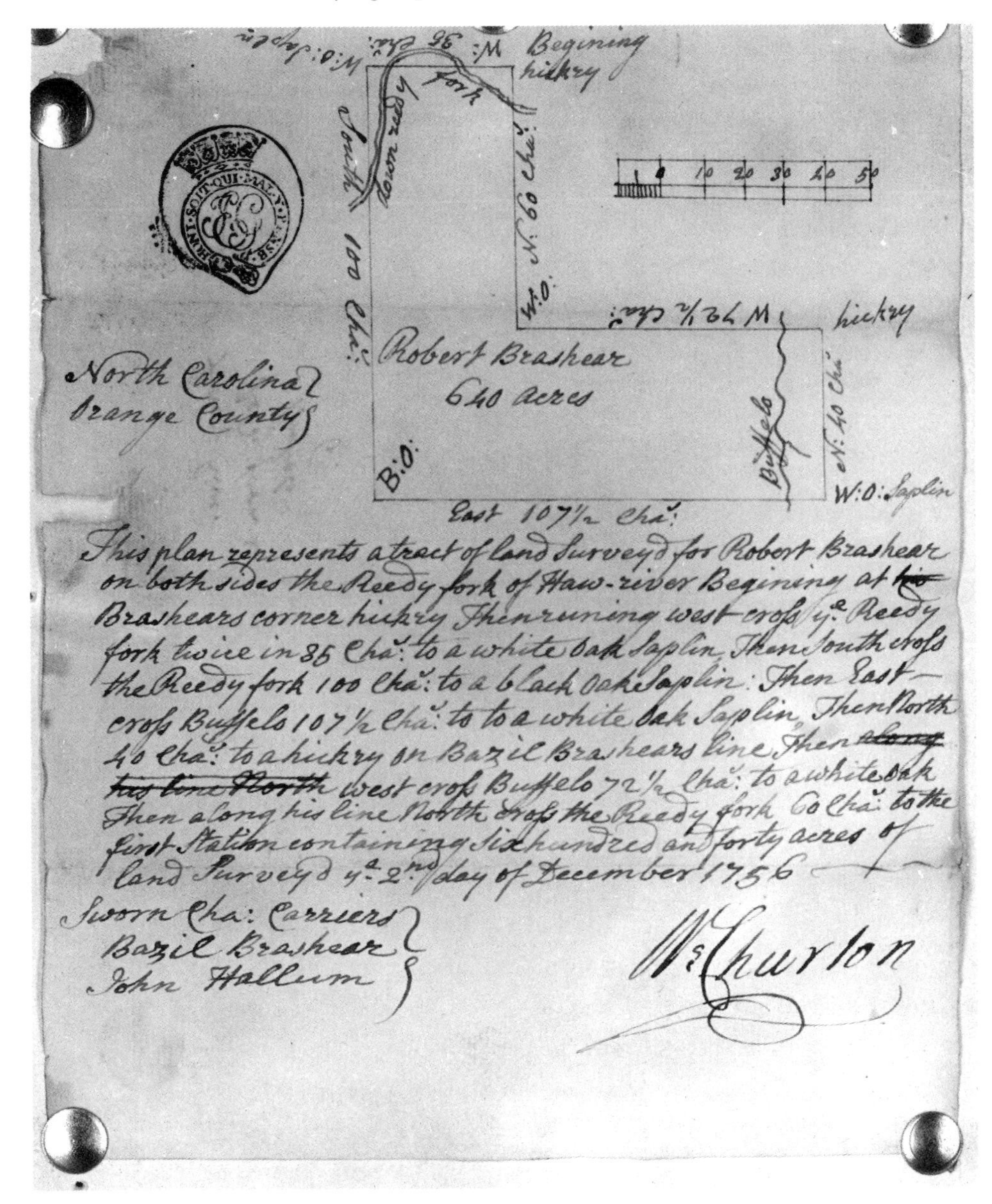

North Carolina
Orange County

Robert Brashear
640 acres

This plan represents a tract of land Surveyd for Robert Brashear on both sides the Reedy fork of Haw-river Begining at ~~his~~ Brashears corner hickry Thenruning west cross ye Reedy fork twice in 35 Cha: to a white Oak Saplin Then South cross the Reedy fork 100 Cha: to a black Oake Saplin Then East cross Buffelo 107½ Cha: to to a white Oak Saplin Then North 40 Cha: to a hickry on Bazil Brashears line Then ~~along his line North~~ west cross Buffelo 72½ Cha: to a white Oak Then along his line North cross the Reedy fork 60 Cha: to the first Station containing Six hundred and forty acres of land Surveyd ye 2nd day of December 1756

Sworn Cha: Carriers
Bazil Brashear
John Hallum

Wm Churton

A Certificate of Survey by William Churton from the Granville Land Office, 1756. This document includes the date of the survey, the name of the individual for whom survey was made, the number of acres, location of the tract, the name of Granville's "sworn surveyor" [Churton], *and names of two "sworn chain carriers"* [Bazil Brashear and John Hallum], *with a drawing of the plat of each tract and courses given. "Collection of the Wachovia Historical Society;" courtesy of Old Salem, Inc. used by permission.*

granted 635 acres to hold in trust for the establishment of Salisbury, and in June 1754, Churton was granted 663 acres to hold in trust for Francis Corbin to establish a township on the north bank of the Eno River. The township was successively named Orange, Corbinton, Childsburgh and eventually Hillsborough. A number of one-acre lots of the new town were staked out. Assisting Churton was a surveyor named Enoch Lewis, and the Quaker surveyor James Taylor also may have worked with him.

PART 2

William Churton (fl. 1749–1767) was an English trained surveyor who emigrated to the American colonies in the 1740s employed by the Granville Land Office in Edenton, North Carolina. In addition to his work for the Land Office, Churton also served as a commissioner for North Carolina in extending the boundary with Virginia in 1749, surveyed tracts of land for the Moravians, and was appointed public register of Orange County.

Although Churton was as much responsible as anyone in his time for extending knowledge of North Carolina's interior, his name does not appear as the author of any published map.

Held Many Positions in Community

From 1757 until his death, Churton was a permanent resident of Childsburgh. During the next few years, until 1763, he occupied the post of register, but in actuality a deputy register, William Reed, served in his place. Churton was a representative to the colonial legislature from Orange for some eight years, from 1754 to 1762, and he also served as town commissioner of the newly incorporated town of Childsburgh from 1759 until his death in 1767. Churton was also officially appointed surveyor of Orange County in 1757 and served as justice of the peace after 1757.

In 1759, Churton received four one-acre lots by legislative grant "*in Consideration of the many Services he hath performed for the Inhabitants of the said Town, and his Labour, Expence and Pains in laying out the said Town.*" This gift of land was reaffirmed in the 1766 legislative bill renaming the town "Hillsborough" to honor the Earl of Hillsborough. The lower portion of the street running north and south near Churton's lots had apparently been named Churton Street even before 1759.

The area described as the Metcalf Lands consisted of 20 tracts totaling between eleven and twelve thousand acres scattered along the water courses of Rowan and Orange Counties. In 1762, the Earl of Granville had granted these tracts of land to his surveyor general, Churton, who in turn sold them to an English Moravian named Charles Metcalf. Portions were sold by Metcalf to various individuals, and by 1780 the land had become the property of the Moravian *Unitas Fratrum.*

It had been noted in an entry for September 1752 in the *Spangenburg Diary* that there was a great need for "*a general surveyor's map of the Granville District.*" It appears that

Churton was engaged from 1757 on the production of just such a topographical map of the province of North Carolina, which he showed to Governor Tryon. He personally had not surveyed the southern and coastal areas, however, and had relied for this data upon available "information and old maps" that he had collected. The northern half was based on almost twenty years of Churton's work. In November 1766, Governor Tryon laid the finished Churton map before the General Assembly, which allowed Churton the handsome gratuity of *f*155 Prov. towards having it printed in England. Tryon further assured Churton that if he would endeavor "*to complete and make perfect the southern and maritime parts of the province,*" he should, with Tryon's approval, take the map with him to England and there present it to the Board of Trade.

When Churton began actively surveying the coastal regions in 1767, he discovered that the lower part of his map, which he had drawn based upon secondary sources, was so defective that he "condemned and cut off that section." During that year, he made several journeys into the southern region of the seaboard to correct errors he had noted in the old maps he had used for making that part of the map. While in the field engaged upon these maritime surveys, he informed Governor Tryon that in the event that some accident should befall him, he was leaving the map to the governor. In December of the same year, Churton died unexpectedly, and the map, as far as he had progressed, was left to Governor Tryon. Of the manuscript map left by Churton, Tryon said, "*I am inclined to think there is not so perfect a draft of so extensive an interior country in any other colony in America.*"

Churton Goes Unrecognized

In October 1768, Tryon wrote to the Earl of Hillsborough in England, stating that he had commissioned Captain John Collet, commandant of Fort Johnston on the Cape Fear River, to continue the work on the map. Collet had redrawn it from Churton's charts, and was taking it to England to submit it to His Majesty with the hope of having it printed. Tryon noted that the lower part of the map was still not satisfactory, however, and he suggested that Collet be commissioned to return to make the additional surveys that were required. It does not appear that this was done, nor whether the map was printed as drawn. Collet published the map in London in 1770. The map, titled "*A Compleat MAP of NORTH CAROLINA from an actual survey of Capn Collet,*" measures 3 feet 8 inches by 2 feet 7 inches. Featured in an elaborate design in the lower right hand corner are the English coat of arms, and figures of an Indian, a wildcat, and an alligator. It bears the inscription "*To His Most Excellent Majesty George III, King of Great Britain,* [etc.]. *This Map is most humbly dedicated by His Majesty's most humble obedient and dutiful Subject, John Collet.*"

Churton's last will and testament was probated in January 1768. He had left six of his Hillsborough town lots as well as another tract of land to four London heirs. The remainder of his estate, including his papers, went to Edmund Fanning. Although Churton was as much responsible as anyone in his time for extending knowledge of North Carolina's

Section of the Collet Map of North Carolina, redrawn by Captain John Collet from Churton's original charts of 1776. "Collection of the Wachovia Historical Society", Courtesy of Old Salem, Inc. Used by permission.

interior, his name does not appear as the author of any published map. The entire length of Hillsborough's north-south street, now its main street, was eventually renamed "Churton Street," and apparently is the only memorial in North Carolina to the Granville surveyor whose important early cartographic contributions have been virtually unacknowledged.

Silvio Bedini *is an historian emeritus with the Smithsonian Institution in Washington, D.C., and a contributing editor for the magazine.*

Reproduced by permission of Gitcamerica, Inc. From: Professional Surveyor, Part I, July/August 2001, pages 78-79
Reproduced by permission of Gitcamerica, Inc. From: Professional Surveyor, Part II, September 2001, pages 86–87

John Vogler 1783–1881
Silversmith of Old Salem

Silvio A. Bedini

Among the few makers of clocks and scientific instruments in North Carolina was John Vogler (1783–1881), whose home with shop forms part of the restored historic area of Old Salem, Inc. at Winston-Salem. Born on November 20, 1783, in the Friedland settlement a few miles from Salem, he was the fourth generation of his family in the American colonies. His grandfather had migrated from Maine to North Carolina in 1770, and a decade later became a member of the Moravian congregation. Vogler's father, George Michael Vogler, was a farmer and was received into the Society in 1779, and married Anna Maria Kunzel in 1781. He died when John was eleven years of age. He made his home with his maternal grandfather, Frederick Künzel, during the eight-year period that he was sent to school in Salem at the expense of an uncle, Christopher Vogler.

His Profession Came Into Question

In 1802, Vogler joined the Unity of Brethren and was received into the congregation the following year. He was apprenticed to his uncle, who was a gunsmith, until about 1806. Although Vogler was listed as a gunsmith in the Salem Congregation catalogue of 1805, no weapons made by him are known. Shortly before his apprenticeship with his uncle ended, he transferred to the craft of silversmithing, which brought about complaints from another craftsman in the community. In July 1806, the Minutes of the Aufseher Collegium, one of the two chief boards of the Moravian congregation, reported that Brother Ludwig Eberhardt, a clockmaker in the congregation, complained: "*...the single* [unmarried] *Br. Joh. Vogler is making silverware. He also is reported to repair clocks, though the Community Direction has granted this work solely to him* [Brother Eberhardt]." The Minutes then went on to comment about the clockmaker: "*It has to be said against Br. Eberhardt that he does not attend to his work as well as Vogler, also that he often does not make these things at all and otherwise is too high in his prices. The Collegium therefore permits Joh. Vogler to make silverware and repair clocks besides his own profession.*"

Several more years passed, however, before Vogler achieved the status of master craftsman in his own right. On January 25, 1809, the Minutes of the Collegium explained:

Physician's lancet inscribed "John Vogler Salem N.C." "Collection of the Wachovia Historical Society"; courtesy of Old Salem, Inc. Used by permission.

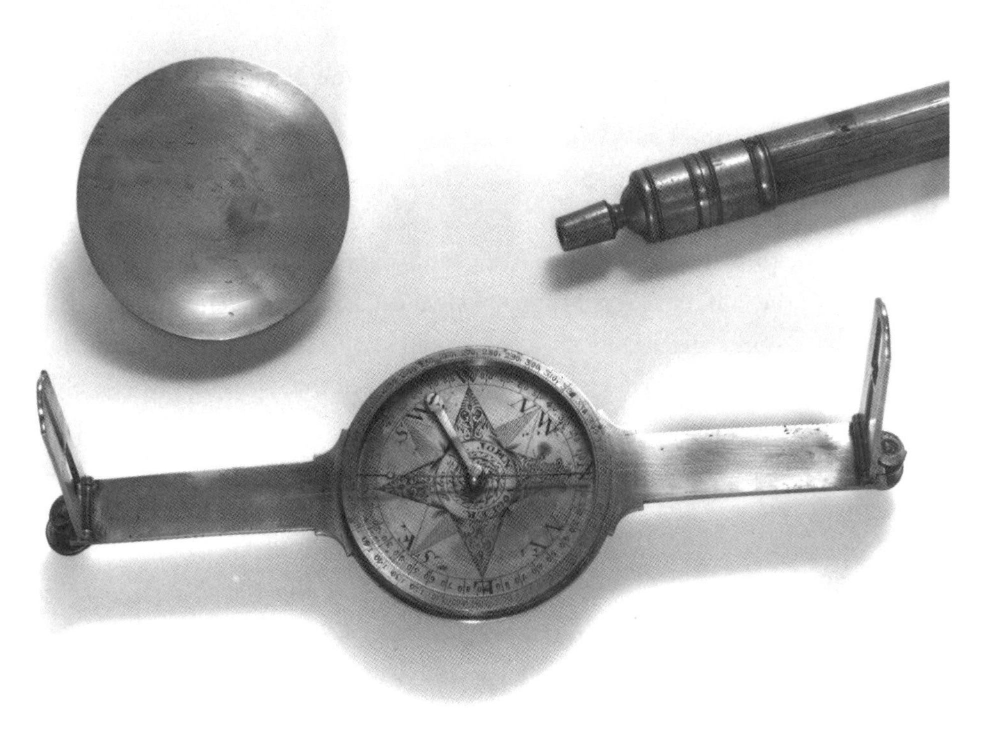

Brass surveying compass inscribed "John Vogler Salem N.C." with its turned cover and Jacob staff. "Collection of the Wachovia Historical Society"; courtesy of Old Salem, Inc. Used by permission.

"For a long time Br. John Vogler has had the desire to attend to his business as watchmaker and silversmith in the Brothers' House. There seems to be an opportunity for him now and we discussed the possibility of an objection in the Collegium to his intention. We did not know anything that could be an obstacle to his plans, since he promised not to deal with wall clocks, which is Br. Eberhardt's business alone."

Despite the decision of the Collegium, the now aging Eberhardt repeatedly appeared before the body to protest Vogler's production of various products that Eberhardt considered to be reserved to his right alone. Vogler continued his work, and as the community's master silversmith, he trained several apprentices in his craft, including Traugott Leinbach, who later became Salem's master silversmith, John Jacob Fockel from Bethabara, as well as two of his nephews, Timothy and George Vogler. On March 7, 1819, Vogler married Sister Christina Spach, and they became parents of a son they named Elias.

When Elias had reached the age of 21, Vogler received the Collegium's permission to take him as a partner in his shop. Elias did not remain with his father's shop, however, and eventually established himself independently as a merchant with an adjacent shop.

Man of Many Talents

As time went on, John Vogler became involved with a variety of business activities in his community. His favorable financial standing made it possible for him to engage in a number of profitable real estate ventures. He was one of the four founders of the Christian Blum & Company to build a mill. He served the community as firemaster, sick nurse, roadmaster, and was also curator of the Single Sisters' Diaconis.

Numerous examples of Vogler's work in various materials have survived, ranging from spoons and other silverware, to carved wooden molds, as well as clocks. Handed down through the family is a physician's lancet with pocket case. During a visit to Philadelphia in 1805, he visited Peale's Museum where he observed the physiognotrace, the silhouette cutting machine. Becoming intrigued with it, he made one of his own upon his return to Salem. He often called passers-by in from the street and offered to cut their silhouettes without cost.

Of particular interest is a brass surveying compass inscribed "John Vogler, Salem, N.C.," presently displayed in Vogler's restored silversmith shop at Old Salem, Inc., with its brass cover and Jacob's staff. Presumably, Vogler had made it for the use of the Moravian Land Office, from which it was acquired.

Silvio Bedini *is an historian emeritus with the Smithsonian Institution in Washington, D.C., and a contributing editor for the magazine.*

PART II

Transit/Electronic Era—Transition Period

Surveying on the Outer Banks

Henry C. Cuningham, PLS

The first recorded survey that I know of on the Dare County Outer Banks was in 1863, when the Yankees needed geographic information on the coastal waters and land area to operate their gunboats in the turbulent coastal waters of eastern North Carolina. This first survey was performed by the United States Coast and Geodetic Surveying Division of the United States Government, and was used in the subjugation of the rebellious Confederacy.

The first inhabitants of the Outer Banks were people who had been on these lonely beaches since the late 1700s and decided to stay to make their living hunting and fishing. They were fiercely independent and had little need for surveyors and fences, or anything else that threatened their independent existence.

My first experience with Outer Banks inhabitants was in 1961, and stories abounded about houses and fish camps being washed hundreds of feet off their foundations by the storms that are so common in these areas. The buildings were promptly jacked up on new foundations, in their new locations, with enough land around them claimed to make inhabitation comfortable. These were some of my first encounters with squatters' rights or recognition and acquisition of land. There must have been some need for land measurement in earlier times, but the land values were low, and the inhabitants took care of their problems with ownership boundaries and other surveying problems. The first maps show measurements made with perches, poles, or rods, all of which were 16 ½ feet in length. Some of this measurement is still with us today with the standard tree log length of 16 ½ feet. The extra ½ foot is cut off to compensate for shrinkage, leaving the standard 16-foot length of lumber. Many of the first maps were maps showing the surrounding ownerships, maybe some quadrant information, and, if the surveyor was lucky, a few measurements. These were the minimum standards needed for an orderly existence on these windswept areas of land.

The first need for more accurate surveys started around the "roaring 1920s," with an abundance of money and the need to escape the bustle of city existence by a restless population. These outsiders started building summer homes, building bridges, and running ferry services into the lonely Outer Banks. This invasion brought the need for more permanent boundaries with surveyors coming in on a temporary basis from the surrounding cities.

A surveyor from Elizabeth City, who has been practicing over fifty years, reminisced about going to Hatteras and Buxton by mail truck on unpaved paths and spending the nights in hotels built for fisherman. "You did all your work over several days with an old

Burger Transit, two helpers, and a Günter's chain," he said. In the Corolla area (in the northern Outer Banks), the only access was by boat, by driving the beach on low tide with a four-wheel drive, or by flying in and landing on the beach at low tide.

My first surveying on the northern Outer Banks was in the Penny Hill area. We flew in and flew out. The Corolla Beach area ends at the Virginia state line. Many local people and surveyors drove from Virginia Beach across the state line to their homes in Corolla. The National Park Service put a stop to this when it acquired the beach between Virginia Beach and Corolla and built a large fence to protect the wildlife. Many of the newer homes in this area are still only accessible by "driving the beach."

The early surveying of these areas was very crude by modern standards but did the job needed at the time. We tend to look down on these first surveys as inadequate and a waste of money and resources, but it is a sure thing surveyors in the future will look back at us as being ignorant and slothful with our surveying.

The basic surveying problem on all of these shifting Outer Banks has always been the need for some permanent surveying control. This need came home to me in the early 1960s, with the arrival of the Ash Wednesday storm, which wiped out buildings and boundaries on most of the Outer Banks. The first "permanent" marker I put in was a ten-foot section of gauge railroad iron, surrounded by one square yard of concrete. Six months later, a bulldozer pushed up this immovable object, and two months later it disappeared in a stormy sea. The only permanent thing I have ever seen on these turbulent Outer Banks has been change.

With the advent of the Global Positioning Systems (GPS), the possibility of some permanent land boundaries on these shifting beaches is approaching. There is always the possibility that a class-five storm will wash away all of man's endeavors on these fragile areas of sand, but there is also a high probability that money will put it back just like it was. The surveyor will have to be the first effort of reconstruction and the primary arbitrator of ownership.

Surveying on the Outer Banks can be physically taxing and frustrating because of a continuing array of new bureaucratic regulations and the continuous shifting of surveying monuments. The surveyor is compensated for this annoyance by the abundance of money, and the fact that the typical surveying attire is tee shirts, short pants, and sneakers.

On my first foray into the Outer Banks in 1961, there was only one nonregistered land surveyor in the area. By 2001, there were twenty-one permanent surveyors listed in the Dare County surveying registry, most of them living on the Outer Banks. These surveyors are supplemented by at least a dozen other surveyors from surrounding counties.

With all the advanced technology available to the surveyors and engineers, very basic common sense is still needed. This fact was shown in the recent movement of the Cape Hatteras lighthouse from the ocean front to a point several hundred yards inland. During the move, it was discovered that the expensive equipment used to keep the lighthouse upright was malfunctioning. A simple plumb bob located inside the structure was used to keep the lighthouse from destruction. Moving the lighthouse was a success due to the common sense of one surveyor and a simple plumb bob.

Outdoor Hardships Retold by a Surveyor's Son

Hank Cuningham

There were many times I thought the Great Dismal Swamp was going to be my deathbed. I can remember as a small boy spending quite a few Saturdays in the swamp, the water over the knees of my hip boots—and sometimes over the boots—hanging on to the ice-cold metal surveying tape which trailed off 200 feet into the distance, no sign of the civilized world for miles around me, just the gloomy, and seemingly endless scenario of swamp trees and muddy water.

For long periods of time, the only evidence available to me that I wasn't alone in the world was the tension on the tape. Somewhere, so far ahead of me that he was invisible, my father pulled the metal tape used to survey land and marked the end points with rods for me to collect. I could be miles away from the nearest road and not have the slightest idea which direction we had come from, but as long as I could see my end of the tape, I knew Dad had to be at his end of it, or at least, there was a good chance he was anyway. Dad never got lost—or if he did, he didn't stay lost very long.

We seemed to be so far away from civilization—out there sequestered in the woods—that I used to believe were the rest of the world to be obliterated in a nuclear holocaust, we wouldn't be aware of it until we had finished and tried to go back into town.

The element of surveying that I considered life-threatening in my early years was the constant exposure to Mother Nature's fury, especially her winter fury. There can't be many places colder than a flooded swamp in the wintertime. The trees only partially screened the merciless chilling wind that whistled over the nearby open farmland. It seemed the Saturday mornings we surveyed were always accompanied by gale-like winds that made me wish for another layer of clothing the second I got out of the truck. If the cold swamp water went over my boots, I knew I could expect to suffer miserably for the remainder of the day, until my feet became so numb that I felt I was walking around on wooden pegs.

And then there was the tug-of-war match. The 200-foot tape had to be pulled as straight as possible to ensure accuracy, and, boy, did Dad believe in accuracy! When the end of the tape streamed through my hands, I would get a firm grip on the leather trailer tied to the end and brace myself as well as I could on one of the tiny marshy swamp islands. Then Dad, somewhere ahead of me and out of sight, would pull that tape! God Almighty, he would pull that tape! I kept the tape zeroed on the marking pin, terrified Dad was going to pull me forward off balance, or else suddenly release the tension so that I would fall down and be completely drenched in the freezing water. One second, two seconds, three seconds, and he was still pulling. "I can't keep this up," I would swear frantically. "I'm either going to fall down, or else let go of the tape and let him fall down." Surely, death would be the only result from all of this. I would die of pneumonia from the cold, or malaria from the swamp, or exhaustion from trying to out-pull Dad, or maybe I would keel over out of sheer frustration. Then Dad would decide he had an accurate reading and the tension on the tape would gradually subside. I was free to follow the tape 200 feet farther into the swamp where the whole terrible routine would be repeated again and again.

I knew the sons of farmers worked every bit as hard as I did, but they did it on dry land, and, heck, I was just a city boy and not exactly athletically inclined either.

The summer season had its own unique hardships: the mosquitoes, the sweltering heat, the poisonous snakes, and, worst of all, the lethargy that came with the warmer weather. If Dad didn't need me for a few minutes, I would rest my legs by sitting down on some dry ground. In no time at all, the warm air would put me into a stupor. The sun's rays on my back would make me drowsy. It was like in *The Odyssey*, when Odysseus found his crew on an island munching on some intoxicating fruit that made them want to do nothing, except lie around on the island and eat more fruit.

When I went into this kind of state, I would wonder where I had ever found the energy to walk miles through fields full of briars or swamps or forests. Did Dad expect me to exert myself anymore today? He must be crazy if he did, but a stern look, and a curt remark were all that was needed to make me pull myself to my feet and trot sleepily forward. A Coca-Cola would have been the very thing to fight off this kind of malaise, but, unfortunately, one was seldom available in the woods.

Of course, I liked the money in part-time surveying. During my college years, I appreciated surveying like I never had before. I would come home on break completely penniless and leave with a fat deposit for my bank account. The college life of classrooms and books kind of spoiled me for the hard work of a land survey. I can remember a particular survey we did between semesters. After chopping my way for what seemed like miles into an unsympathetic forest, I threw down my machete and yelled at Dad, "If you ever take another survey like this one, get someone else to help you do it!" Dad just laughed loudly and kept on chopping.

I am glad to report that I retired from surveying at the ripe old age of twenty-two. Ironically, during the ten years I helped my father survey part-time, I developed a liking for the outdoors. Despite the hardships, I'll never be a surveyor myself, but I can now understand why some people might choose the realm of the outdoors for their life's work.

Moving a Piece of History

ROBOTICS AND COMMON SENSE KEPT THE CAPE HATTERAS LIGHTHOUSE STANDING TALL

Vicki Speed

Lady's hand soap, a robotic total station, and a $60 plumb bob: this odd combination proved to be key in the historic move of the Cape Hatteras Lighthouse.

Located on the shores of North Carolina's barrier islands near Buxton, the Cape Hatteras Lighthouse is the tallest brick lighthouse in the world. Built 130 years ago, the familiar black-and-white striped structure warned mariners away from shifting sandbars and treacherous currents. But due to erosion, the relentless sea pressed to within 160' of the lighthouse foundation, threatening to topple the historic monument.

Now, with help from the International Chimney Corporation (ICC, Buffalo, N.Y.), Seaboard Surveying and Planning (Seaboard, Kill Devil Hill, N.C.), Earl Dudley Associates, Inc. (Charlotte, N.C.) and the latest in Leica Geosystems (Norcrosss, Ga.) robotic automatic target recognition technology, the lighthouse is safely located 2,900' from its original location and 1,600' from the sea.

For Seaboard, the preparation and actual move of this 200' tall, 4,800-ton landmark is unforgettable. It was also its first opportunity to demonstrate the one-man power of the robotic surveying system.

"We couldn't have provided the level of support required without robotic technology," says John Mayne, senior crew chief for Seaboard and the primary on-site surveyor. His role began as simply support, but during the four-week move, the services and technology resources he offered provided some unexpected—and vital—benefits.

They Don't Build'em Like This Anymore

Beneath the sandy barrier island surface, the Cape Hatteras Lighthouse foundation sat on a brick and granite substructure that rested on a mat of yellow pine timbers immersed in fresh water and compacted sand. In preparation for lifting the lighthouse off this foundation, Seaboard surveyors dug four test pits down to the wood timber mat on four of the eight sides of the lighthouse to check mortar joint elevations.

Exposed to the light, the resulting structure offered on-site engineers and surveyors a glimpse of century-old engineering precision. The original shoring timbers were still in place alongside one of the most precise leveling courses ever seen.

The brick and stone foundation consisted of several courses of stone and then a leveling course. To allow room for the steel support beams, the lighthouse was cut off at the top of the next course—above the leveling course—a couple of tenths below existing grade.

John Mayne at test pit with original shoring timbers.

"We measured the elevations on every side of the leveling course, and the greatest difference between any two sides was .02' or .03'," Mayne says. The surveyors shot the corners of the eight points of the hexagonal base. Then they went inside the lighthouse, measured across to locate the center point, and dropped a plumb bob.

No matter how they tried to position the lighthouse center—from the eight points or from the inside diameter of the lighthouse—all points fell within a .1' circle. They just don't build structures with this kind of precision anymore.

After the analysis, ICC riggers attached four prisms to the main shaft of the lighthouse structure: two near the bottom, 90 degrees from each other, and two attached near the top, also 90 degrees from each other. Because of the lighthouse's tapered design, the top prism was located about 7.5' closer to the center of the lighthouse than the bottom prism. The ICC riggers then cut the granite substructure and began transferring load to 90 hydraulic shoring jacks (each capable of lifting 60 tons). Once the shoring jacks were in place, the steel beams and lifting jacks would be inserted to lift the lighthouse an additional 6'.

During this transfer, Seaboard surveyors monitored the lighthouse movement in two directions: the tilt and distance differential. Using the reference angle differences between the top and bottom prisms, they measured tilt in one direction. Then, they measured the distance differential between the prisms to measure the tilt in the other direction. If the distance between the top and bottom got smaller, the lighthouse was tilting toward the base prism. If it got larger, it was tilting away.

One of the engineering firms had installed a $250,000 electronic system designed to monitor tilt and tip of the lighthouse during the move. Its system gauges recorded inside wall temperatures and outside wall temperatures on the black and white stripes. Some strain gauges were set inside to measure changes in shape and roundness. In addition, gauges were attached to a number of the existing cracks to see if they widened or closed. Finally, two tilt sensors were mounted on the inside walls at the top and bottom. Unfortunately, the sophisticated system was plagued by electrical storms, power outages, and damp weather. The system malfunctioned and occasionally failed.

That's when Seaboard surveyors, with technical and systems support from Earl Dudley Associates, stepped in with robotics. Bill Owen, PLS, president of Seaboard Surveying and Planning, recalls, "We had wanted to evaluate robotic technology in more traditional surveying/stake-out operations. Turns out the lighthouse relocation was an ideal application for this technology, especially when it came to monitoring the lighthouse as it was lifted 6' to make room for the steel rail track system."

As the lifting jacks slowly raised the lighthouse, Mayne used Leica's TCA 1102 with coaxial Automatic Target Recognition (ATR) locked on a Leica 360 prism mounted to the top railing of the lighthouse catwalk to record horizontal and vertical positions. Operating in a stakeout mode, the robotic equipment continuously recorded cut/fill quantities as the lighthouse inched higher. It recorded distance as well. If the lighthouse tilted, the robotic readout would display a come-and-go, similar to a traditional stakeout operation.

The true story of the move—"Thanks Mac."

ICC riggers cut foundation and place shoring towers.

As Mayne operated the robotic controller, engineers controlling the lifting jacks watched the robotic LCD readout for slight changes. When the lighthouse tilted slightly, they would pressurize the appropriate jack to rebalance the lighthouse to vertical.

According to engineering studies prior to the move, the lighthouse could tilt as much as 6.5 degrees before it was in danger of damage, or even worse, falling. During the project, Seaboard surveyors did not monitor more than a .3 degree movement at the top prism.

It's Moving!

Thursday, June 17, was a rainy, dreary day. Recent reports stated the lighthouse would probably not move this day—but then again, it might. Owen adds: "We scrambled to figure out how to mount the prism on the bottom rail. We found a piece of angle iron, searched for a welder willing to help, found a prism-size bolt and welded the bolt to the angle iron. Then, we bolted the prism to the angle iron and used a simple c-clamp to attach the prism/angle iron piece to the main steel railing."

Ten minutes later, with no warning from site engineers, the lighthouse began to move. Owen had just returned to the trailer and was scanning the site and locking on prisms. Mayne looked at the robotic controller and said, "Damn, it's moving!"

Initially, engineers moved the lighthouse just 4" along the steel track. They then went forward with two full strokes, totaling 10' that first day. While Seaboard used high-tech equipment, the work crews from ICC opted for a simpler method to smooth the lighthouse's path. As the lighthouse moved along the steel track, they smeared bars and bars of Ivory soap along the rails. It was a simple and extremely effective way to reduce friction and ensure the smooth movement of the lighthouse. In the meantime, Mayne's job was to track the alignment of those roll beams from the center point to the new location for the next 25 days. Movement varied on any given day from 10' to 355'.

From Backup to Lead in a Minute

For the first two weeks, survey operations played a backup role to the other engineering equipment as the lighthouse team continued to rely on the engineering monitoring system to determine slight changes in the lighthouse position. Seaboard's role took an unexpected shift about halfway through the move.

On this day, computer readouts suggested the lighthouse was leaning slightly to the left. Engineers adjusted the jacks to compensate. A few minutes later, the computer readout suggested the lighthouse was leaning a little further to the left. Engineers compensated again. Mayne, using the robotic system as a backup, received data reporting the exact opposite conditions.

"You're going the wrong way," he said rather timidly. The engineers jacked it again.

"You're still going the wrong way," he said. Finally, it became evident to people watching

Surveyor Todd Grant waits out the rain with his robotic.

Mayne is in full control as the push jack operator waits to be told when to stop the light house.

the move that the lighthouse was leaning. They immediately called the engineering team who realized the computer was malfunctioning. Within an hour, Leica's robotic system became the primary lighthouse watchdog.

Back to Basics

The client had asked Seaboard for another electronic system, such as rotating grade levels with large sensors. With just one week left, there simply wasn't time to get the necessary equipment to the site and make it useful for more than a day or two. Instead Owen bought a 5-pound, $60 plumb bob and hung it in the middle of the lighthouse. He drew a target on the CAD system and plotted it .1' apart. The target was positioned on the floor with duct tape. From there, he used basic trigonometry to measure the length of the string, take the sine, and figured out that every .03' equaled .1 degrees. It was a simple but effective fix. From then on, if the engineers or surveyors had any question as to which way the lighthouse was tipping, they simply walked inside and looked at the plumb bob.

It took 23 days to move the lighthouse 2,900' to its new home on a 60'x60'x4' concrete and steel slab, designed so the leading edge would take the entire weight of the lighthouse as it rolled into position. Engineers were concerned about the back of the slab tipping up as a result of the weight.

By now, Seaboard's job was to monitor the movement of the slab—not the lighthouse. "We propped a free-floating, 360-prism pole on the slab so it could move up and down. Once again, we locked the robotic station on to the prism, set it in stakeout mode and measured cut/fill quantities during the entire process. Amazingly, the slab never moved more than .025'," Owen concluded.

Today, the lighthouse stands 210' from sea level to the top of the lightning rod. The Cape Hatteras rotating navigation beacon was re-lit and is visible from 20 miles away in clear weather. While it warns seagoing vessels of possible danger, it reminds Seaboard of the benefits of new technology and the importance of remembering the basics.

The Cape Hatteras Move Timeline

- July 1998: Seaboard Surveying positions the lighthouse, outbuildings, Oil House, three rain water cisterns, the granite block footing surrounding the lighthouse and an old brick walkway.
- August 1998: Soil engineers worked with the surveying team to monitor sand compression tests.
- September 1998: Seaboard surveyors dug four test pits on four of the eight sides of the lighthouse to determine cutoff point.
- December 1998: Seaboard stakes clearing limits for the move corridor and stakes positions of the various structures in the new location.
- March 1999: Lighthouse beacon and other electronic features are shutdown in preparation for the move.
- June 17, 1999–July 9, 1999: Lighthouse moves 2,900' to its location 1,600' from the sea.
- July–August 1999: All other lighthouse structures are placed in theiroriginal relative locations around the lighthouse.
- September 4, 1999: Lighthouse beacon lighting is postponed due toHurricane Dennis. Rescheduled for November 13, 1999.

Vicki Speed is a freelance writer based in Dove Canyon, California. Article and graphics reproduced with permission of *Point of Beginning (POB) magazine*, a BNP Media publication, issue dated December 1999, pages 16, 17, 19, 20.

Redrawing the Line

Lieca N. Brown

Private and public sectors collaborate on the resurvey of a U. S. Coast Survey base line in the Outer Banks of North Carolina.

Many surveyors like to retrace their predecessors' footsteps. Over the past few years, Robert "Bobby" Stalls, PLS, walked much the same line as that walked by one of surveying's greats: Alexander Dallas Bache (pronounced BASH). While working on a reconnaissance project of a portion of the Outer Banks in North Carolina for his employer, the North Carolina Department of Transportation (NCDOT), Stalls' curiosity piqued when he realized the area hadn't been completely resurveyed since Bache's initial survey in the mid-1800s. Stalls wanted to know more, he wanted to compare today's land to that of yesteryear and he wanted to honor the work of past surveyors with a memorial. Since the National Park Service owns the land, Stalls believed a coalition of public and private sectors could be established to resurvey the U. S. Coastal Survey Base Line of the Outer Banks of North Carolina.

Ron Miller, PLS, Gary Thompson, PLS, Joe Huffman and Charlie Brown, PE, PLS, head into the field in search of mile marker #4.

The Story of Yesteryear

In 1807, President Thomas Jefferson commissioned an effort for the eastern coast of the United States to be physically surveyed and mapped. As part of that survey, highly accurate primary verification base lines were established intermittently along the coast, as far south as Georgia (and later all the way into Texas). A. D. Bache, second superintendent of the U. S. Coast Survey (who acted as superintendent at the time of these surveys), established one of these base lines roughly 6.75 miles long on Bodie Island on the Outer Banks of North Carolina. The base lines were used as the basis for the initial surveys on the eastern coast, which vastly improved the maritime navigation along the coast before and after the Civil War.

Around 1843, Swiss-born geodesist Ferdinand Rudolph Hassler, Bache's predecessor, sent James Ferguson and J. C. Nielson, two of the first civilian assistants for the U. S. Coastal Survey, to the Bodie Island area of the Outer Banks to perform reconnaissance work to select the location of a verification base line for primary triangulation surveys extending southward from Hassler's Fire Island Base Line in New York. Bache subsequently selected Kent Island in Maryland as the site for a verification base line approximately halfway between Fire Island and Bodie Island.

The line was designated as Base No. IV and each end was monumented. Underground (or subsurface) marks consisted of a copper nail in the top of a 4" red cedar stake driven through a hollow-glazed stoneware marker shaped as the frustum of a pyramid, the top of which was 3' below ground level. A 5' square platform of 3" planks laid crosswise and bolted together, leaving an 18" hole in the center, was placed 8" above the stake. Surface marks were placed on the platforms. These granite monuments were about 3.3' square and 2.8' high with a ¾" copper bolt placed flush in the center of the top. Engraved capstones 3' tall x 1.5' square with pyramid-shaped tops were placed over the surface marks.

At the north end of the line, three granite reference marks, each 2.6' long and 1' square with a copper bolt flush in the top center, were placed perpendicular to the line on the east and west sides, and on a northerly projection of the line. At the south end, two reference marks of the same type were set perpendicular to the line and on either side of the station mark.

Charles O. Boutelle, who worked with Neilson, performed astronomic observations to determine the precise location and direction of the line, possibly using a 300-lb theodolite with a 30" horizontal circle. Hassler designed the "Great Theodolite" (as he referred to it) himself and had it built by Troughton of London in 1836. The U. S. Coast Survey used the instrument continuously until 1873 when it was destroyed by a tornado while occupying a station in Georgia.

William Wurdemann, a master mechanician in the Coast Survey in the mid-to late-1800s, and Bache developed an apparatus in 1845 that was used to determine the length of the Bodie Island Base Line, the second of seven principal base lines measured using the equipment. The measuring device consisted of bars 6 meters long made of iron and brass, which were coated with lacquer and encased in tin tubes to compensate for and minimize the effects of temperature changes. Each bar was carefully aligned on its supports, making

Surveyors working on the resurvey of the Bodie Island Base Line (left to right): Hugh A. Sorrell, PLS, locating engineer, Location & Surveys Unit, NCDOT; Robert "Bobby" Stalls, PLS, assistant locating engineer, Location & Surveys Unit, NCDOT; Randy Wilcox, survey team leader, Location & Surveys Unit, NCDOT Charlie W. Brown, PE, PLS, state location & surveyes engineer, Location & Surveys Unit, NCDOT Buck Rogers, PLS, chief of surveys, Coastal Engineering and Surveying Inc., Kitty Hawk, N.C.; James Cratt, transportation tech II, Location & Surveys Unit, NCDOT; Greg Skeen, PLS, owner, Horizon Surveying, Kitty Hawk, N.C. Gary Thopmson, PLS, director, North Carolina Geodetic Survey; Rick Poythress, transportation engineer, Location & Surveys Unit, NCDOT Ron Miller, PLS, assistant locating engineer, Location & Surveys Unit, NCDOT; and Joseph (Joe) Huffman, party chief, Coastal Engineering and Surveying Inc.

contact with the previous one in a leapfrog-like manner, each setup taking less than three minutes. Crews took ten days to measure the 6.75 miles between the monuments they had set. With lines measured, surveyors drafted maps, performed triangulation and used trigonometry and other techniques to fill in the blanks. Six granite monuments similar to the reference marks were set at one-mile intervals, measuring from north to south.

Seven Score and a Decade Later

Following much research spurred by pure curiosity and passion for history and surveying, Stalls blueprinted his plan to resurvey Bache's base line. There were many benefits to performing the work. The relationship of present day measurements to those of 1848 could be used to correlate older maps with more recent data and may be useful in barrier island studies. The coordination between the public and private sectors would be a true testament to the cooperative work of surveying. And all involved would have the chance to walk in the footsteps of their predecessors.

Stalls began his adventure in July 2000, when he found the monument at the northern end of the base line established in November of 1848 by A. D. Bache. It had been about 25 years since anybody had located any evidence in the area; previous recoveries had been in 1962 and 1975.

Once Stalls received approval from the National Park Service to cut brush to the North Base, he organized a small group of surveyors and engineers from the North Carolina Geodetic Survey (NCGS), the NCDOT, and local firms to help begin the location work of the base stations and mile markers. The handful of men who stepped forward did it with vigor and interest, some traveling as much as 360 miles from the opposite side of the state, to help Stalls with his endeavor. Of course, there are many perks to visiting the Outer Banks of North Carolina, including the stunning views of the Atlantic Ocean, the Bodie Island Lighthouse, the Cape Hatteras Lighthouse and the site of Roanoke Island, one of the first American settlements. A short drive up U. S. 158, visitors will find a busy tourist attraction: the Nags Head/Kitty Hawk area where patrons are paying homage this year to the Wright Brothers in celebration of their first flight 100 years ago (where, incidentally, surveyors played a role, too. See the Latest News, POB, November 2002).

And So Begins the Resurvey

The Bodie Island Base Line Resurvey adventure began on Saturday morning, Oct. 26, 2002, as eleven local and state surveyors, myself and *POB*'s Publisher, Diana Brown gathered in front of the Bodie Island Lighthouse. Introductions were made for a few people as others exchanged familiar handshakes. Stalls started the group off with a heartfelt thank you and a few instructions to start the static GPS sessions. To have the stations included in the N.C. High Accuracy Reference Network (HARN), two to three sets of occupations over several days were required using static RTK GPS measurements. Sessions were held using four Trimble 4700 GPS receivers (Trimble, Sunnyvale, Calif.) to tie the ends of the base line (North Base and South Base) to four existing control monuments. To search for the intermediate mile marks along the line, two Trimble 4800 units and a Topcon Legacy (Topcon Positioning Systems, Pleasanton, Calif.) would be used as RTK rovers.

Diana Brown and I took a walk to check out the much talked-about monument at the North Base, which is tucked back in the marshy and wooded area west of State Highway

Ron Miller, PLS, ponders over where to spike the shovel next with Randy Wilcox. Bodie Island Lighthouse in background.

NC 12. A short walk about 200 yards off the highway on a bed of pine needles and a nicely groomed trail, thanks to Stalls and his friends, brings visitors upon a 3'x3' slab of granite in excellent condition. The capstone for this monument is displaced, lying on the ground beside the monument itself. This capstone is roughly 20"x 2"x 40" in an obelisk shape (like a squatty version of the Washington Monument) with parallel sides. All sides are marked: 1848, A. D. Bache Supt., U. S. Coast Survey and Base No. 4. One of the surveyors cleaned the monument with bleach to make the letters stand out more clearly. North Base has three reference marks, smaller granite monuments (about 12" squares) with center-punched copper rods set approximately 100' away in westerly, northerly and easterly directions.

The monument at the south end of the line, South Base, is south of the entrance road to Bodie Island Lighthouse, approximately 100' east of N.C. Highway 12. The monument has been totally covered in sand, roughly to a depth of 2' and the capstone is in very poor condition. Stalls retrieved recovery text for this station, indicating the existence of two reference marks, both of which were found by the crews. One was a few inches below the ground surface, while the other was buried under about 3 feet of sand.

The Finding of the Mile Markers

Stalls and Hugh Sorrell, PLS, also of NCDOT, had already located the first mile marker a few days prior to the October 26 event. It was not 5,280' from the north end as he expected it would be, but rather about 4½' short. To find the other five-mile markers, we split off into small crews to cover as much territory as equipment and personnel would allow. We went on the assumption that the mile marks were set at the distance in miles rounded to the nearest 6 meters, yielding all segments at 268 tubes. It was cool and windy, nice work weather that reduced the mosquito nuisance. It was a good time of year, too, because we dodged the hurricanes, so there was really no chance that we would lose our instruments as Bache and his crew did.

Rick Poytress and James Cratt of NCDOT found Marker #2, as calculated. Randy Wilcox and Ron Miller, PLS, of NCDOT found Marker #3, nearly effortlessly, about 5" deep and on line, albeit about 20' northerly. The distance between #2 and #3 had been mistakenly assumed as a 269-tube segment, but this finding indicated that all of the segments would be 268 tubes. Position calculations were adjusted accordingly and the remaining marks were searched for. Gary Thompson, PLS, director of the North Carolina Geodetic Survey, won the Find-and-Seek Game at Marker #4. "The water was a little bit chilly," he said, citing the knee-deep water where he found the marker sticking up.

Onto Marker #5, we found Joe Huffman, a party chief, at Coastal Engineering and Surveying, Inc., of Kitty Hawk, N.C., who had recently located the marker, with Buck Rogers, PLS, and Greg Skeen, PLS. "That one was not pleasant," he said, standing with his Topcon Legacy unit. Huffman said the marker is in good shape and flush with the ground, but was in a very swampy bed.

While searching for Marker #6 in some messy earth and not knowing if the marker would be deeply buried in the swampy water or sitting above ground, we rummaged around in the wet, prickly brush. Thompson randomly spiked his spade into the ground and after about 20 minutes, all present heard "Clink!" followed by a respondent, "I like that sound!" from Thompson.

Isolated settings for marks may not always be ideal for locating, as they can cause more obstacles than expected. But in the case of the Bodie Island Base Line Resurvey, it was favorable, as the monuments have been preserved.

Searching for history: Ron Miller, PLS, and Gary Thompson, PLS, work together to find mile marker #6.

At 3:45 in the afternoon, after treading amid prickly pear, sand and smelly marsh water, the eleven surveyors and two understudies from *POB magazine* found the six rocks successfully. The high-pitched, whining insect noise of the magnetic locators were the last attempts to find a potential third reference mark at the South Base. With no such luck, we packed it up and called it a day—a good surveying day.

Reflections of a Base Line

After a well-needed cleanup and a hearty meal, the Bodie Island Retracement Base Line Survey Crew went their respective ways. They left with a strong sense of spirit for friendship, for surveying and for history. Although the GPS equipment aided in their efforts, the crew did not under-appreciate the work done in the 1800s by A. D. Bache and crew. They recognized the differences in the passing of time and realized the importance of the past surveyors' work.

"Bache and the others that were there over 150 years ago did the real work," Stalls said. "The main reason why the variety of people that have shown interest or participated in the recovery of the line has been to understand what a monumental task, physically and technically, those folks completed. From what I've seen so far, even with today's tools, we'd be challenged to duplicate their accomplishment."

Now, hopefully, other surveyors and the public alike can recognize the importance of the Bodie Island Base Line—and of surveyors as a group—through a special monument dedicated to surveyors on the North Base of the Bodie Island Base Line. Phase II of the Bodie Island Base Line Proposal submitted to the National Park Service includes a request to refurbish the South Base monument, establish trails to both the North and South Bases and erect interpretive plaques to describe the significance of the monuments.

Fund-raising to assist in implementing the requests of Phase II has begun through the assistance and administration of the North Carolina Society of Surveyors (NCSS) Historical Committee. To make the North Base more accessible for public view, Stalls and crew recommended that a permanent trail be established from the Whalebone Information Center, an already established facility for parking and traffic conditions, approximately 1,750 ft. long. Stalls and friends recommend establishing a similar trail to South Base and have analyzed the possible scenarios for the most accessible route with the least amount of maintenance. The proposal to the National Park Service also suggests utilizing local Boy Scout troops (or other civic organizations) to assist in the clearing and landscaping of the trails. This will offer an excellent opportunity for Scouts to earn merit badges and to work closely under the direction and regulation of a government agency.

Charles Challstrom, director of the National Geodetic Survey, has offered to provide commemorative plaques to be installed at each end point of the Bodie Island Base Line, describing the importance of these historic monuments and celebrating the efforts of the recovery and restoration. Efforts to place the North Base monument in the National

Register of Historic Places have begun and could take up to a year, according to Doug Stover, Cultural Resources Specialist with the National Park Service.

After "redrawing" the base line of Bodie Island on the Outer Banks, the volunteer surveyors and all those they've worked with on the project hope their desires for a proper dedication to the past surveyors of the Bodie Island Base Line come to fruition. The monuments will serve as a dedication to all surveyors near and far, here today and gone, but not forgotten. Through a strong and dedicated coalition of devoted individuals from both the private and public sectors, there will—hopefully soon—rest a monument that stands for so much more than was originally intended.

That was then, this is now; appreciating the site of the North Base. (left to right) Randy Wilcox, POB's Lieca Brown, Gary Thompson, PLS, Bobby Stalls, PLS, and Joe Huffman.

Lieca N. Brown is editor of *Point of Beginning (POB) magazine*. Bobby Stalls, PLS, of NCDOT contributed valuable historical research to this article. Article and pictures reproduced with permission of *Point of Beginning magazine*, a BNP Media publication, issue dated February 2003, pages 34-39

Surveying In the Coastal Plains

John W. Parker, PLS

My first and most vivid memory of surveying comes from my later years of high school. My father was dividing out lots for his will and had hired the local surveyor, who just so happened to be a one-man crew. We provided the additional labor. I clearly remember the compass, the Jacob staff (Jake), chain (which the surveyor referred to as the "tape"), and chaining pins. His procedures particularly caught my interest, since in my math classes in school we were studying geometric figures and relationships, the unit circle, and magnetic directions. The procedures used by the surveyor and his accuracy of work, I later discovered, were far from that needed or required. As was still the case then for some rural coastal survey work, the surveyor was not registered, nor did he work for a registered surveyor. Rather, he was a woods surveyor who worked for the Forest Service and performed property surveys on the side—a moonlighter.

His method for measuring the tie down of one tract located on a dirt road has reentered my mind many times over the years as I have studied old deeds, maps, and descriptions. This particular section of road had a frequently used travel way, approximately 20 feet in width with an additional area on each side, referred to as the "shoulder." A curve of several hundred feet was located along the tie line. The surveyor was very specific in his instructions to me to place the chain on the ground at the edge of the travel way and to shape the chain in the curve so that it fit perfectly with the edge of the travel way as it formed the curve. After placing the chain correctly, I placed the chaining pin at the lead end. The chain was then moved ahead to measure the next 100 feet.

The surveyor had no deeds for adjoining properties and began his survey at the center of a ditch, which my father described as the dividing line. In dividing out lots along a road frontage, he set no corners, though my father later buried concrete pillars from an old corn barn in the area where the surveyor had taken his shots. His compass seemed fairly sophisticated, reading direct to one degree, and the surveyor estimated to ½ degree. Years later, to satisfy my curiosity and upon calculating his closure, I found that he was accurate to one foot in approximately each 100 feet, though his closures varied from one foot in 50 feet to as great as one foot in 300 feet—probably not too far out for the methods used then.

This survey has been within the last thirty-five years—at a time when transits were the prevalent surveying instruments and theodolites were already in use by the more advanced coastal surveyors. It seems that the use of such unlicensed surveyors was quite typical in eastern North Carolina, particularly the rural areas, and this practice continued into the 1970s. Many property owners did not know, or have any concern, as to whether the surveyor was licensed. What they did know was that the surveyor who had an office in town was more expensive—a more likely concern for the property owner.

Many of the earliest surveys in the coastal area were conducted by the property owners themselves, actually not surveys, but more of a call for adjoiners with some calls for a general direction, no distance, and eventually intersecting with the adjoining property owner's line. Few records indicate that "real" surveys were conducted by "surveyors," but rather by individuals identifying themselves as engineer, civil engineer (C.E.), and even an occasional B.C.E. Many deeds or maps simply stated "as surveyed by… " or even did not name who did the survey.

The changing of the rules in the 1970s by the North Carolina Board of Registration for Professional Engineers and Land Surveyors removed the engineers from those allowed to perform property surveys, though many from the coast quickly registered as surveyors through demonstration of their past experience as surveyors. By the latter part of the 1970s, surveys by unlicensed surveyors were all but eliminated.

METHODS AND EQUIPMENT. The most frequent of the earliest of descriptions was simply the call for adjoiner's lines, with an occasional natural feature mentioned. The call for the "corner tree," or the road leading to someone's house, or some other well-known landmark gradually came into use. The call for a general "northerly" direction became more specific and became a "northeasterly" direction. The use of the most elementary compass increased the angular accuracy to at least 5 degrees, and the use of the measuring pole increased the accuracy of the total distance of a given line to 16.5 feet, supposedly. The more interesting perch, (a pole removed from the roosting area of a chicken coop), also was 16.5 feet. Pacing, as in "thence north about 50 paces" (or steps), was a frequently used method of measurement. Accuracy increased more when the Gunter chain came into use with the reporting of distances in chains and links.

Most of the earliest surveys reported no data along boundary lines that were formed by water bodies such as rivers, creeks, and branches, with only an occasional general direction and, in few instances, an approximate distance. Some indicated the direction of flow.

Even into the 1970s, surveyors reportedly used a graduated measuring wheel, particularly along the smooth surface of paved public roads.

Many of the earliest descriptions did not identify an area or acreage of the subject tract. Conversely, some descriptions, which merely called for adjoiners, would report that the tract contained "100 acres." Other descriptions would report "containing about 100 acres" or "containing 100 acres by estimation." Occasionally, a deed or map would report "containing 103 and ½ acres" with one-fourth of the tract perimeter bordering on a stream, but with no stated direction or distance. One must assume that the surveyor performed much more work than was shown on his map, or stated in the description, but there was probably another reason for stating the area to the ½ acre.

The introduction of the transit and the properly used 100-foot steel chain arguably accounted for the greatest change in the accuracy of surveying, though it was uncommon for the typical surveyor to apply temperature, tape, and slope corrections. The chainman seemed to know exactly how much tension to apply to adjust for these corrections as the measurements were made.

Town, city, and public survey work followed a more accurate, but parallel, path as the technology advanced. The Dumpy and Wye levels were owned only by the more advanced surveyors working the towns or public projects. The theodolite, an advanced transit with a new look, came into use by the more advanced surveyors in the late 1960s and early 1970s, though some old-timers who continued to practice well into the 1980s, never owned a theodolite. The electronic distance measuring device (EDM) significantly reduced the laborious chaining of long distances. However, the early models had to be switched with the theodolite at every set up and were so large, bulky, and heavy that the field crews preferred to use the chain. They became believers with the invention of the small EDM, that easily attached to the top of the theodolite, with batteries that could endure nearly a half-day of continuous use. This light-weight, semi-total station was soon replaced with the complete, even lighter-weight total station that the Japanese introduced at a cost that most busy surveyors could afford. Then came the fully-automated total station with electronic data collectors that presumed to eliminate the need for keeping notes by hand. Next came the robotic instrument, that electronically followed the surveyor around and took shots on demand. Nothing, however, has replaced the bush axe.

Global Positioning Satellite Surveying (GPS) was better received in coastal North Carolina than the robotic instrument, but the initial expense, lengthy learning curve, and selective areas of use have kept many companies from purchasing it. As the technology continues to advance—with increases in the speed, accuracy, and mobility—GPS is undoubtedly the equipment for the future.

In the late 1970s, one industrious company invented a Magnesium Tracer Targeting System, intended to ease the taking of extremely long shots over varying types of terrain and woods. The procedure consisted of positioning a .45 caliber handgun chambered with magnesium tracer shells directly over the unknown point or location. Through radio contact between the unknown point and the instrument position, the firing of the tracer was coordinated and, after several attempts, the instrument, or multiple instruments, could lock onto the magnesium trail. After being certain of a lock, the surveyor could move the instrument to another position, and another session begun. Elementary triangulation, but one minor problem—the work had to be done at night. The magnesium tracer shells were not inexpensive, weather conditions had to be favorable, and most surveyors just did not want to work at night. Whether any surveyor in the coastal area ever used this system is not known.

MAPPING. The first survey maps were more often simple sketches, using a straightedge occasionally. Lettering was freehand and large. The scale was either in poles or chains or not mentioned at all. The use of an elementary compass or protractor later provided more accuracy in plotting the shape of the property. Leroy lettering equipment or templates, though infrequently used, helped reduce the misinterpretation of numbers. Physical features continued to be sketched on, some elaborately, with their location clearly provided by estimation, or guesswork. Elaborately-drawn north arrows, some with the entire compass reproduced, were much more common than was plotting accuracy. The advancement of the mechanical drafting machine allowed for plotting accuracies in graduations as close as one minute of angle and correlated closely with the accuracy of observed direction taken by the one-minute transit.

The seasoned draftsman could letter with the Leroy Templates nearly as fast as one could letter freehand. The electronic lettering machine, which came into use in the coastal area in the early 1980s, relieved the tired hand, but being mechanical in nature, brought its own problems and difficulties. Though bulky and difficult to move around on the surface of the drawing, the machine was at its best when large amounts of text were required. For extensive text, the machine was quickly replaced by sticky-backed material, on which one could type standard notes, legends, and other voluminous text, photocopy, and artlessly stick onto the face of the drawing. Personal computers, and computer-aided drafting software of the 1980s, and especially the 1990s, have all but eliminated hand drafting and lettering. The technology and equipment speed continue to advance.

The multiple pen-ink plotters of the 1980s, along with the climate-sensitive electrostatic plotters, while providing excellent service and speed, have all but been eliminated by the new, and nearly defect-free, inkjet plotters with roll paper feeds and automatic cutters. Few surveyors on the coast today still prepare any sizeable map by hand.

COPIES. It was not unusual, even in the 1970s, for landowners to produce an original map or an original tracing of their property. Limited options were available for reproducing the earliest maps, and many old original maps have been long lost. Maps of the older surveyors carry the notations that show that they were traced from the original, or the map book in the Register of Deeds office.

Reproduction through the chemical reaction process seems to have occurred in eastern North Carolina in the early 1900s, though the release of the original continued for many years. The two-stage, advanced ammonia or diazo machine significantly accelerated the process, with machines in the 1970s reaching process speeds up to 30 feet per minute—quite a difference from placing a copy in the developer tube for several minutes. Even these machines are fading away, as health concerns associated with ammonia gases and processes increase. The current trend in copiers is the black line photographic process with capabilities of storing billing accounts into memory, programming copies, and having multiple-roll paper feeders and automatic cutters.

THE MATH. The first surveyors apparently had little, or no, need for math. Data was reported exactly as collected, often with one or more sides of the property not having any data. Bearings or directions were reported, at best, to one or one-half degree. Closures, if determinable, did not begin to appear until the last half of the twentieth century and with greater frequency in the last thirty years. The Double Meridian Distance (DMD) method of determining closure and area entered the scene in the 1950s. It was more widely used in the 1960s, though it was still common practice not to survey natural borders along streams and marshes. Logarithmic tables and trigonometric fans with calculations done by hand were the predominant method of calculation until the mechanical calculator, such as the Marchant, became available. Only the more progressive surveyor used such equipment, as well as card-reader systems and those manufactured by such companies as Wang, which appeared in the coastal area in the early 1970s.

Hewlett Packard easily reduced to extinction the log table and trig fan when it introduced its Hewlett Packard (HP35) with built-in trigonometric functions. Its HP45 sold for $400 in about 1973. It could convert coordinates from rectangular to polar and back, convert degrees, minutes, and seconds to decimals and back, and could store up to twelve numbers in memory. Calculations of closures and areas by coordinates were now done with speed that almost dazzled those who had previously labored by hand for hours to perform such calculations.

Apple Computers arrived on the coast in the early 1980s, brought by a programmer who had written the survey computation software for surveyors. This, and similar systems, and software spread throughout the eastern surveying offices, with the hand-held Hewlett Packard model becoming the personal field tool of virtually every surveyor.

The International Business Machines Personal Computer (IBM PC) and IBM compatible PCs, in addition to a proliferation of various surveying and mapping software followed, and the Apple Computer soon was retired to the closet. The advancement in computer and software technology accelerated so quickly in the 1990s that, in many cases, only the larger, more progressive companies have attempted to keep fully abreast. The latest generation of Pentium processing systems, computing software, and computer-aided drafting software have so many capabilities, operate at such speeds, and generate so much heat, that air conditioners or fans are needed to keep the work area cooled, even during cool weather.

The most advanced surveyor today performs field services with the total station and electronic data collector. He computes and prepares his maps with a Pentium 300 MHZ processor, plots on a Hewlett Packard inkjet plotter, and produces his copies on the Xerox black line engineering copier—and still can't complete the work fast enough to satisfy the client.

THE CALL FOR CORNERS. The lack of descriptive detail of corners has been a thorn in the side of all retracement surveyors. The first descriptions, which ordinarily referred only to the adjoiner's line and then arriving at that corner, were impossible to follow without the landowner showing where he knew the lines to be. A "point on the road leading to the old landing" was just as impossible to find. When corners were mentioned, they routinely called for every species of tree native to the area. Stakes were typically light-wood stakes or a light-wood knot, but unless the material was identified specifically, it was unknown. Once the direction and distance had become more frequent, the bearing and distance determined during the retracement survey was often found not to be close to that of the former survey. The most easily retraceable maps and descriptions referred to fence lines, hedgerows, ditches, and "the tree" that probably long since had disappeared. The next generation of surveys would find the stump, the stump hole, a light-wood stake, or an unspecified stake, in the stump hole.

Some lines in wooded areas were blazed or chopped, with blazed or chopped witness trees, but that practice varied with the surveyor. It seems that the more accurate surveys, mapping, marking of lines, and identification of corners were the work of surveyors for the timber companies, which purchased large acreages of coastal pine land in the early 1900s. Few lines are chopped or blazed today.

The call for a fence post—usually cedar or cypress was chosen for their permanence. The most predominant, permanent-type corners were cart axles, a few car axles, pump pipes, or simply iron pipes. Stones, not abundant in the coastal area, were seldom discovered, though occasionally one might find the reference to stones, even carved with the property owner's initials. Partial sections of discarded, used railroad rails, called "railroad irons" or "T-irons," often extending four to five feet above ground, were the most permanent and easily recognizable corners.

Corners used within the last half century have been more consistently the iron pipe, pinched iron pipe or iron stake (normally rebar) varying in lengths from 18" to 30", and a sprinkling of concrete monuments. Apparently at some point, obtaining iron pipe and rebar was difficult, and surveyors purchased long sections of electrical conduit, cut into lengths of approximately 24", to substitute for the conventional iron pipe. In paved areas, nails were inserted through soft drink bottle caps and driven into the pavement surface. The more visible "shiner" caps later replaced bottle caps, and most caps were eliminated after Parker Kalon (PK) nails became available.

The coastal surveyor of today places iron rebar or rods or iron pipes for regular corners and typically uses concrete monuments for control corners. PK nails are most frequently used for points set in pavement or driven into the top of electrical transformers. Chiseled "V" or "X" shaped marks in concrete are also regularly found.

THE ALTA. The American Land Title Association survey requirements were generally unknown to the coastal area until the early 1980s. In many areas, ALTA expanded significantly the level of effort the surveyor must invest in research, survey procedures, and mapping and reporting. Before the ALTA, the typical angle was turned twice or doubled, with the second turning primarily to verify that the first angle had been correctly read. The ALTA, however, for most survey classes, required angles to be turned four times (two directs and two reverses), which increased the field work and the cost for such surveys. The ALTA specified that the surveyor analyze each adjoiner's deed and report on the map their north orientations, mathematical closures, and data for each common line. This requirement resulted in many surveyors reporting three sets of bearings and distances along any given line: one set for the adjoining tract from its deed, one set for the subject tract from its deed, and a final set of data from the current survey. These, and many other requirements, resulted in a cost nearly double the norm for the otherwise conventional survey.

During the 1990s, requests for these surveys became increasingly more frequent—particularly for larger commercial projects. They have become a current standard requirement of many national chain stores, as well as lending institutions, and for large apartment and condominium developments. It is now not uncommon to perform the ALTA survey prior to development. A second ALTA survey is conducted upon completion of development, which records all the physical improvements that have been made.

THE COUNTY SURVEYOR. Now, almost unheard of, the county surveyor, in his day, was assumed to be the master—supposedly knowing all things, capable of interpreting all deeds and maps, and the absolute authority on the true and correct location of lines. He was the settler of disputed lines and the court-appointed commissioner for partitioning proceedings. A legal proceeding was often ordered by the clerk of the court in order to divide equitably an estate left by the deceased who did not provide in a will, or by other means, the desired division of his property among his heirs. The county surveyor might also be engaged by the clerk of court of neighboring counties to assist in dispute settlements and partitioning proceedings. The position was that of an elected official similar to the county sheriff, but without a salary.

Most offices of the county surveyor had been eliminated, or forgotten, by the 1970s; though at least one county, Onslow, maintained the office into the early 1980s. Either the office was officially abolished, or surveyors simply stopped filing for the office. There are currently no known county surveyors' offices in the coastal area.

FEMALE SURVEYORS. From the early years, female surveyors were unheard of, probably not even remotely considered a possibility. A female surveyor was as unheard of as a lady king; survey work was reserved for men only. Female employment in the surveying business was relegated to office/secretarial and drafting duties, with females comprising nearly half of the drafting workforce in surveying offices. At least one company in the Jacksonville area had a female crew chief in the late 1970s. Still, one seldom finds a female on a typical survey crew in eastern North Carolina, though they are infrequently seen working with a Department of Transportation survey crew.

Today, there are several North Carolina registered female surveyors, with at least one gaining a significant part of her earlier experience on the coast.

SURVEYING FOR SHELLFISH. The coastal waters of North Carolina are controlled by the North Carolina Marine Fisheries Commission, which regulates, among other things, the taking of seafood by both individual and commercial operations. The commission provides for the leasing of certain public trust water bottom areas to individuals for clam culture, oyster culture, and the culture of other shellfish. These are universally referred to as the "Oyster Leases." Upon commission approval of the lease, the lessee is required to furnish a survey of his lease area, which may contain from one to ten acres of open-water bottom.

The oldest surveys rarely provided enough information to determine even the general location of the lease without prior knowledge. In fact, without the leaseholder showing the location, the lease area may never be found. After all, the lease could be a two-acre site surrounded by the open waters of a 50-acre bay. Interestingly, the Marine Fisheries rules, at one time, provided for resolutions of disagreements on whether the survey actually purported to show the same area as the agreed lease. The boundary of the lease was typically marked with wooden posts that projected a few feet above the water surface at high tide. Since the tract was not actually "real" property, without adjoining owners frequently observing the leaseholder's routine, the location of the lease corners could easily be moved. Retracement surveys regularly found that the relative location of corner posts marking the lease did not accurately fit with the shape or size of that described in the lease description or on the map.

The water vehicle of choice for conducting such surveys is the ultra-flat bottom or Jon boat with poles or long paddles, used to push the boat through the shallowest mud bottoms. Water depths may be two feet or less at high tide, with an 18-inch tide range, and if the survey work is not properly coordinated with the tide, one may spend more time poling the boat than performing the survey.

Before the EDM was available, the survey was mostly performed by observing the corners of the lease from multiple setups on dry land, simple triangulation. The careful surveyor would, in addition, attempt to measure between the lease corners as a check against his triangulation calculations. Except for the difficulty of getting to the lease site, using the current total station has made shellfish lease surveys nearly as elementary as any other radial survey, but there are complications. The Marine Fisheries Commission requires that the lease corners be marked by posts at least three inches in diameter, extending at least four feet above high tide water level. The posts frequently extend several feet above the minimum, which all but eliminates the possibility of placing the prism pole on top of the post. The rules also require that the survey now be conducted in accordance with Board Rule 21-66.1600, which requires a minimum degree of accuracy. Obtaining such accuracy can become tricky with a 3" diameter post that may be leaning at a 15-degree angle, especially when the surveyor must take the shots on a day with 40 mph winds, which always seems to be the case when performing such work.

THE CHANGING TIDES. The earliest surveyors paid little attention to water bodies, since the property adjoining the water body had little or no value at the time. The deed or map, often merely referred to reaching the water body, and then running with the water body. No direction or distance was given. Upon reaching an adjoiner's intersecting boundary line, the survey then proceeded to move upland again. These areas were simply not important. Most marshes and swamps were considered wasteland and were possessed only because they were a part of the total tract. Occasionally, a surveyor would identify, most likely by estimation, the location of marshes, swamps, and other wet areas. As property gained value and as the usefulness of the land more frequently affected its value, marshes and swamps became more adequately surveyed and mapped. Some of the surveys following along the edge of the "unusable" land called for an extension of the property lines to the water body. The precise location of the property line intersecting the water body was seldom, if ever, needed.

Into the third quarter of the twentieth century, surveyors increasingly began to identify and report their estimation of the fabled approximate "mean high water line." At best, the location of the line was a guess and could vary with as many surveyors as were on the property. The often made statement that ten different surveyors would identify ten different locations for the mean high water line was undoubtedly accurate.

The adoption of the Coastal Area Management Act (CAMA), in the early 1970s, and the adoption of the Coastal Area Stormwater Rules in the 1980s, universally changed the procedures of performing surveys bordering water bodies. The state began to strongly enforce its claim of ownership of all waters below the mean high water line and applied environmental controls over the use or development of the adjoining land.

By the 1970s, the migration of the general population toward the coast was well underway. Developments on the Barrier Islands, which by the 1970s had gained reasonable vehicular access, no longer required the use of boats or ferries. The building of homes and condominiums began to spread on the oceanfront, as well as along the sounds and streams leading inland.

The mean high water line is the most elusive line for the coastal surveyor to determine. Theoretically, considering the average of all high tides over an 18.6-year period, it is virtually impossible for the surveyor, at the time of the survey, to be exactly at the mean high water line, since he is never in the exact middle of the 18.6-year cycle. On the day of the survey, it would be another 9.3 years before the averaging of the tides' cycle is complete. Frequently, the surveyor, based on his years of experience, surveyed his best estimate of the location of the mean high water line. In many instances, the surveyor would locate and report what was described as the "high tide line," presumably the level to which the water rose during the last high tide. He would often use the "trash line" along the ocean—the deposit of buoyant shells and trash left by the receding waters of the highest recent tide. Obviously, neither of these correctly identified the "mean" high water line.

As the level of regulatory control increased in the latter part of the 1980s, storm water restrictions were added. Later, Outstanding Resource Water (ORW) designations were made, which asserted additional levels of storm water restrictions for these special areas. While different commissions administer the CAMA and storm water regulations, they often work closely in regulating and controlling development near water bodies. CAMA extended its jurisdiction (AEC) to 575 feet from the mean high water line of ORW, with the storm water regulations assigning a maximum of 25% allowable built-upon area as within the 575-foot AEC. Additionally, the rules prevented the possibility of an engineered system, or the construction of any storm water collection devices, such as curbs and gutters, catch basins, and storm water piping networks, except under certain limited situations. The regulations continued to restrict other areas to no more than 30% allowable built-upon surfaces without an engineered treatment system.

An accurate location of the mean high water line, one agreeable to both the CAMA and storm water regulators, became notably more important. The total area of the tract became the basis for determining the limitation of built-upon areas and particularly impacted individual lots that might be carved out. Setbacks from the mean high water line, as designated by CAMA local zoning or storm water rules, multiplied the significance of the accuracy of the line. The "buildability" of the property, and the assurance that each individual lot was buildable within the regulatory constraints, became the responsibility of the surveyor. If the surveyor inaccurately reported a mean high water line that was waterward of the "true" location, (that location as proclaimed by the regulator), the area of the parcel could become too small. The setback from the water body could become too little, and, when applying the 25% or 30% allowable built-upon calculation, the space available for building could become too small. The owner or developer would then hold the surveyor responsible for making the property "unbuildable." Conversely, if the surveyor placed the mean high water line landward of the correct location, the owner, or developer, lost much needed space and held the surveyor responsible for "giving away land."

Another area of major concern is associated with the surveyor's determination of the mean high water line. The AEC, within which land disturbing activities require a CAMA permit, extends inland from the mean high water line. Hence, the demarcation of the high water line may determine whether a permit should be obtained. Any development activity that occurs within the AEC—which also requires any other state or federal permit, approval, or consistency review—elevates the permit to a major status. The process is excruciatingly involved and solicits multi-environmental agency review and scrutiny. If, based on the surveyor's determination of the mean high water line (and thence the AEC), a determination is made that development is not to occur within the AEC, an application for a CAMA permit would not be made. Development could begin, with the regulators later determining that the development is, in fact, within the AEC, and no permit has been obtained. In this situation, the issuance of "cease and desist" or "stop-work" orders may occur. The surveyor may then be assumed to be responsible for causing the illegal activity.

Differing opinions with the regulator on the correct location of the mean high water line have increased in recent years. More complex is the instance where a development was platted and recorded several years earlier. Home construction is to begin on an individual lot; a Minor CAMA Permit is required, and the current regulator disagrees with the location of the mean high water line reported on the recorded development plat. In this case, the location of setbacks, the size of the lot, the AEC location, and the buildable allowance are all affected by an otherwise minor disagreement.

Disagreements are most prevalent in areas of large tidal flats, which have minimal elevation change in tide. In these locations, a one-half foot change in tide could extend over several hundred horizontal feet. Such distances can have tremendous effects on the developable area and need for Major CAMA Permits for many projects. The determination of this mean high water line should be commenced with extreme caution. The prudent surveyor will request regulatory approval of his established line, or establish the line jointly with the regulator. Significant disagreements could then be negotiated. The mean high water line could be established by more scientific methods, incorporating the use of tide stations, tide tables, tidal benchmarks, or accepted elevation to determine as accurately as possible the theoretical location of the line.

Some well-seasoned regulators profess that they can visually determine the mean high water line within as close as 1/10 of a vertical foot by identifying the most landward extent of the marsh vegetation known as Spartina Altorniforia. The surveyor who also identifies the high water line by this method will often obtain an immediate agreement by the regulator. Uncertainty enters when sparse patches of the Spartina are located up slope of the normal edge of the prevalence of vegetation, or strips of vegetation may be separated, by a "Hammock" of only a few inches in height from the normal extent of the marsh. Since the Spartina requires frequent flushing of the tide and nutrients carried by the tidal salt waters for its survival, the regulator will insist that the location of the line follows along the most landward edge of any extent of the Spartina.

The accurate location of the first line of stable natural vegetation (vegetation line) on oceanfront dunes, similar to the mean high water line, establishes the criteria for control and development in these areas. CAMA regulations require that buildings be set back specific distances (determined by the average annual rate of erosion), which vary along the entire length of the coastline. Essentially, each word within the term "first line of stable natural vegetation" is significant in making the determination. "First" means the nearest edge of the vegetation on the ocean side. The "line" is a normalized straight line created by the vegetation, which is often extrapolated as a best-fit line. "Stable" means that the vegetation must cover a relative majority of the area. The term "natural" requires that the vegetation be indigenous to the area (a sodden lawn or dune would not be indigenous).

Photo by John W. Parker. Courtesy of John W. Parker.

Prior to the hurricanes of 1996, an experienced surveyor could determine the vegetation line within generally acceptable tolerances, and a regulator would customarily confirm his determination. Following the storms, with the massive bulldozing and replanting of dunes, the covering of existing natural vegetation with sand, and the adoption of certain special rulings which apply to non-vegetated beach areas—it is now virtually impossible for the surveyor to make any determination. The typical procedure today, in most storm-damaged locations, is to have the regulator stake out the line before the survey work begins.

THE RIPARIAN CORRIDOR SURVEY. The riparian corridor is an area extending from the high ground property, over water, within which the adjoining high-ground land owner has certain rights of use. The rights are most commonly the right to construct a pier or boathouse. The corridor theoretically extends from the main channel, at perpendiculars to the channel, with the corridor width established by the intersection of the perpendicular lines, from the channel to the sidelines of the property. If the channel flows at a skew to the waterward property line of the lot, the corridor remains perpendicular to the channel. It is not, in such instances, unusual for piers to extend from the shoreline at somewhat severe angles. In locations where the property fronts a large bay or where the channel is located hundreds of feet out, it may become necessary to survey water bottom elevations from the shoreline out to the side of the channel. These situations, typically, are found in areas of extreme shallow water, such as those of many shellfish lease areas, (with the Jon boat, again, being the surveyor's vehicle of choice). Corridor surveys are done in conjunction with the typical survey work for a pier permit application.

Surveys for the average homeowner's pier mainly consist of a profile line determining the water-bottom elevations out to a depth of approximately 48 inches, or to a distance of 400 feet (typically the maximum extents for pier permits). The corridor survey may extend the survey work out several hundred additional feet, either to determine the location of the channel or to reach a water-bottom depth of 48 inches. A line is then constructed along the edge of the channel—or a line is determined as a best fit with the 48-inch depth elevations—to which perpendiculars are constructed, which extend to the side property lines of the high-ground tract. The area between the two sidelines forms the riparian corridor, within which the pier may be constructed.

As with shellfish lease surveys, prior to the EDM or total station, surveys were performed using stadia, though some distances were determined by the joining together of several 100-foot tapes. There was minimal need for extreme accuracy of locations. Channels at great distances away, or water depths in large bays, require the taking of dozens of elevation and location readings.

The determination of the riparian corridor does not always allow for a reasonable assignment of corridors. It can result in corridors overlapping existing piers, and, in the head of small bays, can result in the overlapping of several adjoining corridors. In these instances, the regulator may establish the corridors as radial lines extending from the side property lines to a central point in the water—similar to the radius point of a circle. The corridors then are configured as segments or pie-shaped areas. In other instances, with no simple or methodical way of establishing the corridor, the regulator, often through some negotiation with adjoining property owners, will assign corridors that provide reasonable areas of right to the various affected parcels.

In recent years, some developers have simplified the establishment of the riparian corridor during the platting of their property. This procedure is acceptable to, and encouraged by, the regulators since it eliminates the need for extensive corridor surveys. It prevents property owners from becoming unhappy with the situation in the future. The surveyor extends side-lot lines into and over the water body, identifies them as riparian corridors, and the corridors are platted along with the lots on the subdivision plat.

THE PLANNED SUBDIVISION. Much of the coastal area remained primarily rural until the last half century, with property divisions occurring mostly in the old established towns. The earliest-settled towns were usually divided into grids of streets and lots. Lots were usually very narrow, many set at 25 feet in width, with homesites occupying several, but varying numbers of lots. Subdivision maps, when recorded, were simple, but often had elaborate north arrows, some reproducing the entire compass. In many instances, the map makers obviously concentrated their effort and time in drawing the north arrow, a practice that would make today's employers cringe. Lot corners were mostly unlabeled, but the map may carry a notation or certificate stating, "lots as laid out and staked by me." Few dimensions were reported, causing many assumptions to be made as to the direction or distance of lines. With many of the lot corners nonexistent, retracements were difficult.

Often subdivisions were set out by metes and bounds descriptions and no recorded map. Though maps had been prepared, the originals were long since lost. Retracement surveys resulted in new descriptions with corrected bearings and pro-rated distances. Corners that were found rarely formed even a remotely straight line and were seldom perceived to be the original subdivision corners; they were often suspected to have been placed by the property owners. Current retracement surveys may find no two corners on a lot being of the same type or materials.

The subdivisions of the early part of the last half century were platted by the more advanced surveyors, often brought in from another part of the state. Except in the largest of towns, the number of surveyors continued to be low. Curves began to appear, and more cul-de-sac streets limited through traffic and provided more privacy. Plats began to report control points or monuments, which were generally no more permanent or accurate than any other corner. Their existence, at time of retracement, was no more guaranteed than any other corner. Cities and towns eventually developed specific criteria for the establishment of control corners. Some required that monuments be set in special manholes in the center of streets. Data began to appear on each line with errors in mathematics and sliding, transposition and other copying errors made when transferring data to the final copy. Errors, though, could now be more easily discovered, or pinpointed, by calculating the mathematical closure and comparing the closing line to those on the plat. Recorded subdivision drawings were titled with a variety of identifications such as: "Plat of," "Map of," "Plan of," "Plan for," "Map for," and "Division of." The terms "map" and "plat" continued to be frequently interchanged.

In mid-century, subdivision maps intermittently reported data along streams, branches, creeks, and other water bodies, or identified some sort of reference line along the edge of the usable land. Lot lines extended, without dimension, to the approximate location of the water body. Some subdivisions were not surveyed or staked prior to recording, and those that were often had the corners destroyed or obliterated during the construction of the infrastructure or while building homes on lots. A few surveyors continued not to survey or stake lots, even into the 1980s. It was an awakening experience to be the first surveyor in a new subdivision with only a few of the corners, or just the boundary, in existence. As surveying standards were adopted, and as more of the rural towns and counties adopted development regulations, the thoroughness and accuracy of the subdivision survey work improved. Tie downs, tie lines, and ties to the North Carolina Grid Coordinate System all provided additional information to aid the surveyor in retracement.

Today's subdivisions are generally well mapped, though they have a proliferation of certifications, statements, and other superfluous information dictated by local regulations. These clutter the maps and obscure the important information related to the location of the property lines. The additional required information is sometimes so extensive that it requires several extra plat sheets to provide reasonable clarity. Not uncommon are flood lines and wetland lines, which are subject to change. Also, there are locations of utilities, septic systems, roadway paving, and as many certificates as there are agencies or departments which review the plat. That aside, the lots are normally well monumented and staked, have adequate tie lines and control corners, and are quite easily retraceable. The loan survey requirements of recent years have aided in insuring that corners are reestablished after homes are completed, with many first loan surveys being performed by the original subdivision surveyor.

SURVEYING THE AIR. The condominium was not known in the coastal area until the 1960s or 1970s, and the majority of them have been built in the last twenty years. With increased migration of highlanders toward the coast and the desire to live near the ocean, sounds, and other large water bodies, the condominium provided a new and unique method of ownership for large numbers concentrated in small areas. Condominium ownership was not in fee simple as in conventional subdivisions, but rather the ownership of an airspace surrounded by constructed walls. Buildings, amenities, parking areas, and other features were owned in common with the individual ownership being focused on a living unit, one of potentially dozens within the same building.

The Unit Ownership Act prescribed the means for platting and perpetuating this ownership. The earlier surveys were recorded as site plans in the Unit Ownership and Condominium Plat Book. They were separate from conventional subdivision recordings and identified proposed building locations, unit numbers, parking areas, and other amenities. The architectural plans of the buildings were recorded to identify the unit space and its dimensions. In some, though not all instances, the elevation, based on mean sea level of the floors and ceilings, was reported on either the Site Plan or the Architectural Plans. The Unit Ownership Act originally allowed the recording of the project as proposed, and after construction, the recording of actual floor and ceiling elevations.

Current condominium recordings occur after the completion of construction and are As-Built drawings reporting the measured interior dimensions, elevations of floors and ceilings and exterior site improvements. Muddy work boots are not permitted during these surveys.

Though uncommon today, there once was an occasional request for a survey and description of a condominium unit. At first, the survey was conducted essentially as any other survey, with one added dimension—elevation, which provided the third ordinate for determining the location of the unit space property "corner." The horizontal description with bearings and distances could be appropriately tied, and with the unit space boundaries, described with bearings, distances, and mean sea level data, elevations for both floor and ceiling "corners" could be described by XYZ coordinates. The best description was that of the floor space as a horizontal plane—with elevations given for each floor corner—and then describing the ceiling corners as a vertical extension of the corners at the floor, (the walls being presumably plum).

THE EASTERN TOPO. In the earliest years, there did not seem to be a great need, or desire, for topographic surveys. Except for the more complex in town construction projects, the experienced contractor established elevations and grades "by eye" as he laid out his work. Streets and larger building projects in town were constructed using actual plans, but the survey work was done by the more advanced surveyor in the area or by a surveyor brought in from a larger town or city. The earliest subdivision streets and drainage were constructed by the experienced "eye" of the developer and his contractor, who "engineered" as they built. The oldest living developers continue to tell of the days that the bulldozers were "led in" to establish streets and drainage locations; the developer often walking in front determining the street locations as he went. Streets were drained to the lowest areas that, hopefully, drained to an even lower area.

As regulations were adopted to address increased growth and poor drainage that was caused in part by the flatness of the coastal area, the need for pre-construction topographic surveys increased. Except in the larger towns, sanitary sewers were not available, and packaged-type sewage treatment plants did not come into much use until the 1960s and 1970s.

There were few "government"—United States Geodetic Surveys (USGS), North Carolina Geodetic Surveys (NCGS), and National Geodetic Surveys (NGS)—benchmarks. The elevation datum for most surveys was assumed, some data being based on the flood mark of the local stream, creek, or river. Benchmarks were normally railroad spikes driven into trees or utility poles, nails set in pavement, or a mark on the head wall of a nearby drainage culvert—all still the common practice today. The transit, but more often the Dumpy or Wye level, was used with most sites surveyed as 50 or 100-foot grids first laid out and elevations taken at each grid point. Due to the minimal elevation change, the topographic map was prepared with one-foot contour intervals, or by simply reporting the spot elevations at each grid point. Radial Topographic surveys were seldom done.

Though there were continued advancements in levels and the introduction of the theodolite, topographic surveys were still mostly accomplished in the same manner, with trigonometric leveling uncommon until the advent of the total station.

The surveyor continued to rely on the consistent accuracy of conventional level networks, rather than gamble on the potential errors in trigonometric levels. However, the advancement of the total station, with the Electronic Data Collector, has changed the method of today's topographic survey. While many surveys are still conducted using the grid system, the "grids" are regularly configured without parallel or perpendicular lines. The horizontal location of each observation is recorded electronically.

The "self-reading rod" (Linker or Direct Elevation Rod), allowed the flatland surveyor to save much time, both in the field and in the reduction of level notes. The rod, incorporating a sliding tape on its face, could be placed on a point with a known elevation. The tape slid until the instrument cross hairs marked the elevation of the known point. The sliding tape could be locked in to keep it from sliding, and while the instrument remained at the same setup or location, the elevation of all other observations taken could be read directly from the rod. Though time was significantly reduced, numbers could still be misread. When moving the instrument, the rod was reset to the elevation of any known point and the procedure continued until the work was completed. The instrument operator had to be careful to set the tape on the correct side of the 10-foot graduation and to be particularly careful in a sloping area. The loss or gain of ten feet of elevation could easily occur on the steeper slopes. The direct elevation rod continues to be useful in recording and establishing elevations in open flat areas.

THE NATURE AFFECT. Imagine trying to make that last setup of the day in mid February on the top of a 20-foot ocean front sand dune, with a 40 mph eastern wind gusting in from the ocean, and a misting rain. This is one of the worst working conditions the coastal surveyor experiences. Conversely, tunneling through a pocosin bay in the dog days of August, a half-mile from daylight, the humidity at nearly 100%, with not even the slightest hint of a breeze for hours is almost as physically challenging. While each area may have its extreme working conditions, these two are probably as extreme as can be found anywhere. The coastal surveyor tromps through marshes and swamps, over sand dunes, through the thickest of vegetation, while fighting off gnats, mosquitoes, yellow flies, ticks, and red bugs. He tangles with vines, thorns and briars, and frequently loses blood, or, at least—loses a little blood. He stays on the watch for snakes, particularly during the walk in or out of the woods. Snakes are seldom seen while doing actual work, because the continuous thrashing of the bush axe frightens them away. The astute surveyor, however, will have developed nearly instinctive radar that searches out their location. Many surveyors have become so used to the woods that the presence of even poisonous snakes seems of little, or no, concern. Hornets, wasps, ground bees, yellow jackets, and similar insects seem to be of greater concern to the coastal surveyor, and inflict the greatest injury. More than a few bush axes have been left in the coastal woods while surveyors flee from a swarm of irate ground bees.

All this aside, there is, arguably, no better place to be in the spring or fall than in the coastal area.

THE LINGO. The general terminology, the phrases used during typical discussions, and the signals the coastal surveyor uses during daily survey procedures are not unlike those of surveyors in other areas, but a few may be slightly different.

"Throwing the chain" has no relation to throwing anything else. It is a very complicated industry procedure whereby the thrower unfolds the survey chain from its collapsed circular position into a figure-eight position and then, while holding opposing sides of the figure eight in each hand, twists and pulls at the same time, in opposing directions, while the chain, if properly manipulated, opens into an even larger circle. The thrower then proceeds to "undo" the chain, much as one would a rope or electrical cord, by stringing it out from each of its five-foot circumference loops. The reverse procedure is called "doing-up the chain."

"Breaking the chain," similarly, has no relation to breaking the vase that has been in your wife's family for a hundred years. The term refers to using shorter portions of the chain to measure, horizontally, the distances along steeply sloped areas such as the side of a hill. The procedure allows the individuals at each end of the "broken" section to hold their end of the chain at a level position; typically, the person on the lower side of the slope holds the chain at approximate head height, and the individual on the upper-slope area holds the chain at shin level. This takes place while hanging a plumb bob, with string draped over the chain, carefully positioned at the correct distance along the chain, and holding the point of the plumb bob over a stake or other marker. This is done while applying just the exact amount of tension (the two individuals pulling in opposite directions) to correct for the sag in the chain, and hoping that the person up slope doesn't let go quickly.

"A head" is a term typically heard on survey sites or by those rambling in the wooded areas where survey work is being done. Often heard as a single, but very loud burst, it is only an abbreviation for "come ahead," meaning that the instrument man has successfully made his observation. The crew person giving the shot may now move on to another location.

"Lite and legs" is another abbreviated term referring to the theodolite, or survey instrument, and the tripod upon which it rests.

"Gun" is used when the survey crew arrives at the house lot, exits the vehicle, and one asks, "Do we need the gun yet?" No, it is not necessary to collect all pets and children and lock them safely in the house, though certainly that would be the wish of the survey personnel in some instances. The word merely refers to the surveying instrument and whether it is needed immediately.

"Break out everything," often unpleasant to the ears of the survey crew, signals that all equipment and materials at the survey crew's disposal will be needed for this work.

"Pack it up" is a phrase most likely enjoyed by the survey crew. As one may guess, it means, "We're ready to leave."

"Busted" has nothing to do with drugs, but it is probably the least-desired term any surveyor can hear. It means that the survey work does not close mathematically, or that there is an obvious error or inaccuracy at some location; it then becomes necessary to retrace and re-measure possibly each angle and distance along the survey perimeter.

"Did you double?" has absolutely nothing to do with how late the instrument man stayed at the local tavern. It merely questions whether the angles were turned twice.

"Shot!" is another term frequently heard at the survey site. Usually, in a very loud exclamation, it is the instrument man inviting the rod man to place his target over the point to be observed.

"The good chain" illustrates that some surveyors are possessive of their best equipment and carry more than one chain in their vehicle. The "good chain" is usually the newest or least worn and without kinks or repairs. It is kept for the most accurate of measuring.

"Bay or Pocosin" is another term the surveyor does not like to hear. Pocosin (po-ko-sin) has no relation to the term "moccasin," a certain type of shoe or a snake that frequents water or wet areas. It is an Indian term meaning "swamp on a hill." Most pocosins or bays are not like typical swamps, with minimum under story vegetation and standing water, though the surface is often wet. They are usually so thick with vines, briars, and vegetation that they are virtually impenetrable. The survey site lines become tunnels carved through the vegetation.

"Hook" is the tool of choice, by necessity, used by the coastal surveyor for making tunnels through thick vegetation. Also known as a "bush axe," the term comes from the curved hook-shaped tip of the cutting blade, which is much more effective on coastal vegetation than the common machete.

"Sky Hook" is my favorite. This is the piece of equipment that the inexperienced, or "green," surveyor is often sent back to the truck to retrieve so that the crew may use it to cross a large ditch standing in water. The crew chief stands at the edge of the ditch, staring and pondering for several seconds, and eventually reports that the skyhook is needed. Yes, they got me too, at least for a minute.

Trying To Remember (Stories, Humor, etc)

A. J. "Jimmie" Davis III, PLS

Several years ago, the North Carolina Society of Surveyors decided to hold conventions, both to promote interest in the profession, and to give the people who provide us with equipment and supplies a chance to meet with us and to display their latest merchandise.

The first convention was hosted by the surveyors in Wilmington, NC in the Cape Fear Hotel. The announcement for the event suggested bringing wives, and stated that there would be a program for them. I took Jean and she was the only wife there. There was no program, but the convention was such a success that we decided to make it an annual affair. Each year it grew and improved, and we moved the convention to Raleigh, where we met in the YMCA.

The year that I was president, 1968, there was one change that we had elected to keep. Some of us had visited the Virginia convention held at Williamsburg and were favorably impressed. We decided to hold our convention in the Velvet Cloak Inn in Raleigh, North Carolina. I believe that one of the reasons we chose it was that several of the officers liked to dance, and the Velvet Cloak had excellent facilities. We were fortunate in one instance: Louis Smith was a close friend of Bob Scott who was running for governor of North Carolina, and Louis told Scott that if he would let us hold a gala in the governor's mansion, we would consider supporting his candidacy. Scott was elected and remembered his promise to Louis. The first social function held in the mansion was a tea for the surveyors' wives. We were fortunate again in the out-of-state guests that were invited. The presidents from Virginia, Tennessee, and Maryland came with their wives. The wife of the Maryland president grew orchids as a hobby and brought some for the wives of the North Carolina officers, and one extra. It just so happened that Mrs. Jessie Rae Scott, the governor's wife, was an orchid fancier, and we made a big hit with her, so that year we had the full support of Governor Scott.

We had three meetings a year then—one in the mountains, one on the coast, and one in Raleigh. I was very pleased to be able to attend all three, and was very fortunate in being able to visit in almost all the offices of the members. The membership was not as large as it is now, so it wasn't as difficult as it sounds.

One other good thing for the year was the wives' formation of the NCSS Ladies Auxiliary. The ladies have meant so much to the society, and I am sure that the friendships formed at the conventions have helped make it the great organization that it is today.

Moses Farmer had been the secretary of the society for several years and was a very dedicated officer, but correspondence with the membership was difficult. He lived in Raleigh on the east side of Highway No. 70, and it was convenient for me to go up to see him. I made several trips to his office to work on society business. We decided to use his secretary on a temporary basis, and she turned out to be very helpful.

Joe Hardee was the president before me, and he sent me a copy of every letter he had written or received during his two years as president. You cannot imagine how helpful they were in letting me know what the job entailed. With the help of Moses' secretary and the secretary in my office, I was able to continue the same practice. I also kept a copy for my files and was able to turn over to the society a bound copy of the year's correspondence.

Today, the officers are much better trained in their duties, and the transition is much smoother than in earlier years. The practices started by Joe Hardee have gone a long way toward making the governing body as efficient as it is today.

Snake "Tails"

Every surveyor knows that as soon as he sets up his tripod, he probably will hear, "Take my picture, Mister." It goes with the territory, as when the surveyor tells his client that his deed has an error, the question will invariably follow, "In whose favor?" A question I dreaded as much as when the teacher used to push the chalk backward across the blackboard.

Another question the surveyor comes to expect is "Do you see many snakes?" Every surveyor has his collection of snake tales. Depending on the reaction he wants to get from his audience, he either is honest and admits that hornets, bees, yellow jackets, fire ants, gnats, and mosquitoes are much more of a threat than snakes; or he decides he wants to entertain and goes to his collection and tries to make each "tail" top the one told before.

My grandfather's brother was a doctor who lived in Texas, and was my idol when I was a young boy. He had gone all over the world on big game-hunting trips, and his stories about snakes were fascinating. My favorite story was about an anaconda he killed on a hunt in South America, and I love to tell it even now. The true story he told about killing a sidewinder rattlesnake in Waco, Texas, reiterates why snake tales should be for entertainment rather than for information. He killed an unusually large sidewinder. They don't grow as big as diamond backs. He preserved the sidewinder and presented it to the local museum. He was present when the first group of visitors saw it and, as usual, someone in the crowd was not impressed because he had killed a snake with two or more rattles. The next day, my uncle performed an operation on the snake and added two rattles. Each time the curator of the museum reported that someone had seen a snake with more rattles, my uncle would add more to the original snake. When he had added enough to make the length of the rattles equal to the length of the snake, he stopped, but the reports of sightings didn't. This has nothing to do with surveying, but his message got through to me and flavors my surveying snake tales.

My wife accuses me of stretching my tales. I maintain that any tale not worth stretching is not worth telling. Let's illustrate first with a horror story:

When the Quaker Neck Electric Plant decided to use the Neuse River lowlands to spill their ashes from the coal-fired generators, they needed a survey. I was working with Ed Little at the time, and we got the job. A cursive investigation revealed that the lines would cross fairly deep sloughs, so I accepted Ed's offer to let me use his fishing waders. He is a lot bigger than I am, and his waders came up pretty high on me. On the first crossing, I started out holding the transit over my head, carefully feeling for the bottom with each step. The water was coming up near the top of the waders, and I wasn't sure if the slough would get deeper, so I decided to stop and look around to see if there was a better way. To my horror, I saw five cottonmouth moccasins swimming in the area. My very first thought was, "What if one got inside these waders?" I know that what I did next will convince you that I am at least one quart shy of a full tank, but believe it or not, I backed out and took off the waders, and surveyed the rest of the job in tennis slippers. I just could not bear the thought of sharing.

On the last day, one of the crew members cut a moccasin in two at the thick part of its body. It was right at a stake I had to occupy. The whole time I was occupying this stake, the snake's head kept striking at anything that moved. This was the first time I had any doubts about not wearing the waders.

Once, when we were surveying for a new fertilizer plant in Brunswick County, the first thing we observed was the number of snakes that slithered out of the dragline bucket as it mucked out the mud. We went into Wilmington to try to buy snake leggings, and were unable to find any, but guys at one hardware store made a suggestion. They sold us stovepipe that we cut off to the correct length and fastened to our blue jean legs. You have to experience hearing the "tink" and feel the thrust and look down and see the venom running down the stovepipe to know what sheer terror feels like!

For the most part, snakes are not foremost on my mind when working in wooded areas. In truth, the activity of cutting lines with bush axes seems to cause them to move away from the activity, and I don't see as many as might be expected. One exception caused me much distress on a survey in Jones County. The day was extremely hot and the area was thick with green running briars—so thick, in fact, that we could not swing the bush axes. We were pecking away at the briars to try to get working room but having very little success. I elected to go back to the vehicle and put on a blue jean jacket and gloves. I pecked a small hole and then lay my body on the briars to force an opening. In short order, I was drenched in sweat and almost blind from it running into my eyes, but we were making progress, so we continued. When we came out for lunch, the man whose property we were surveying asked if we had seen "our friend." I was puzzled at first until he pointed out a large diamond-back rattler he had killed. He said we had run it out of the woods into the path where he was parked. He had cut the head and rattles off and had it hanging on the tailgate of his small pickup truck. Both ends of the snake were touching the ground, and the mid-section was bigger than my lower leg. It was not as big as my thigh, but it was big enough to give me nightmares when I thought that I had probably lain on top of him when he decided to leave for the field. He didn't have to, you know. It was his home, after all.

When Tempers Flared

A number of years ago in Duplin County, NC there arose a land dispute that caused much ill feelings in the community. Both parties in the dispute were taken down into the woods at the end of the disputed line. They drove a gun barrel next to a light-wood stump and announced that from that time on the gun barrel was the corner.

For years, the dispute simmered. Finally, it broke out again, and both parties decided to hire a surveyor and have the lines run again. I got copies of both deeds and met with the parties on the agreed-upon site. Both deeds seemed to agree, and being young and inexperienced, I really wasn't expecting to have any trouble running the lines. The first thing Mr. Jones said when he got out of his truck was that unless I used a map he had in his truck, he wasn't going to agree with anything that was done. When he showed me the map, I immediately realized that it was a mirror of his deed, and either the deed was written backward, or his map was. Because the calls in the deed for the lines that joined Mr. Smith's land agreed with Mr. Jones' deed, I decided that the map was incorrect. When I tried to point that out to Mr. Jones, he became highly insulted. He let me know that he was with the old surveyor when he ran the survey, and when he drew the map.

Everything I said only made him more upset, so I told him I would let him pick any corner that he accepted, and I would set the transit on that corner. I would drop the needle and let him see what his deed called for and what the map called for. He could then decide whether he would rather use his map or his deed. I was so confident that I had convinced him with my indisputable reasoning, that I turned to Mr. Smith with a "know-it-all smile." Mr. Smith had not taken part in the discussion up to this point, and as we proceeded to a known corner, Mr. Jones kept up a running dialog about how certain he was that the map was correct. I set up the instrument and dropped the needle, pointed the telescope in the direction the map called for, and asked in what must have sounded like a sarcastic tone if he really wanted to run in that direction. Mr. Jones had said too much and felt he could not back down and insisted on using the map call.

Away we went across his neighbor's field, and we had started across the next, when I noticed that Mr. Jones was becoming extremely agitated. I got Mr. Smith off to one side and asked him to call off the survey. I told him I was afraid we were going to cause Mr. Jones to have a stroke or "something." Mr. Smith replied, "Not on your life. He started it, and I'm going to finish it." The whole thing was getting out of hand, and I wanted to end it. In exasperation, I said to Mr. Smith, "Tell me why it is that when push comes to shove, a man doesn't act this way over anything but a little piece of land or a woman." Mr. Smith's reply was, "Sonny, when you get my age, the women don't mean a thing. It's just the land." Well, in a short while Mr. Jones did have an attack of apoplexy, and we had to carry him out of the woods. He was put to bed, and in just a couple of weeks he died.

Several months after his death, his son decided to hire the son of the first surveyor, who was also a surveyor, and we all met again on the site. This time, we used the deeds and had no trouble finding the called for corners. When we cut out the line and located the corner, we got one of the oldest men in the neighborhood, who remembered the incident, to identify the stump and gun barrel. I was helping to hold him up as step-by-step we made our way into the woods, and I told him what Mr. Smith had said. This man was white-haired and walked with a crutch and walking cane. He shook with palsy and his voice quivered when he spoke, but he stopped, leaned back on his crutch, and held his walking stick in a very shaky hand, looked me straight in the eye and said, "Well, Sonny, when the women don't mean anything to me, you can have the land." This "Sonny" was one rebuke I didn't mind. With that one short terse statement, he took away my fear and dread of growing old. Oh, one other thing—I'm old now, and you know what? He was right!

What Goes Around Comes Around

Early in school, someone pointed out to the history class that those who choose to ignore history are condemned to repeat it. When the government decided to re-activate Seymour Johnson Air Force Base, I was working for the Army Corps of Engineers in the survey section. They sent a surveyor from Florida to head up the section, and he arrived in the winter with no warm clothing.

One very cold day, when he and I went out to run levels on a large outfall ditch, he was wearing canvas shoes and a very light raincoat. When it became necessary to cross the ditch, I, having on boots, slogged across and wondered how he would manage. He told me he would show me a trick. He took the level rod and put it in the bottom of the ditch and attempted to pole-vault across. About halfway across, the rod settled in the bottom and his forward motion stopped. Then slowly, he fell length ways into the water, lost his footing, and fell completely in. I sat down and laughed until I cried, and the conversation that followed is not fit to print. It concerned my ancestors and the North Carolina winter weather, and my insensitivity, along with my future well-being. It just didn't seem prudent to discuss his athletic ability at this time, so I explained that his mishap had reminded me of a similar incident that happened to me a long time ago.

I grew up in the small town of Mount Olive, NC that had a large ditch or canal that was the headwaters of the eastern branch of the northeast Cape Fear River. The town used this ditch as both a storm and sanitary sewer, and it was the area where most young boys congregated to be Tarzan, Jungle Jim, Davy Crockett, or just an everyday ordinary explorer. Nobody I knew wore shoes in the summer, and we played both in and out of the ditch catching crawfish or digging caves in the bank.

The local pickle plant dumped the waste from their operation into it, and the town turned the sanitary sewer directly into this open ditch. Still we played in it with no discernible ill effects. No one seemed the least bit concerned, but when cold weather came, then my mother always admonished me not to get my feet wet.

On one cold, windy February day, we explored a long way out-of-town to an area that had large trees with vines just like Tarzan's. We all carried knives and soon had a vine cut, and the older boys tried to swing across the canal. Somehow the vine didn't work at all like

Tarzan's, and not to be outdone, the oldest boy found a small dead tree and used it to pole-vault across. Each boy had to try, and as I was the youngest and smallest, I was the last to try. I gave it my best shot, but to tell the truth, I had neither the strength nor the skill, and when I was about halfway across, my forward motion stopped. For a very short while, I hung there in the middle of the canal and started to fall into the canal. Mother had told me not to get my feet wet. I got everything wet. The oldest boy told me to take my clothes off and hang them on a bush and let them dry out. Well, I did and played buck-naked until time to go back to town. The clothes were still very wet, so I put them on and went first to my cousin's house. His mother gave me some of his clothes to put on, and that warmed me up a little, but my mother warmed me up even more. For a long time I wondered, "How did she know?"

Years later, my crews were surveying a tract of land south of Kinston, NC bordered by a large canal. There were several septic tanks in the area, and each one seemed to empty into the canal. There was no bridge across the canal, and the young men on the crew took a running start and jumped across, but I wasn't young anymore and could no longer jump ditches or logs. I sat down on a log and dragged my legs across, and I fell into the ditch and crawled out the other side. This time, the water in the ditch was too deep for my boots, so I decided to use a range pole to vault across. You are way ahead of me. Yes, when I got halfway across, the range pole settled into the bottom, but this time I didn't slowly fall in the water. The pole broke, and I fell with a splash, and the slimy-green water covered me. When I crawled out, the men would not let me in the vehicle. The odor was strong enough to take your breath, and I had to ride back to town hanging on the back. It brought back memories of the good old days!

Early North Carolina Land Surveyors

A.J. "Jimmie" Davis III, PLS

When Otis Jones asked me to write a short article on early North Carolina land surveyors, he did not specify how early. The only knowledge I have of the eighteenth and nineteenth century surveyors is that which I have gleaned from the maps and descriptions they left. The oldest of these are found in land grants and estate subdivisions, and I never cease to be amazed at the amount of work these men turned out. They had to devote their entire time to surveying and mapping.

The surveyors in young North Carolina were, of necessity, educated either in a liberal arts or a military school. There were no technical schools and no schools of higher education devoted to engineering. It must be remembered that public schools, as we know them today, just did not exist in North Carolina prior to the War Between the States. Another thing that must be kept in mind when trying to picture the early surveyor is that surveying equipment was not readily available. The ideas of the vernier and cross hairs in a telescope were conceived in the middle of the 1600s and were incorporated into surveying and navigational instruments, but they were not mass-produced, and they were very expensive. The geodetic surveyor used them but, for the most part, the land surveyor used the magnetic compass.

In the same vein, today when we look at an early survey, we may be critical of the accuracy and smile at the open-ended surveys. We forget that calculators had not been invented. Though the knowledge of trigonometry was available, trig tables were not. Even as late as the 1960s, the standard joke was, "to find a surveyor in town, just drive around and find an office with a light burning until midnight." All calculations had to be done in long hand. The next time you are critical of an early survey, do a closure yourself without the aid of your computer.

Prior to the 1800s, engineering was divided into two branches, military and civil. As late as the 1950s, the public thought of the surveyor in military terms, and a lot of surveyors affected military dress, to wit, bat wing riding pants and riding boots, or leather leggings, Smokey the Bear hats, and khaki shirts with epaulets. In the early 1800s, the industrial revolution created a need for more and better surveyors. The big demand was for railroad and highway surveys. In my area of the state, two surveyors are remembered by name. Goldsboro and Dudley were named after railroad surveyors or engineers. City streets and drainage demanded accurate surveys, and some engineering firms specialized in surveying.

For the most part, in rural North Carolina, land surveys were performed by men who learned their skills by working under a practitioner. A lot of these men just did not have extensive mathematical background.

By World War I, most of the schools of higher education offered plane and route surveying as an elective, and the engineering and military schools required it. Even so, there were never enough trained, educated surveyors willing to survey the rural areas. The general practice in a lot of areas was for anyone with even the barest of knowledge to perform these surveys. These men all signed their work as "engineer" or "surveyor," and the public had no way to know who was, and was not, qualified. The General Assembly, in an effort to correct this situation, passed a registration law in 1921. They appointed a five-man board, and in 1922 these men registered themselves as engineers; two of them registered themselves as land surveyors. At the same time, they registered the first land surveyor applicant. The requirement for registering as a professional engineer was not stringent and even less so for registering as a land surveyor. The law did prevent those not registered from signing a map as a registered land surveyor or as a registered professional engineer. It did not prevent the nonregistered surveyor from practicing his trade.

Soon it became evident that the new law, while helping, did not solve the problem, and a small number of surveyors over the state came together in 1939 to form a society with the purpose of upgrading land surveying. These men were not starry-eyed dreamers, nor were they super educated theorists trying to impose their ideals on the rest of the surveyors. Rather, they were practicing surveyors who, for the most part, did not have the advantage of a higher education. One was a Salvation Army captain. Another was a surveyor and timber cruiser for a lumber company. One, who was secretary to the society for years, had only two honors on his office wall. He was equally proud of his North Carolina Society membership certificate and his Mount Olive High School diploma. All had one thing in common. All agreed there was a problem, and all spent the rest of their lives trying to improve the quality of surveying in the state.

World War II set back their efforts, but the end of the war saw a huge building spurt that created a demand for more and better surveying. The General Assembly responded with a more stringent registration law that prevented nonregistered surveyors from practicing engineering or land surveying. It allowed professional engineers to practice land surveying but prevented land surveyors from practicing engineering. There began a turf war between the two professions that still continues. The General Assembly passed a mapping law in an effort to give the public a way to judge the quality of the surveys they were buying. There was never a complete agreement in the society and, undoubtedly never will be, as to how to effect that desired improvement. Some members bitterly opposed the Manual of Practice published by the Board of Registration. An untold number of hours by dedicated members have been spent on a standards manual that is still controversial. Ironically, the first county to ask to be exempted from the Mapping Law was prompted to do so by one of the charter members who was also a surveyor member of the Board of Registration (Meriwether Lewis, 1962 to 1968).

For a long time, the society struggled for existence. The yearly meetings were held at North Carolina State College and received support from its school of surveying. It was decided that a convention would attract membership, and the surveyors in the Wilmington area offered to host the first convention in the hotel there. The convention grew and, for several years, it was held in the YMCA in Raleigh. For a while, three meetings were held each year. The central meeting was held in Raleigh, while another was held on the coast, and one in the mountains. As the membership grew, so did the effort to take control of the profession. One member put his career on the line to obtain, for surveyors, the right to design streets and residential drainage in subdivisions. The society demanded, and got, more representation on the Board of Registration, and a battle with the executive secretary was fought and won. The society got the General Assembly to require that all land surveys be performed by registered land surveyors.

One of the facts of life that had to be contended with was the dearth of educational opportunities for surveyors. N.C. State University dropped surveying from its curriculum, so the society worked for, and got, surveying programs started in the community colleges. They also have sponsored seminars each year to help older surveyors upgrade their knowledge. With the advent of modern survey equipment and the better-trained young men now in the profession, land surveying in the state of North Carolina is better than it has ever been, and with the dedication of the land surveyors, it will continue to improve.

I wish to thank Mr. Monty Speir, executive secretary to the Board of Registration. Without his help, I could not have written this chapter.

ALL PHOTOGRAPHS FROM PAGE 86 THROUGH 92
IS EQUIPMENT OWNED BY ALLIED SURVEYING CO., OTIS A. JONES SURVEYING CO., INC.
AND NCSS MAPS, INC. PICTURE USE IS BY PERMISSION FROM PHOTOGRAPHERS
W. KEVIN DAVIE AND KENNETH T. MILLS FOR NCSS MAPS, INC., OWNERSHIP.
(see permissions, page 241)

Dietzgen Dumpy Level.

Collage Field Surveying Instruments.

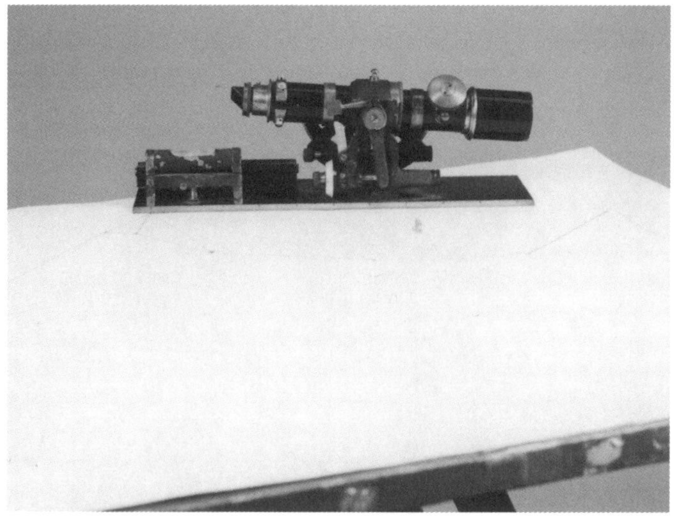

Plane Table with Alidade.

John Jones Baltimore Compass—Circa 1870.

W. E. Gurley Mountain Transit—Circa 1926.

W. E. Gurley Mountain Transit—Circa 1926.

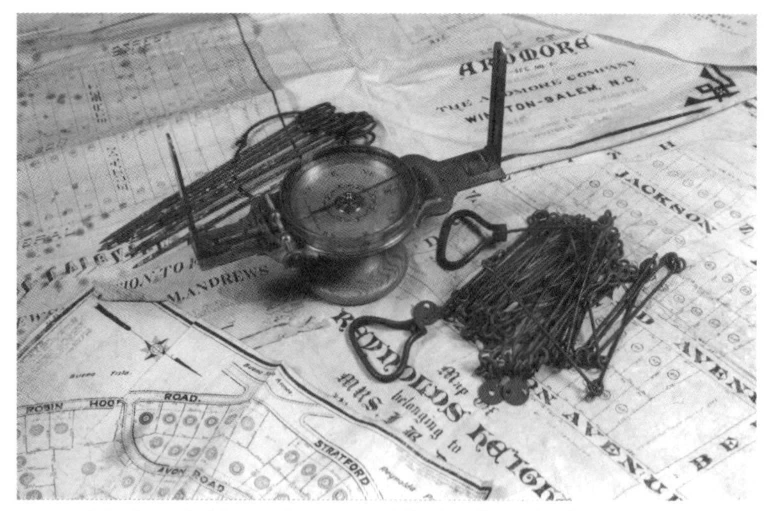

John Jones Baltimore Compass, 66' Gurley Chain, Early 1900s Map.

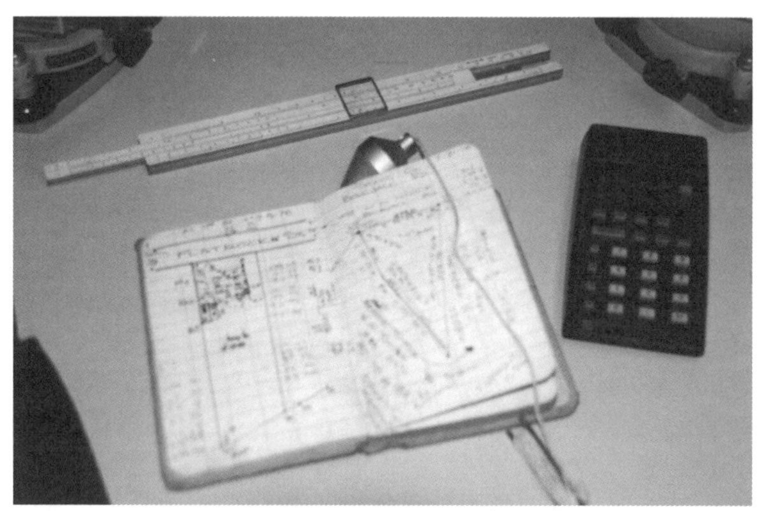

Slide Rule, Plumb Bob, HP45 Calculator, Field Book.

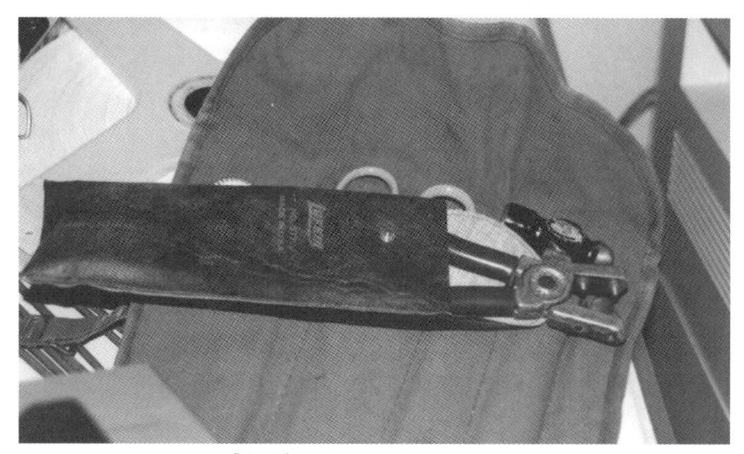

Lufkin Chain Repair Kit—Circa 1980.

3805A Hewlett Packard Distance Meter—Circa 1973.

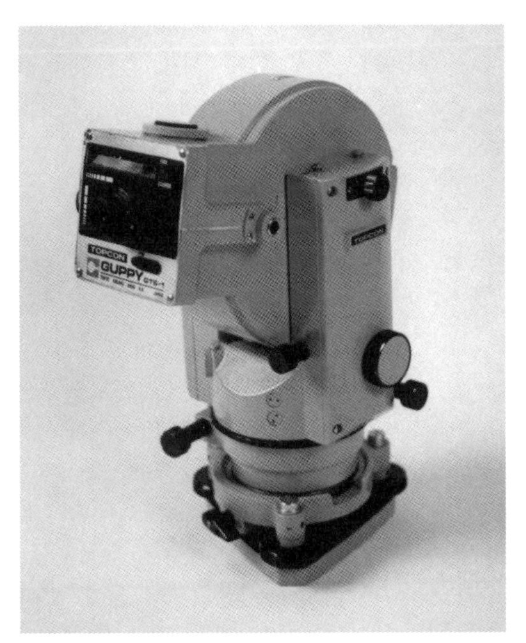

Topcon Guppy GTS-1 Electronic Distance Meter—Circa 1980.

Lietz/Sokkisha Red Mini-Electronic Distance Meter.

Dietzgen Transit—6100 Series—Circa 1958.

Wild Heerbrugg T-2 Universal Theodolite—Circa 1973.

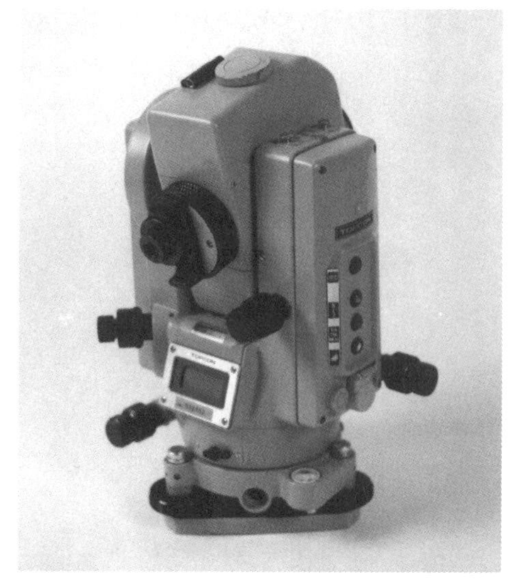

Topcon Distance Meter GTS-3—Circa 1985.

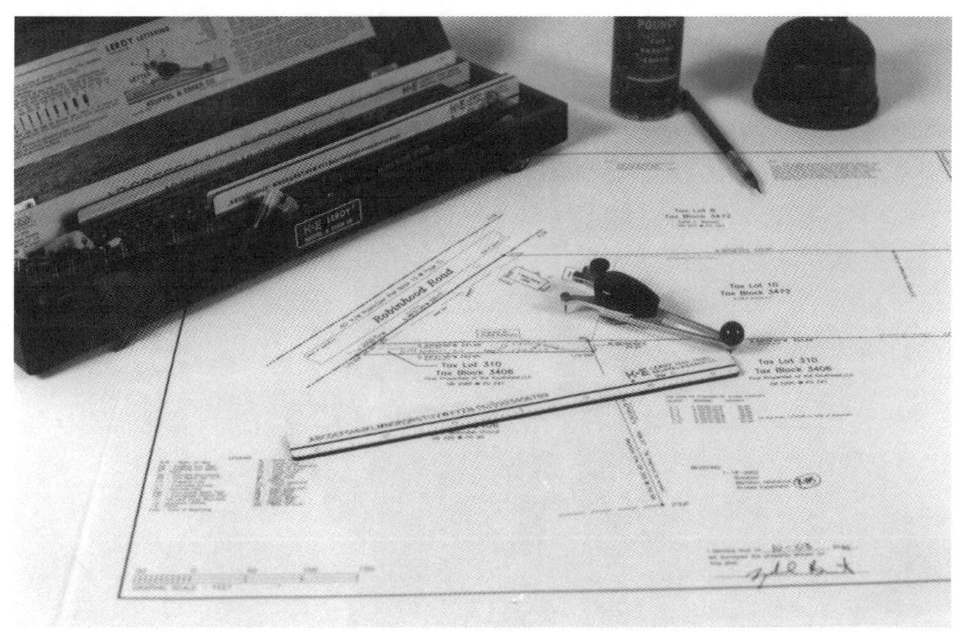

Leroy Lettering Guide Set, Pounce for Linen, Round Pencil Points.

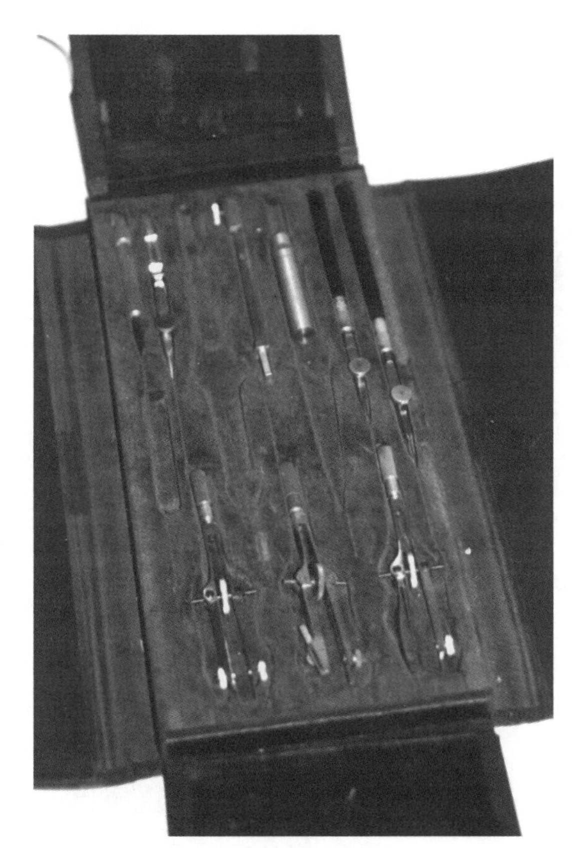

Drawing Instrument Set.

Beetle 1000 Electronic Distance Meter—Circa 1977.

Buff & Buff Transit—Circa 1920.

Guurley Mountain Transit—Circa 1926.

Buff & Buff Transit—Circa 1926.

175 Years of Surveying and Engineering: 1812–1987
The Ward and Blanchard Family Heritage

Tom Boney

"Enthusiastic" is the one word that can best describe William Ward Blanchard's dedication to his chosen professions, engineering in general and land surveying in particular. And well he should be enthusiastic!

This fifth generation land surveyor has roots reaching back to his great-great-grandfather, Alfred Ward, born near Delway, in Sampson County, North Carolina, January 12, 1790.

William (Bill) Blanchard, of Wallace, believes his business might be the oldest surveying and/or engineering firm in continuous operation, and still in operation nationally and, perhaps, internationally.

MASTER-APPRENTICE The learning of surveying and engineering 200 years ago was then, and to some extent is now, a master-apprentice relationship.

In most all states, some experience under the direct supervision of a licensed professional is required before public licensing is granted for either the practice of surveying or engineering .

There is a continuous heritage of surveying and engineering knowledge that has existed in the Ward and Blanchard families for a period of at least 175 years. The heritage has been passed from generation to generation in these families for at least that long. Talking with Bill about his ancestors brings forth a fascinating account of the changes in land surveying over the years.

WITNESS In the early 1800s, surveyors wrote their own deeds and signed them simply: "A. Ward, Witness."

The writing of deeds was carried out years ago not only by surveyors, but also by tax collectors, justices of the peace, and others. In fact, anybody could write a deed. Requiring that deeds be prepared by a lawyer, based upon a professional land surveyor's description, went far toward solving many land problems about 1950.

The 1790 founder passed the business to his son, William Robinson Ward, about 1840. He, in turn, gave the business to his son, Maury Ward, who later gave it to his nephew, J. William Blanchard, uncle of the present owner, who was given the business in 1954.

William has nothing but praise for the line of succession, but his benefactor, "Uncle Willie," particularly touched him. He can recollect many stories about his Uncle Willie's earliest days in the field. He rode a mule down to the middle of Pender County and spent a week with the family for whom he was doing surveying.

His trusty transit had to be wrapped in burlap to protect it from the ravages of the weather, very different from today when the current surveying instrument is carefully encased in shockproof material, which also could possibly be dropped from a high-flying aircraft without sustaining much damage.

"NOT IN THE SUMMER" The stories Uncle Willie passed along to his nephew are equally as delightful. He said, "Any surveyor ought to have more sense than do survey work in the summer with all the swamps and rattle snakes that are in southeastern North Carolina." The hot summer months are better suited for farming, leaving the other nine months to pursue land surveying, according to Uncle Willie's philosophy.

From 1954 until 1957, Bill operated as "William W. Blanchard, RLS." From 1957 until 1968, he was "William W. Blanchard, Civil Engineer." At that time, the business was incorporated and became known by its present designation: "William W. Blanchard, Inc., Engineering and Land Surveying."

Beginning with farm surveys, the firm has expanded to include complete surveying and mapping services including property line surveys, control surveys, and site development designs and surveys. Also included are the necessary surveying and reports for the analysis, design, and construction of engineering projects. Several thousand acres of land are surveyed by the firm each year. There are 23 people on the payroll.

This firm has a geodetic capability for doing second order surveys, staffing survey parties for such work, and equipping them with traverse equipment, one-second theodolites, and electronic measuring devices. All computations are done by electronic computer, and all field parties are equipped with modern surveying equipment—a far cry from the transit wrapped in burlap.

Capabilities and equipment of the firm range from an expertise on the smallest lot survey to the ability to work on multi-million dollar projects. The company has the equipment necessary for the operation of nine survey parties and, indeed, has at least four or five going at all times from lower South Carolina to northern Virginia and as far west as the North Carolina mountains.

Surveying services have included monumentation and mapping parts of the Inland Waterway right-of-way for the Army Corps of Engineers. Also included is the segment of Interstate 40 in parts of two counties for the Department of Transportation of North Carolina.

A. WARD WAS FIRST Alfred Ward was recorded in the Ward Family History as a "surveyor, farmer, and good businessman." Based on William's research, he started his practice of surveying when he was about twenty-one years old, or around 1811.

Three of Alfred Ward's sons were surveyors and were taught the profession by their father. The first child, William Robinson Ward, was born June 26, 1817, and was a "teacher, surveyor, and businessman." He was also a member of the North Carolina House of Representatives and North Carolina State Senate.

Joseph John Ward, the third child of Alfred and Elizabeth Robinson Ward, was born July 22, 1821, and was a "schoolteacher, justice of the peace, and a surveyor."

George Washington Ward, the seventh child of Alfred and Elizabeth Robinson Ward, was a "farmer, teacher, and a surveyor."

William Robinson Ward, William's great-grandfather, seems to have been very active in the surveying business. William has photostatic copies of approximately two dozen original survey plats made by his great-grandfather, dated around 1840. Many of these survey plats are on record in the North Carolina Department of State Land Grants Office.

It is interesting to note that according to the signatures on some of these plats, William Robinson Ward worked with a surveyor named "Hugh Maxwell." During that time period, Hugh Maxwell worked with a surveyor named John H. Blanchard. Decatur Blanchard, family historian, told Bill that John Blanchard was first cousin and neighbor to Bill's great-great grandfather, whose name was John Blanchard .

Two of William Robinson Ward's sons were surveyors. Members of the Ward family have told Bill that these two sons were taught the art of surveying by their father. Alfred Decatur Ward, the fifth child of William Robinson Ward, did some land surveying. Bill has observed some of his original survey plats. However, his primary profession was the practice of law. He graduated from the University of North Carolina in 1885 and completed his law course soon thereafter. He practiced law in Kenansville and in New Bern, and he represented Duplin County in the House of Representatives. He was a member of the Board of Trustees of Wake Forest University for over forty years.

Maury Ward, the seventh child of William Robinson Ward, was born on September 8, 1863, and was a teacher and surveyor. In 1897, he served in the State Legislature. He was very active in surveying during his lifetime and many of his original survey plats are on record in the Duplin County Register of Deeds office in Kenansville.

On December 17, 1882, John William Blanchard, son of Zachariah and Bettie Ward Blanchard, was born near Chinquapin. He was a nephew of Maury Ward and grandson of William Robinson Ward. He learned the art of surveying by living and working with his uncle, Maury Ward, and by attending North Carolina State College (now North Carolina State University) in 1924.

"UNCLE WILLIE" John William Blanchard was Bill's "Uncle Willie," in that he was brother to Bill's father, Ward Caswell Blanchard. He was very active in the surveying business in the 1930s and 1940s. For a short period of time during the late 1920s, he was in business as Blanchard and Vann, Surveyors.

Henry J. Vann gave Bill all of his surveying records and his surveying business in 1952. He told Bill that J. W. Blanchard taught him much of what he learned about property line surveying.

William Thurston Blanchard, son of John William Blanchard and Docia Rouse Blanchard, was born September 14, 1918. He graduated from Rose Hill High School and received a B. S. in civil engineering from North Carolina State University in 1940. He did some engineering work in the Army during World War II and attained the rank of captain before being discharged. He learned to survey land from his father, John William Blanchard, and was registered to practice surveying in the State of North Carolina. He practiced as a land surveyor for approximately four years.

Cicero Franklin Blanchard, Jr. of Rose Hill, locally known as Frank Blanchard, was registered as a surveyor, and practiced surveying for several years. He learned his surveying by attending North Carolina State College two years, and then by working with his uncle, John William Blanchard.

BILL BLANCHARD William Ward Blanchard, son of Ward Caswell Blanchard and Pearl Carr Blanchard, was born September 26, 1926, near Wallace. He graduated from North Carolina State University in 1950 with a degree in civil engineering.

Bill worked for a structural contractor for a year and for an engineering firm, the J. E. Sirrine Company, for another year. In 1952, J. W. Blanchard, Henry J. Vann, William T. Blanchard, and Frank Blanchard collectively gave Bill their surveying business. In addition, unselfishly, "they gave of their time," according to Bill, "helping to teach me the field aspects of land surveying."

Bill continued, "If I have accomplished anything during my lifetime in the surveying and engineering business, much of it is due to the help given to me during a period of approximately ten years by my Uncle Willie, or John William Blanchard. I also worked directly for Henry J. Vann for approximately three months during 1952."

Bill was registered as a land surveyor by the state of North Carolina in 1954, and then as a professional engineer in 1957. In 1969, he was licensed by both Virginia and South Carolina as a professional engineer.

Bill is now doing business as William W. Blanchard, Inc., Engineering and Surveying. His office is located in Wallace.

Bill is particularly pleased that his son, William David, has recently shown more interest in surveying and may carry the family tradition on to the sixth generation. David is now a student at Sandhills Community College in Southern Pines working toward a civil engineering degree.

When he called me and said, "Daddy, I want to go back to school and learn to be a land surveyor," 'I almost keeled over,'" the proud father said. "That's just what I had always wanted to hear, and it makes me real proud."

Former United States Congressman David N. Henderson, a long-time attorney and resident of Wallace, recently said of Bill Blanchard, "Bill not only began his business of surveying with much enthusiasm, but also has always maintained the highest degree of professionalism and ethical standards. That reputation has become widely known throughout North Carolina and, in fact, over the nation."

As to where, or from whom, Alfred Ward learned his trade or profession, Bill does not know at the present time. He has done considerable research to determine the occupation of Alfred Ward's father, whose name was William Ward, but, at the present time, he has not accomplished much on that matter. He speculates that William Ward's father, Edward Ward, brought the trade or profession with him from England when he came to America about 1740.

Many of the roads in Duplin County were originally designed and surveyed by Maury Ward or John William Blanchard. To understand this, we must be aware that the public roads of North Carolina were built and maintained by the counties before 1931. Several roads have the name "The Maury Ward Road" in old land deed descriptions because those roads were actually designed and surveyed by Maury Ward.

The first volume of the *Ward History*, printed in 1945, noted of Maury Ward that "he spent a lot of time, energy, and money trying to make roads that would shorten the distance to market, church, and pleasure resorts."

Bill's Uncle Willie "personally told me he did some road planning and surveying for Duplin County when the county had the responsibility for the roads in this area. One of the roads he told me he planned and surveyed in its original and present location was North Carolina Secondary Road 1005. It connects the towns of Beaulaville and Pink Hill, a distance of approximately nine miles."

Another road that we know he planned and surveyed while working as a professional for Duplin County, is a part of NC 41 east of Wallace from Island Creek east for two miles. His son, William Thurston Blanchard, personally remembers assisting his father on that road about the year 1930.

OTHERS ALSO Other members of the Blanchard family are also in the surveying and/or engineering business and have received at least a part of their experience and training from the Ward and Blanchard heritage.

Wyatt Eakins Blanchard, son of Cicero Franklin Blanchard, Jr. and Olivette Eakins Blanchard, was born September 20, 1946, and is a graduate of the School of Engineering of the University of North Carolina at Charlotte. In the past, he has worked for both Cicero Franklin Blanchard, Jr., as well as for Bill himself. He is now registered as a professional engineer and a land surveyor in the state of North Carolina and is employed as an engineer by New Hanover County.

Charles Vance Brooks, III, husband of Doris Blanchard Brooks (Bill's sister and a niece of John William Blanchard), like Bill, graduated from North Carolina State in 1950 and was registered as a surveyor in 1952. He is still active in surveying and received much help in beginning his surveying career from John William Blanchard and Frank Blanchard.

Charles Vance Brooks, IV, son of Charles Vance Brooks, III and Doris Blanchard Brooks, was graduated from North Carolina State in 1979 with a bachelor's degree in civil engineering. During his college years, he worked part-time for his father. Following graduation, he joined the Asheboro office of Moore, Gardner and Associates. In 1983, he entered the University of North Carolina at Chapel Hill to work toward a master's degree in environmental engineering. He completed his degree in the fall of 1985, and obtained his PE registration shortly thereafter. Presently, he is associated with Henry Von Oesen and Associates, Inc. as a civil environmental staff engineer designing water and wastewater piping and treatment facilities for the firm's municipal, industrial, and private clients.

Bill believes this heritage of surveying and/or engineering knowledge has had continuity for at least 175 years through the Ward and Blanchard families.

"It is also my belief that this history of continuous surveying and/or engineering heritage may have set some kind of record; such as possibly the oldest surveying and/or engineering business in continuous existence, either in the nation, or, perhaps, even the international area." Bill concluded with an invitation for further comment "from any who may have knowledge about the matter."

A more enthusiastic booster of engineering and land surveying would be difficult to find.

NOTE: Tom Boney, the writer of this article, was a fellow graduate with Bill Blanchard in the Class of 1943, of Wallace High School. Boney graduated in 1950, from the University of North Carolina at Chapel Hill School of Journalism, working four-and-a-half years as editor of *The Wallace Enterprise* before purchasing *The Alamance News* of Graham in 1956, now the largest newspaper published once a week in North Carolina.

This previously published article was revised by the author for distribution at the dinner celebrating "175 Years of Surveying and Engineering: The Ward and Blanchard Family Heritage," held February 23, 1987, in Wallace, North Carolina.

~

William W. Blanchard, PE/PLS, of William W. Blanchard, Inc. continues the surveying tradition of the Ward and Blanchard family. Now in its 191st year, this tradition has moved into the electronic age of surveying. The following is a copy of a letter written by William W. Blanchard, dated April 9, 2002, to Otis A. Jones of Otis A. Jones Surveying Company, Inc. summarizing the developments and improvements in land surveying in the last fifty years.

Dear Otis:

The purpose of this letter is to relate to you the changes that I have seen in the surveying business during the fifty years that I have been doing surveying work.

When I started surveying land in this area, during December 1951, it was generally said that the price of land had gone high. It was then bringing $35 to $50 per acre for cut-over woodland. Then, many of the deeds that existed had been written with the courses given to the nearest degree and the distances given to the nearest pole. It was generally said that a surveyor *should use a one-minute transit and turn angles to the nearest one minute for urban land, but that the cost of obtaining such accuracy could not be justified for rural land. Also, the distances were then measured with steel tapes, without using plumb bobs, and the distances recorded to the nearest foot. I did use plumb bobs for measuring when I started surveying during 1951.*

I believe that what has really changed the accuracy that can be used to measure land during the last two decades has been the use of theodolites that measures angles to the nearest five seconds of angular accuracy and the electronic measuring device for measuring distances accurately to the nearest one hundredth of a foot. Also, the requirement in our Standard of Practice in Land Surveying for measurements to be performed to a minimum accuracy of one part in five thousand parts has increased the need for accuracy. As I remember, the accuracy that was required for surveying rural land during the 1950s was one part in four hundred parts.

One of the great improvements that I have seen develop in the land surveying business has been the requirement for all new surveys to be tied to, and coordinated with, the N.C. Geodetic Survey Grid System, if the survey is within 2000 feet of any grid system monument.

Another of the improvements that I have seen develop within the last few decades has been the increase in education requirements for licensing for the surveying of land for the public.

When I started surveying land in southeastern North Carolina during December 1951, many of the land surveyors in this area were using the Jacob staff compass for rural land surveys. Also, they did not use plumb bobs with the steel tape measurements.

Maybe this information can be of help to you. If you have any questions, please feel free to call me.

Very truly yours,
Signed/William W. Blanchard

Surveying in the Piedmont

Michael J. Evans, Sr., PLS

Do you remember what you were doing thirty years ago on one specific day? Most people don't, unless it was a very special day. I have vivid memories of Monday, March 17, 1971. It was the day I began my career in surveying. At nineteen years old, I was nine months out of high school and unemployed. I had seen employment ads for "Rodman Wanted." I thought it was extremely bold for the Mafia to be advertising in the local paper for help. I did not know anything about surveying. I don't think I had ever seen surveyors at work or knew what they did.

I was searching for a job, but at nineteen, I wasn't looking very hard. A friend from school said his father was looking for help and asked if I was interested. I said I was and on Monday at 7:00 a.m., I was on my way to a new job. The surveyor's office was in the basement of his home. There were piles of maps, plats, and other papers all over the office area. The surveyor was finishing a map for delivery that morning. I asked what I could do until we went to work. I was promptly introduced to a book of trig tables and a Monroe rotary calculator. I was shown a closure sheet and given some direction on how to use the calculator. The boss said to check all the numbers. After a few minutes, we were ready to go. We drove to downtown Winston-Salem and delivered a map to an attorney's office. Next, we picked up the part-time rodman. He only worked three or four days a week.

Our first job was in Davie County. After a thirty-minute drive, we arrived at the end of a long dirt road. I was told we were looking for a stone. A stone, I was told, was described as a rock in the ground that had been placed as a corner. We walked about 200 feet into the woods and started our search. Every time I saw a rock, I yelled, "I found it." The boss and other rodman would run over, and after a brief examination would say, "No, that is a rock, not a stone." I sometimes think how humorous this would look now, knowing what I know now.

Surveying has changed greatly in the last thirty years. Formerly, it took over a year to train a rodman. Instrument training took a year. Most surveyors had three years or more time invested in training a party chief. With modern equipment, you can train a crew to run a traverse with a very good closure in a few months. The problem, though, is that you can have trained technicians that do not know surveying. They may never find that stone I was searching for. They may tie iron pipes or stakes to a traverse, but are they corners or dog tie stakes or fence brace irons?

I have always believed a good surveyor should learn the old ways. He must learn them to follow in the footsteps of the generations of surveyors that preceded him. We are in danger of losing these old skills if we don't pass them on now. How many young surveyors can run a closure by hand, chain a 1,000-foot line correctly, or mark a tree? How many times have you retraced a recent survey and found a new iron pipe a few feet from a stone? Do you know how surveys in your area were done fifty years ago? What direction is a bearing of east 5 degrees north? What is the difference between "north" and "northerly"? On which side of a tree or post is barbed wire nailed? If you don't know these things, how can you retrace an old survey? Many old procedures were followed across the entire state. Some procedures were modified somewhat in different areas of the state, and some procedures were used in some areas and not in others. I will attempt to discuss methods and procedures followed by surveyors in the Piedmont.

The Piedmont was settled in the 1740s and 1750s. The interior of the state had few people due to the lack of roads and navigable rivers. In 1755, many settlers followed Thomas Spratt's route, now known as the "great wagon road," south from the colonies in Pennsylvania, Maryland, and Virginia and moved to North Carolina, South Carolina, and Georgia.

Between the years 1752 and 1755, the Moravian Church purchased a tract in North Carolina of approximately 98,985 acres. This tract was known as "Wachovia." The town of Rural Hall, in Forsyth County, is almost exactly on the north line of the Wachovia tract. The south line of Forsyth County follows the old Wachovia line from the east to where it borders Clemmons Township. The west line is west of Muddy Creek. The town of Walkertown is on the east line. The deeds to the Wachovia tract are recorded in Rowan County. There were many changes in the counties of this area in the early days. Wachovia was originally in Anson County, and later in Rowan County. During the Revolutionary War, it was a part of Surry County; during the War of 1812 and the Mexican War, in Stokes County; and through the Civil War, in Forsyth County. The cities of Salisbury and Charlotte were also founded along this route.

In November 1753, a group of eleven single men founded the first settlement of Bethabara. Bethania was founded in 1759, about three miles northwest of Bethabara. Johann Christian Reuter, a surveyor, was appointed as a forester to select trees to be cut for use in new construction. He also took inventory of the plants and animals. In 1761, a Moravian diarist wrote that Brother Reuter hoped to complete his survey of Wachovia that year. The area became a small farming community. The Moravians were fond of the forest and took care to protect it. Today, Johann Reuter would be an environmental planner as well as a surveyor.

The town of Salem was begun in 1766 as a central community. It quickly grew into a commercial center for a wide area and was home to many craftsmen and merchants. In 1913, Salem merged with Winston, the county seat of Forsyth County. The town of Salem was well planned. The town was surveyed and mapped by a surveyor appointed by the ruling church council. Many old maps of the area have been preserved. The town surveyor was also the "road master." He was in charge of planning, surveying, building, and maintaining the area road system.

Surveying in the Piedmont in the 1700s was done with a compass and chain. The compass was set on a wooden pole called a "Jacob's staff." The old compass did not have a telescope. Sighting was over "sighting vanes," thin metal posts or strips of metal with slits in the middle with a thin wire. Angles at the corners were not turned as in modern surveying. The compass was set on a corner. The surveyor's helper would set a pole or rod on the next point. The surveyor would read the magnetic bearing of the line and record the information in his notes. If the line was no longer than could be sighted at one time, the compass was moved to the point at the helper's rod. The surveyor would then set the compass on the same magnetic bearing, and the helper would move up the line. The surveyor then directed the helper until he was on line with his rod. Because the surveyor's helper carried and lined the rod, he was called the "rodman." When the far corner was reached, the surveyor lined the rodman opposite the corner. The distance between the rod and corner was measured. The surveyor then applied a correction to the bearing of that line. Measurements were made with a chain or pole laid flat on the ground. The back end was lined up with the last mark or corner, and a new mark was made at the front of the chain. The "front chainman" walked forward and pulled the chain with him. The "back chainman" walked to the point that was marked by the "front chainman." When the end of the chain reached the back chainman, he called out "CHAIN!" The back chainman aligned his end of the chain and called out "GOOD!" The front chainman would pull the chain tight, lay it on the ground, and mark a point. The process was repeated until all measurements were made. When a corner or stopping point was reached, the front chainman would hold the front end of the chain on the point, and the back chainman would read the links. Each link on an old chain was marked with its number from the front end. The chainman kept a count of the number of chains measured. Sometimes one of the chainmen would put a stick in his pocket each time a full chain was pulled. The sticks were counted when the total measurement was completed. If a stick fell out of the chainman's pocket, or one broke into two sticks, the final count would be off by one chain.

When measuring with a "pole," the surveyor placed the pole flat on the ground and flipped end over end. Measurements with the pole were probably not as accurate as ones made with the chain. A chain is 66 feet long. Each chain is divided into 100 links. Each link is 0.66 hundredths of a foot, or 7.92 inches long. A pole is ¼ of a Gunter's Chain. Each pole is 16 ½ feet long. Poles are sometimes called a "rod" or a "perch." One mile equals 5,280 feet, or 80 chains, or 320 poles. Surveys were done with these methods for many years.

In the late 1800s, the transit came into use. Many rural surveyors used the transit in the same way as the compass. Some surveyors used the old methods even into the 1960s. The transit was a multi-purpose instrument. It could be used to turn horizontal and vertical angles, run levels (elevations), read stadia distances, or read magnetic bearings from the compass. The transit has cross hairs in the telescope, both in the vertical plane for alignment and in the horizontal plane to read stadia distance. There are three stadia hairs in a transit. One in the center, one above the center, and one below the center. The distance between the top and bottom stadia hairs is a constant (usually 0.01 of a foot per foot). A level rod is graduated in 0.01 of a foot increments. The level rod is sighted with the bottom stadia hair on a number, and the difference between the top hair and bottom hair is read; multiplying this difference by the constant will give a distance. This method can be accurate to approximately ½ foot when the distance is under 200 feet. The transit has two plate level bubbles and a level bubble on the telescope. When running levels with a transit, the plate bubbles are leveled, and then the telescope is inverted so that the level bubble is on top of the scope. The bubble on the scope is leveled, or checked, before and after each shot.

When traversing a boundary with the transit, the instrument is set up on the corner or point. A backsight is taken. An angle is turned to the front point and recorded in the field book. The distance between the points is measured with the steel tape and recorded. The transit is then moved to the new point. The process is continued until the survey is complete. This is much the same with a theodolite or total station. Most surveys performed between the late 1800s and late 1970s were transit and steel tape surveys.

Trees were often used for corners and to mark a line. The way trees were marked is slightly different in each region of the state. In the Piedmont, a corner tree has three hack marks. The marks should be placed on two sides of the tree: where the property line enters the tree, and where the property line exits the tree. Hacks should be approximately at chest level. A variation was to place a hacked X marked with a blaze under the X. Sometimes trees were marked to witness a stone or iron. Three trees at approximately 120 degrees were marked. They were marked with an X, a blaze, and a hack mark for each foot from the face of the tree to the corner. I have recovered many stones that were witnessed in this manner. I have even found the hole where an iron was destroyed. Witness trees have been a great aid in finding or replacing missing corners. You can be certain, to within a few feet that the corner was replaced correctly. Trees on the property line were marked by two hack marks. The marks were placed on both faces of the tree, where the property line entered the tree, and where the line exited the tree. If the tree was not on the line, but located within three feet of the line, two hack marks were placed on the side of the tree next to the property line. When marking a tree, care should be taken not to cut too deep into the wood. All the bark should be removed and a shallow cut made into the first layer of wood. If the cut is too deep, the wood will grow over the hack. This is called "rollover" wood. Bumps of "rollover" wood can also indicate marked trees. Another common practice that left distinctive marks on trees was called "notching a tree." In the 1960s and early 1970s, this practice was very common in the Piedmont. You should remember that we did not have calculators or computers. It was common to extend a straight line until the corner could be seen. At the last stake before the corner, the angle was turned to the corner. If a tree was on line, and the line was near the edge of the tree, a notch was cut into the tree so that the line could be sighted. I have also cut many thirty-inch oak trees with a bush axe.

Fences can be an important clue to the location of an old line. Fences may have been constructed on or near the property line, or may be simply fences of convenience. A fence of convenience is a fence constructed when the property owners did not know the true location of the line. They simply agreed that it was a convenient place to construct a fence.

Crooked fences tied to trees are probably fences of convenience. A straight fence or post may, or may not, be located on or near the property line. When you know the fence was constructed near the line, you need to decide what side of the fence the line is on. The side of the post where the wire is attached provides a clue. The wire should have been attached to the side of the fence next to the owner of the fence. If cows or other animals pushed on the fence, it would push against the post and not pull the staples out of the post. The same is true when the fence was attached to trees. If an old fence was attached to trees but is no longer visible, a metal detector can still locate the trees to which it was attached. It should also be noted that a nail, staple, or wire that was attached to a tree would remain at the same level. Trees grow out and from the top up. Anything attached to the tree, or a hack mark made into the tree, will remain the same height above the ground over the years. Also, the bark will grow over the wire. A distinctive mark or bump will indicate that something was attached to the tree.

I have heard it said that you can pull up an iron, but you can't pull up the hole. If an iron was in the ground several years prior to being destroyed, you might find the hole it came out of if you know how to look. You can sometimes find irons that have rusted out. This process works best in small areas at a time; a two-foot radius usually works best. You may need to enlarge the hole. The first step is to approximately locate the iron. Next, dig down a few inches in the area of the missing iron. If the area has been plowed, you will need to dig down deeper. Next, remove the dirt in the bottom of the hole in one-half inch increments. Check the bottom of the hole after each increment. Look for a ring of dirt that is different in color from the soil around. The discolored area will be the shape of the missing iron. Also, check for small rusty pieces of the iron. Many times, the outer layer of an iron will flake off in the hole when the iron is removed. When you find the discolored area, try pushing an iron or stick down into the area. If it is the iron hole, you can push the new iron down with your hand. I recovered several lost or destroyed irons in this manner. When an iron is pulled up, the hole remains. Top soil will wash into the hole. Most of the time, the soil will change color at about a one-foot depth. You can find this evidence of the original iron if you know how to look. I have even found the remains of wooden stakes and hubs with this method.

There were two methods used to prolong a straight line through the woods. The first method was called an "offset." A traverse stake was placed near the obstruction. The transit was set up on this point. Ninety degrees was turned and a second point placed at five or ten feet. A back sight was placed as far as possible from the second point. The transit was moved and 90 degrees was turned again. A third stake was placed past the obstruction at a distance of 100 feet or more if possible. The transit was moved to the third point and 90 degrees was once again turned. A fourth stake was placed at the same distance as between stake one and two, and a long back sight was set. The transit was moved to point four, and 90 degrees was turned again. You are now back on line. The second method was called "off and on." When a tree was on line, an angle was turned to the right or left of the tree. The angle was usually a whole degree, two or three degrees if possible. All surveyors and party chiefs carried a small book of "trig" tables in their pocket. By looking up the cosine of the angle, it was easy to compute a correction. For example, if the angle was two degrees, the cosine was 0.999398. Multiplying by 100 was easy, simply move the decimal two places. At two degrees off line, if you pulled 100 feet, the distance on line was 99.94 feet. By the same token, if you pulled 100.06 at two degrees off line, the distance on line was 100.00 feet. A stake was set, usually at 100 feet plus the correction: in this example, at 100.06 feet. For this example, the angle was two degrees off line to the left, or the angle right from the back sight was, therefore, 178 degrees. The transit was moved to the stake. The first stake was back sighted, and an angle right of 184 degrees was turned two times the amount that was turned off. A stake was set at 100.06 feet. The transit was moved to the third stake. The second stake was back sighted, and an angle right of 178 degrees was turned. You are now back on line 200 feet from the first point. With the calculators, computers, and data collectors we have now, this method is almost forgotten. Many younger surveyors have never learned these methods.

Modern surveyors measure everything as if it were flat, or a horizontal plane. Modern surveying is called "plane surveying." Modern surveyors use a 100-foot steel tape that is marked every foot. The tape has an extra foot to the left of the "0" mark. The extra foot is divided into hundredths of a foot. When measuring a distance with fractions of a foot, the back chainman holds a whole number and the front chainman reads the hundredths. The modern steel tape is still called "chain," and measuring with a tape is called "chaining." The tape is always held level. Plumb bobs are used to elevate the ends of the tape so that the tape will be level when measuring over an obstacle. If the slope of the land is such that the tape cannot be held level for the whole 100 feet, a shorter distance is used. The chainmen use hand levels to determine the longest distance that can be measured while holding the tape level. This is called "breaking chain." Modern EDMs and total stations have insured that chaining is becoming a lost art.

Measuring With The Steel Tape

EQUIPMENT: When measuring distances with the steel tape, you need the following equipment: 1 chain (steel tape), 2 plumb bobs, and one or more hand levels. The lines to be measured should be clear of bushes and obstructions. A tension gauge should be used to apply the correct tension on the chain. Although most surveyors in this area do not use the tension gauge, measuring without the gauge is risky and requires much practice to get good results.

PROCEDURES: All measurements must be made as if the land were a flat horizontal plane. If the slope of the land is steep, short distances under 100 feet must be used. The hand level is used to determine the longest distance increment that can be measured at one time. The chainman at the lowest point uses the hand level to determine what increment can be used. The chain must be kept level with no bends over or around obstructions. The most experienced chainman should be on the front of the chain (0 end). Correct tension must be applied at all times. Distances must be corrected for temperature. Temperature corrections are usually applied in the office. Correct alignment must be maintained. A thermometer is attached to the chain or tape. When possible, the entire chain or tape should be either completely shaded or completely in the sun. The temperature of the tape is what is important, not the air temperature.

When beginning measurements, the chain is let out. Care must be taken to insure that the chain is not looped or crossed over. It must not be pulled around small trees or other obstructions. The front chainman pulls the chain from the beginning point in the direction of the second point. He checks the elevation as he walks, and stops at a point that the elevation dictates, or when the end of the chain is reached. The back chainman should not hold the chain except when a measurement is being made. When possible, the back of the chain should be held on the ground or other point (corner, iron, stake, nail, etc.). I have found that much better results are obtained if you always measure down hill when the slope is steep. The back chainman always holds a whole number. If fractions of a foot are needed, the front chainman applies them using the "extra foot." Except for the last increment before a traverse point or corner, the back chainman should hold a number ending with an "0" or "5." This makes addition easy and fewer mistakes are made. Each incremental distance should be recorded in the field book and totals kept. When either or both ends of the chain must be elevated, plumb bobs must be used. Care must be taken to insure that the bob string remains on the correct mark on the chain. The chain must be level and the correct tension applied. The plumb bob must be steady with no movement. Both chainmen must meet all these requirements at the same time before a measurement can be made. When the back chainman meets these requirements he calls, "Good." If the front chainman is also good, he makes a point with the bob. The bob point should be as close to the ground as possible, without touching. If either chainman is not good, the measurement must be repeated. The front chainman always clears an area and packs the ground so the point can be found. This is called a "kick-out."

Surveying in North Carolina was very much the same across the state, but each area had minor differences specific to that area. The biggest differences occurred when new equipment came on the market. Surveyors in big cities or large multi-purpose firms tended to upgrade their equipment before rural surveyors did. One reason for this is money. Surveyors in fast-developing cities could charge more. Country surveyors often just managed to make a living. They had to save a long time to afford new equipment. This has changed. Today, some of the best-equipped surveyors using the most up-to-date equipment may be small city or rural surveyors.

The greatest difference between surveying in the past and in the present is the knowledge and education of a good modern surveyor. Gone are the days when studying one simple text book and buying a compass and chain made an individual a surveyor. The "old-timers" are gone, but not forgotten. We must remember how they worked so that we can retrace that 100-year-old deed or will. We should always remember where we came from, so as not to lose sight of where we are going.

Surveying in the Mountains of Western North Carolina

Kenneth T. Mills, PLS

During the 1700s and 1800s, North Carolina's culture was agrarian. At that time, land surveyors were farmers or businessmen. They farmed during the summer. After the crops were in, they surveyed land for their neighbors. Some were even asked to undertake extensive surveys for the lords, proprietors, and later, for the governors appointed by the King of England.

During the early 1700s, settlers looking for new land to farm began moving toward the mountains of western North Carolina. At that time, the Cherokee owned the mountain land and only traders ventured into the mountains. From the land at the foot of the mountains, the farmers could not see any useful land to plow. However, when the traders came back with tales of rich valleys, plentiful game, and an abundance of timber for building, farmers began venturing into the region.

As the people moved into the mountains and claimed or purchased land, surveyors followed to provide farmers with their valuable service. In May of 1730, George Hunter produced a map showing the main trading trails to and through the Cherokee country. The trails began at the coast in South Carolina and continued through the mountains, almost to the Mississippi River. At the time, states had no boundary lines, so the map doesn't show any. After careful study, my best guess is that the trails shown in the area of the mountains pass through southwestern North Carolina. Later, a note was added to the map stating that Thomas Brown had a survey made of land along the main trail in 1738, near a creek named "Ninety-Six."

A map, prepared by Henry Mouzen, and others of "North and South Carolina with their Indian Frontiers" was published on May 30, 1775. It shows only the lowlands of both Carolinas with roads and towns. It's very well done, and many of the original locations of major cities we know today are easily located on it. The unusual feature of the map is that it does not show any of the mountainous areas. The map ends at the foothills with only two roads shown leading into the mountains.

The map does not show any of the mountainous regions because in 1763, Governor William Tryon established a proclamation line, which ran along the foot of the eastern side of the Appalachian Mountains. This line divided the land the settlers could farm, and the land owned by the Cherokee Nation. The proclamation line didn't keep settlers from moving around north of the mountains, through Virginia and the Cumberland Gap, and down to the land in North Carolina west of the Appalachian Mountains. At the same time, people began slowly moving into the mountains as well.

Since the survey of the boundary had been completed in the early 1770s, the map does show the boundary lines between North and South Carolina. It also shows most of the boundary line between North Carolina and Virginia which, at that time, had been extended to near the northwest corner of North Carolina.

Because the settlements west of the mountains were so far away from the legislature in Raleigh, and because the people in the west felt they were being neglected, North Carolina passed an Act of Cession in 1789. This act gave all of the land of North Carolina west of the Appalachian Mountains to the federal government. This was fine with the people living there. They began working toward becoming an independent state. Then, in 1796, Tennessee became the sixteenth state.

In 1799, North Carolina and Tennessee organized a joint commission to survey the boundary line between the states. The survey began on Pond Mountain at the Virginia border on May 20th and started south. The line surveyed lay along the great backbone of the mountain range. On June 28th, the survey party reached the French Broad River below Warm Springs, now known as Hot Springs. The following day, the commissioners and surveyors returned to their homes.

Then, in 1821, another commission was organized, and the rest of the boundary line was surveyed. Leaving the French Broad River, the commission again surveyed along the backbone of the Appalachian Mountain range. For at least one third of the trip to the Georgia boundary, they traversed ridges rising over 5,000 feet and mountain peaks over 6,000 feet. When the commission reached the Hiwassee River, they realized that they had come to the end of the Unicoi Mountains, and from that point, they surveyed due south to the Georgia boundary.

We know that as early as the 1730s, hunters, trappers, and traders prepared the only maps showing anything in the mountains. Over the years, as more and more people settled in the mountains, the need increased for land surveyors to mark the land they claimed or purchased.

What was it like to survey in the mountains? First, let's look at the area. The mountains in western North Carolina are part of the Southern Appalachian system of mountains. They cover parts of eight contiguous states, an area larger than New England.

In the area north of Virginia and east of the Black Hills of North Dakota, there is only one mountain, Mount Washington in New Hampshire, which reaches 6,000 feet above sea level. Only a dozen or so others exceed 5,000 feet in the same area. In North Carolina alone, the mountains cover approximately 6,000 square miles, with an average elevation of 2,700 feet, and with twenty-one mountains taller than Mount Washington.

In 1728, when William Byrd, a resident of Virginia, was surveying the boundary between Virginia and North Carolina, parallel chains of savage, unpopulated mountains rose, tier after tier, to the west halting his progress. All the area was densely forested and matted by laurel and other undergrowth. In his journal, Byrd wrote: "Our country has been inhabited for more than 130 years by the English, and still, we hardly know anything about the Appalachian Mountains."

One can find areas that are flat, or relatively so, in the valleys or on tops of ridges, knobs, or mountain tops. In 1904, when going up the side of the mountains or ridges, the natives described the rest of the land as; "Goin' up, you can might' nigh stand up straight and bite the ground; goin' down, a man wants hobnails in the seat of his pants." Ask any surveyor you see working in the mountains today, and he'll agree with the 1904 statement.

We have accounts of the large surveys establishing the boundary lines between North Carolina, South Carolina, Virginia, and Tennessee. In William Byrd's journal, he lists twenty men employed by Virginia on the first expedition. For the second, he lists seventeen. Not all of these men were rodmen, or chainmen or instrument men. Usually, the crew consisted of one instrument man, a head chainman, a tail or rear chainman, and the surveyor in charge.

The surveyor kept the notes of the measurements. He checked the instrument man's use of the instrument, and checked on the progress of the chainmen. Besides the surveying crew and the axe crew, the expedition needed hunters to provide game, a cook to prepare meals, and general laborers to load and haul the supplies and to set up the camp.

Since the area the crew traversed was, for all practical purposes, wilderness, covered with thick laurel and trees, they needed a number of axe men. This crew, consisting of from six to eight men, would cut and clear the line being surveyed and then mark the line after the surveyors passed. In the case of the boundary between North Carolina and Virginia, the line followed a parallel of latitude. Everything in the way was cleared or cut down.

The boundary between North Carolina and South Carolina was a mix of lines. The first ran in a northwesterly direction. The next line followed a parallel of latitude. Then the

Courtesy of Kenneth T. Mills.

surveyors had to survey the Catawba Indian lands, making sure the land was located totally in South Carolina. The next line was another parallel of latitude. The last skirted the south side of the Cherokee lands.

When the boundary between North Carolina and Tennessee was surveyed, guides were hired to lead the way along the ridge tops. Every so often, during both times the boundary was surveyed, the crew would take a break and come down from the top of the ridges to rest at a local cabin or nearby community.

Obviously, these expeditions were very large and covered a great distance. The state governments also financed them. How did a farmer in the mountains get his property surveyed? In the 1700s, he would contact a surveyor, arrange for a survey of his property, and agree to a price for the work.

The surveyor would schedule the work for after the fall harvest. Before he could leave his farm, he needed to harvest his own crops. After the harvest was in, he loaded his compass, chain, and chaining pins into saddlebags, grabbed his rifle and rode his horse or mule to the farmer's property.

When he arrived, he was made to feel at home since he might be there for a couple of days, or even weeks. He would be given a place to sleep in the one-room cabin and a place to store his equipment. If the farmer had any sons, they all pitched in to help the surveyor. If he didn't have a family, his wife would help. The farmer could also count on some of his neighbors to pitch in if needed.

The surveyor would pick two people to do the actual measuring and instruct them in the use of the chain and the chaining pins. In the morning, just after daylight, the surveyor and his helpers would go out to a starting point, which could be a neighbor's corner marker. If there wasn't a neighboring marker in the area, the crew would choose one. It could be a tree or a stone. Metal markers were not used because of the high cost of iron at that time.

The surveyor would lean his rifle against a nearby tree, record a bearing from the compass, and begin chaining. Since the land in parts of the mountains cost as much as a penny an acre, or as little as taking possession, there was no need for a lot of accuracy. What was important was to pick, or to set, corner markers that would be easy to see and would remain a long time.

The surveyor would record the distances and the bearings in his notebook. He also described the corner marker. Since the surveyors and the farmers were very knowledgeable when it came to the names of the trees, they left an accurate record of the corner markers. However, in some deeds, local names for trees resulted in names unfamiliar to many people today. For example, the Spanish Oak is really a Southern Red Oak.

In the evening, the surveyor began making a map of the day's progress. This way, once the fieldwork was complete, the surveyor only had to add the last day's work to the map. Before leaving the farmer, the surveyor handed over the map, and the farmer would give the surveyor the agreed on price. This could be produce, farm animals on the hoof or butchered, furs, or even money.

Surveying continued in this manner for many years. When traveling in the mountains during the early 1800s, the surveyor used a horse, a mule, or his own two feet. Not until the mid-1820s were any roads suitable for use by wagon or buggy, and these were only in the open valleys. Once the surveyor reached the end of the graded road, he was back to walking or using a horse.

In 1768, John Love published a book titled, "*Geodaesia: or the Art of Meaſuring Land Made Easy*" (Note the spelling of the word " Measuring" in the title of the book. In 1768, it was normal to use a swash "s" in place of a traditional "s" in some words.) In a chapter titled "Of Instruments and their Use," he writes about the chain: *But that which is most in use among surveyors (as being indeed the best) is Mr. Gunter's, which is 4 poles long, and contains 100 links, each link being 7.92 inches in length.*

He adds the following about surveying in America: *If you find the chain too long for your use, as for some lands it is, especially in America, you may then take the half chain and measure as before…*

According to Love's book, the surveyor would instruct the people helping him measure the lines this way:

> *Take care that they who carry the chain deviate not from a strait line; which you may do by standing at your instrument, and looking through the sights. If you see them between you and the mark observed, they are in a strait line, otherwise not. But without this trouble, they may carry the chain true enough, if he that follows the chain always causes him that goeth before to be in the direct line between himself and the place they are going to, so as that the foreman may always cover the mark from him that goeth behind. If they swerve from the line, they will make it longer than it really is, a strait line being the nearest distance that can be between any two places.*

In this passage, he describes how a line could be measured without the use of someone standing at the instrument. In the sparsely settled regions of the mountains, the surveyor and the farmer alone could survey a tract of land.

In the mountains, the surveyor also instructed the chainmen not to let go of the handles at either end of the chain. When they were measuring up the side of a ridge, the front chainman could not put his end down on the ground without first hooking the handle over a limb or something to keep it from moving. In the flat lands, the chain could be laid down on the ground with little trouble. In the mountains, with the leaf cover on the ground, as soon as the chainman above released his end of the chain; it would slide down the side of the mountain to pile up around a tree, or at the feet of the other chainman. When that occurred, the process of untangling and straightening out the chain began.

Mr. Love also comments on some of the instruments used for measuring angles. He writes:

> *There are but two material things (towards the measuring of a piece of land) to be done in the field; the one is to measure the lines (which I have showed you how to perform by the chain), and the other is to take the quantity included by those lines; for which there are almost as many instruments as there are surveyors. Such among the rest as are most esteemed, are the plane table for small inclosures, the semicircle for champaign grounds, the circumferenter, the theodolite, etc.*

During the mid 1800s, the surveying instruments used in the mountains began to change from the compass to the engineer's transit. Land values in metropolitan areas began to rise, and reached 25 to 50 cents an acre. For that kind of money, the landowners required much more accurate surveys. Surveyors began employing assistants to help measure the property lines instead of relying on the farmers to help. In remote regions, the landowners continued to help the surveyor.

In 1835, Elisha Mitchell, a professor at the University of North Carolina in Chapel Hill, came to the mountains to measure the elevations of some of the higher peaks. His method was to use two barometers. In late June, he reached Morganton after a week of travel by wagon. Here, he took barometric measurements at a friend's house for several days and calculated the elevation.

When he left by horseback, he asked his friend to record the barometric pressure each day at noon from the barometer he left behind. He recorded the barometric pressure at noon, wherever he happened to be, from the instrument he took with him. This way, he could calculate the difference in elevation from his location to his friend's house in Morganton. During this trip, he calculated the height of Mt. Mitchell to be 6,476 feet above sea level. In 1857, he returned to the mountain, and was in the process of running levels up the mountain when he died. Today, the height is officially listed as 6,684 feet.

Because of the general prosperity that existed in North Carolina during the 1850s, substantial improvements in transportation and communication were possible. Improvements in the roads made it easier for people to reach the mountain areas. People, mainly from Charleston, South Carolina, began visiting the mountains during the summer to get away from the oppressive heat. Among these people were developers and engineers.

Some of the engineers settled in the mountains and brought their knowledge of mathematics. After practicing land surveying for a while, they realized that many of the local surveyors measured up the side of the mountains, which created problems with accurately plotting the shape of the property on a map. Still, in the very remote regions, the earlier practice of slope measuring prevailed. The local surveyors did not reduce the slope measurements to their horizontal distances because they either didn't have an instrument for measuring vertical angles, or they didn't have the mathematical knowledge to perform the calculations.

During the late 1800s, the farmers began stringing barbed wire along their property lines to keep the cattle confined. The surveyor would run the line, and the farmer would follow with his friends and family putting the fence where the surveyor marked the line. Today, it's not uncommon to find barbed wire, patented in the late 1800s, in the remote areas and on the side of steep ridges. Many times, the old fence has led to finding long lost corner locations.

From the beginning of the Civil War until the beginning of the 1900s, the economy in the mountains was depressed. After the turn of the century, development began to increase again. The engineers switched from using the Gunter Chain to the new steel tape for measuring distances. Some of the new steel tapes were marked in links and were either one chain or a half-chain long. The newer tapes were marked in feet, with the first and last foot marked in hundredths of a foot.

Even after the introduction of the steel tapes, measuring distances in the mountains didn't change very much. The surveyor still had to get out to the remote property, and he still had to climb the sides of very steep ridges looking for the old corner trees or stone markers. With the new chain, he needed to bring along one or two people who knew how to use the steel tape. Survey crews, with three or four people, became the norm.

Using the steel tape created a few new problems for the chainman. As you may have noted, the title "chainman" remained. Although the tape was much more accurate, it would break easily if it was looped and the loop pulled tightly. If that happened, the crew could not continue measuring the line and would have to climb down the mountain and repair the tape before continuing.

The problem of the tape running down the mountain, if released, became worse with the arrival of the steel tape. The Gunter chain would slide down the mountain if released, but usually the chainman could catch it before it went very far. The steel tape had nothing to slow it down, because it was smooth the entire length. When released, it moved as fast as if you dropped a rock to the ground. One second it's there; the next, it's streaking down the mountain like a scalded snake. The only thing the chainman could do was yell to the one below to catch it, then hike down to get it and bring his end back up the mountain. If they were lucky, the tape wouldn't break.

A metal loop was attached to both ends of the chain. Through this loop was threaded a leather thong. In the mountains, the end of the thong was knotted to form a loop. The chainman never let go of this loop. If he did, he would slip it over a sapling, a limb, or a large rock to keep the chain from getting away.

How was a distance measured using the new steel tape and the engineer's transit? First, the instrument was set up over a corner marker. The tape was laid out in a straight line in the direction of the first measurement. Most tapes were made with an extra foot at the zero end of the tape. This foot was marked in hundredths of a foot, from the zero mark, toward the end of the tape.

If the distance was shorter than the tape, the rear chainman would hold the tape so that a footmark was beside the hinge point of the telescope of the instrument. The rear chainman called out the foot he was holding, and the party chief would note the number in his field book. The front chainman would pull the tape tight, and drop a plumb and string over the tape in the area of the extra foot and over the mark. As the front chainman steadied the plumb bob over the mark, the instrument man would adjust the crosshairs in the telescope on the string over the tape. When the instrument man finished his adjustment, he called "good," and the front chainman called out his measurement. Then the instrument man would call out the vertical angle he read from the scale.

If the distance was longer than the tape, the first measurement was completed as described above. The second measurement began by the instrument man sighting the height of the front chainman's string over the tape. Then, the instrument man would tell the rear chainman to raise or lower his string over the tape so that both ends of the tape were on the same sloping line. This process required great care in the mountains because of the steep slope of the land. The chainman needed good balance and strength in order to remain steady during the measuring process.

The beginning of the 1900s brought the loggers. When they arrived, they were not interested in preserving a tree as a corner marker, even though the wood in the tree was valuable as lumber. The corner tree was cut with the other trees. This trend did not help the surveyor when he tried to retrace a boundary line.

After the loggers arrived, the people in the mountains saw the aftermath of the clearing operations, and began setting aside land for the newly formed Forest Service. In September of 1914, a survey crew from the Forest Service began a survey of a remote tract of land. The party chief had a crew of nine men: a transitman, two chainmen, a front rodman, a back rodman, three axe men, and one cook. According to old field notes kept in local field offices of the Forest Service, distances were measured in chains and links.

Of course, this crew worked for the federal government and could afford to have that many men on one survey crew. However, the small business operator, at that time, could not. The small businessman could only afford, at the most, two helpers. All three would go out to the property. The surveyor would be the head chainman and decide what to locate and where to measure. One helper operated the instrument and kept the notes, and the other worked as the rear chainman.

In the mid 1900s, the survey crew grew to four members. The party chief directed the activities of the other three and kept the notes in the field book. The instrument operator was in charge of the instrument and when the party chief was not present, he would be in charge of the crew. The other two men—the head chainman and the rear chainman—were responsible for accurately measuring the distances. In both survey crews, everyone worked together searching for corner markers called for in the deeds and clearing lines so that property boundaries could be measured.

Today, with the total station instruments and electronic data collection, a crew of only two people can locate more features and measure more boundary line than a crew of four people could twenty years ago. However, even today, as in the 1700s, the surveyor has to climb and descend the sides of steep ridges by foot. In a remote area, which, for the most part, is any area outside of any town in the mountains, the surveyor has to crawl through thick stands of mountain laurel or rhododendron, while climbing steep ridges or descending into deep hollows in search of boundary evidence.

Why does he do it? Two reasons come to mind—the challenge, and the view at the top.

REFERENCES:

Kephart, Horace, Our Southern Highlanders. Knoxville: The University of Tennessee Press: 1984

The North Carolina Historical Commission. William Byrd's Histories of the Dividing Line Betwixt Virginia and North Carolina.

Love, John. Geodaesia. (Photocopy) London. 1687

Woodrow Wilson Bedsaul (1912–1998) Compass-Transit-Electronic Surveyor in North Carolina in the Twentieth Century

The following information about Woodrow Wilson Bedsaul was selected from his memoirs and compiled by Carolyn M. Huskey. He was a highly respected surveyor who made a significant surveying contribution to North Carolina.

The Early Years

Woodrow Wilson Bedsaul was born in the town of Lambsburg, in Carroll County, Virginia, on November 5, 1912, two miles north of the North Carolina/Virginia state line. It was election day and Woodrow Wilson had been elected president. Dr. B. F. Fulks delivered him for a fee of $5.00, a charge that Mrs. Bedsaul thought was outrageous, as the doctor lived nearby and didn't even have to hitch his horse to the buggy. She said he could have been neighborly enough to do it free, since he was sort of kinfolk because he had married her cousin Fannie.

During the year of Woodrow's birth, the United States was still a growing youngster and not fully developed. In 1912, the Union admitted Arizona and New Mexico as the 47th and 48th states.

Woodrow Wilson Bedsaul witnessed a lot of history firsthand—the development of electricity, the telephone, radio, automobile, aviation, movies with sound, television, and all of those home conveniences that we now take for granted.

He walked to his school in the Carroll County School System in his early years, when one-and-two room schools dotted the county. Wood-burning stoves heated the schools. The community furnished the wood, and the larger students chopped it. The water bucket, with a dipper in it, was a part of the furniture. Each child had his/her own drinking cup. High school became available for children who were in walking distance. Sometimes a patron of the school would build a homemade bus. It became necessary for Woodrow to leave home to go to high school at Coal Creek High School. He boarded with his uncle, Fountain Bedsaul, the first year for $8.00. That stretched his finances to the breaking point. The next three years, he boarded with the principal of the school, feeding hogs and milking cows to pay for his keep.

When Woodrow got big enough to help, he was allowed to go with Alf H. Morris, a surveyor and neighbor of the Bedsaul family, to help with surveying. When he reached high school age, Alf even paid him for his help. Woodrow worked for him during summer and vacation times. He even allowed Woodrow to try his hand with the staff compass. He made him his "compass man." Woodrow was on his way to becoming a surveyor. In those days, no certification or license was required. When Alf Morris retired, Woodrow bought his equipment for the sum of $50.00.

Woodrow had to put his plans to go to college on hold. His father had six children to feed and clothe, so his Uncle Willie Shaw agreed to help Woodrow with school finances. Woodrow boarded a train to Galax, VA with a ticket to Welch, West Virginia, to see what arrangements he could make with his Uncle Willie. In Pulaski, Virginia, he had a layover at the railroad station and occupied his time filling out an application to Berea College in Kentucky. Engrossed in the forms and papers spread out on the seat beside him, he suddenly noticed more policemen than he had ever seen, or so it seemed. They rushed him from all sides with guns drawn. While two policemen held him, they announced to the crowd that had gathered, that they had the "murderer" now. Woodrow's papers were scattered all over the floor, and he wanted to pick them up, but the policemen told him that he would not need them where he was going. As they escorted him up the street to the police station, they repeatedly called him "Delp." They would not believe him when he told them Delp was not his name.

At the police station, they accused him of killing the police chief at Galax and questioned him for several hours. They informed him that a man from Galax was on his way down to get him. When the man from Galax arrived, he told them that they had the wrong man, that Woodrow was not Delp.

Woodrow had missed his train connection, his lunch, and lost his papers, and he had spent the evening answering crazy questions. Apologies were profuse, but Woodrow could not accept them gracefully. He was tired and hungry. He did not have enough money for a room to spend the night. While he sat there wishing he was dead, someone brought him a sandwich and a cup of coffee. That helped a little. They told him there was a bed in the jail that he could sleep on, but he said, "No, thank you." He spent the night on a bench in the train depot and boarded a train for Welch the next morning.

The Depression Years

With the crash of the stock market, the Great Depression of the thirties began. When he arrived in Welch, more bad news awaited him. Uncle Willie had suffered a financial setback and said he would have to withdraw his offer to finance Woodrow's college education at that time, but said that he would give him a job if he wanted to help drill a gas well.

He lived with his Uncle Willie, and his wages were $20.00 a month, plus board and lodging. Uncle Willie had several natural gas wells and was supplying gas to part of the city of Welch. They succeeded in striking gas. It was a new experience for Woodrow, and he felt a part of something special.

Uncle Willie was a contractor who had received the contract on three star mail routes, so he made Woodrow a mail carrier on a route between Welch and Pineville. Woodrow enjoyed carrying the mail and carried it about one year. Then, his older sister, Fannie Fears, wrote and told him that if he wanted to attend E. C. Glass Business College, she would help him enroll, and he could board with her for free. Since an education had been Woodrow's aim from the beginning, he told Uncle Willie that he was going to Lynchburg.

At E. C. Glass Business College, Woodrow learned to type and keep books. When he made his services available to the business world, his job hunting was a failure. The Depression was going on, and no one needed the meager skills he had to offer.

About 1931, Woodrow joined the Civilian Conservation Corps (CCC) and became assistant educational advisor. His duties consisted of helping to teach night classes. While there, he took extension courses in English, psychology, and math at Bluefield College.

In 1934, the National Youth Administration came into being, and outstanding high school graduates were granted scholarships. As valedictorian of his class, Woodrow became eligible and was granted a working scholarship to King College in Bristol, Tennessee. While at King, he took a competitive examination given by the United States Forest Service. The four people who made the highest scores on the examination were appointed Junior Assistant Technicians in the United States Forest Service and given a scholarship to the University of Virginia. Woodrow was fortunate to be one of the chosen four.

The subjects required at the University of Virginia were forestry and engineering. Woodrow chose also to take astronomy and land surveying as additional subjects. Because he had received a working scholarship, he spent more time on work projects than he did in the classroom. The Virginia State Forester gave him his fieldwork assignments, and he was required to submit a weekly progress report. His first assignment was to survey and mark the boundary lines on five-acre Timber Stand Improvement (TSI) demonstration projects in various counties in Virginia. He lived in the officers' quarters at the CCC camps, while working on projects, and used CCC enrollees in his survey parties. Surveying equipment usually included a staff compass, a 100-foot chain, and a line rod. Using CCC enrollees, he also surveyed and laid out tree planting plots and supervised the planting of thousands of trees in all parts of the state.

His most interesting work assignment while at the university was that of helping to survey and lay the boundary lines of Forest Service Park lands that the United States Government was transferring to the state of Virginia. He learned how to cruise timber, measuring the height and diameter of a tree with an Abney level and tree calipers, and to estimate the board feet in a tree. After resurveying the original of the United States Forest Service boundary lines, the crew would be required to submit information necessary to estimate the present board foot content and future growth prospects.

Officially speaking, Woodrow was still in school, but he could not attend classes in Charlottesville and do the work that was expected of him in other places.

During the next several years, his assignments carried him to various CCC camps throughout the state. Using CCC enrollees in his work crews, he laid out TSI demonstration projects, planted trees, cruised timber, etc., in northern Virginia, the Tidewater Section, central and southwest Virginia.

Woodrow transferred from the United States Forest Service to the United States Engineering Department, with orders to report to the engineering office in New York City. With an expense allowance, a railroad pass, and a hotel reservation, Woodrow went to the big city. He took physical exams and had needles jabbed into his arm; and he received a new uniform, a brass badge with the engineer's castle symbol on it, a passport picture, an English to Spanish dictionary, and a bundle of literature to study about the natives of the British West Indies.

After about a month in his new environment, he felt confused and uncertain about how he was supposed to fit into the big picture that someone else was painting. He could not determine whether he was a surveyor, engineer, country hick, or a newborn city slicker. When they gave him his passport, he decided that he must be a world traveler.

After his transfer to the United States Engineering Department, he was sent to Trinidad, in the British West Indies (B.W.I.), where he worked for several years. He boarded a ship in New York bound for Trinidad, with orders to report to the area engineer in Port of Spain. The United States had obtained a ninety-nine year lease for a military base, which would include two airstrips. One would be the Edinburgh Runway for army bombers. The other would be the Xeres Runway for navy planes and dirigibles. Woodrow headed one of the seventeen survey parties, worked ten hours a day, seven days a week, with every other Sunday off. The war was close, and almost daily, ships were being sunk by submarines nearby in the Caribbean. The construction was important to combat the submarine menace.

Of the seventeen party chiefs of the United States Engineering Department, fourteen were engineers with impressive brochures, mainly from large cities. Three were land surveyors with the title of "assistant technician." Woodrow chose his crew with the assistance of an Indian boy, who had been educated at Queens College. Then, he chose the equipment that he would use. One of his first assignments was to profile and map the river that flowed by the east end of the site on which they wanted to build the Xeres runway on the airport. The surveyor had to have a full knowledge of the terrain that he would be working in. Elevations were most important, and precise locations of planned construction were necessary.

Construction of the Edinbourgh Air Base in Trinidad was in the final stages. Army B-17 bombers were using the Edinbourgh runway and the navy dirigibles were using the Xerxes runway daily. As the base neared completion, engineers and surveyors were transferred to other locations or released for military duty. Woodrow remained on the base with the title "As Built Engineer." His assignment was to map the Edinburgh base and cantonment areas.

Meanwhile, the war fever was increasing. Woodrow's brother and brother-in-law as well as his schoolmates, neighbors, and friends back home were all in the military. He was torn with conflicting emotions. To remain in Trinidad, as resident engineer of the air base, would have been an important step in realizing his lifetime ambition to become successful in the field of engineering and surveying. The decision to leave or stay troubled his mind.

Woodrow turned in his resignation from the United States Engineering Department in order to volunteer for the army. His resignation was refused; he was offered a raise in salary and was told that the war effort needed him more where he was. Thirty days later, he again turned in his resignation and, again, it was not accepted. Woodrow was dissatisfied and unhappy. After his third letter of resignation to the Area Engineer's office, he was granted a leave of absence, without pay, for the duration of the war.

World War II

Woodrow said goodbye to friends in Trinidad and boarded a plane for Miami, Florida. Before leaving Miami, he visited the draft board and volunteered for the United States Army, to be in the next group inducted from Dade County, Florida. He returned to Virginia, and had his records transferred from Dade County, Florida, to Carroll County, Virginia. His call came soon afterward.

Woodrow Wilson Bedsaul was inducted into the United States Army on September 15, 1943, at Camp Lee, Virginia. He was assigned to the surveying section of the headquarters company of the 1059th Port Construction and Repair Group (PC&R). The PC&R group was special, consisting of individuals from throughout the United States who were outstanding in their field. He felt lucky to be included. He was allowed to cross train in the surveying section and the deep-sea diving units and was sent to Tallahassee, Florida, to attend diving school at Wakula Lake.

He was then shipped to San Francisco to set sail for New Guinea, in the South Pacific, under the rule of Australia. While there, his company constructed a bridge across a river and built an airstrip using interlocking aluminum panels instead of paving. They also cleared the harbor of sunken craft, built floating can docks, drove pilings to form ship tie-ups, and did whatever else they could so that American ships could enter the harbor with supplies or reinforcements.

Woodrow saw his first action in Maffin Bay. The next move was to the island of Morotai, located in the Netherlands East Indies. The Japanese had an air base on the nearby island of Halmahera, and the proximity gave them a great advantage.

Army engineers worked day and night under adverse conditions. They cleared and leveled up a dirt strip that fighter planes could use. They set up hospital tents, a mess tent, and squad tents in a coconut grove and constructed a floating can dock for ships carrying supplies. They drove pilings and established dolphins to secure ships at anchor. Despite the air raids, they made great progress.

Orders then came for the 1059th Company to join a convoy heading for the southern Philippines. They continued on northwest until they reached the island of Mindoro. The heavy equipment was unloaded and brought ashore. The underbrush and vegetation were pushed away, and the ground was leveled up in short order. In a few days, they had erected a mess tent and tents for living quarters. Work crews repaired a landing strip nearby that the Japanese had used.

They had been in Mindoro for about three weeks when orders came for them to go to Manila. The occupying Japanese Army had ravaged Manila, and food was scarce.

Woodrow returned to the 1059th Engineering Company at the west coast of Luzon. By early July 1945, the American Air Force had gained control of the air over Japan. Plans were being made for an amphibious invasion of Japan labeled "Operation Downfall." It was an accepted fact that the cost in lives lost would be terrible, but, at this time, there was no alternative. The 1059th engineers were placed on standby alert. All work activities stopped, and they began to pack up and prepare for further orders. For days, they sat on their duffle bags and waited.

On August 6, 1945, the atomic bomb was dropped on Hiroshima. "Operation Downfall" was put on hold. President Truman demanded that Japan surrender. Despite confirmation that an atomic blast had occurred, the Japanese cabinet refused to give in to President Truman's surrender demands. President Truman was forced to order another atomic bomb. On August 9, 1945, an atomic bomb was dropped on Nagasaki. On the morning of August 10, 1945, Emperor Hirohito sanctioned the proposal to accept the Allied Proclamation, with the stipulation that the Supreme Power of the emperor not be compromised. Without further dissent, the Japanese Cabinet agreed to the terms spelled out in the Potsdam Proclamation. The war was over in Europe and, finally, in Japan. Details of surrender and occupation of Japan had to be worked out and agreed upon. The Peace Treaty was signed on board the U.S.S. *Missouri*, on September 2, 1945. Tens of thousands of GIs owed their lives to mankind's most destructive weapon.

On October 30, 1945, the first phase of Japan's occupation began. The 1059th engineers received the orders that they had been waiting for and headed for Japan. They went ashore at a beach on Yokohama Bay, and as occupiers, they moved across the mountain to the city of Nagoya.

After his service with the occupation forces, he was discharged at Fort Bragg, North Carolina, on January 20, 1946. Ending thirty-three months of service in the United States Army, Woodrow came home with a Bronze Star.

After the War

Soldiers returning home found many things in short supply. Gasoline was rationed and transportation was affected. Woodrow did not return to the United States Engineering Department, but instead, chose employment as a substitute teacher for two years. He used a motorcycle as a primary mode of transportation until he was able to purchase an automobile. Then, he began to do small jobs as a surveyor, the work that he liked best. For a long time, he had been observing and participating in the progress of the surveying profession. There was more land than there were people to make use of it, and many landowners had more land than they wanted to pay taxes on. The large land grants were being divided up and resold. Federal and state land grants contained no warranty, and the title was not always clear.

Woodrow went to Richmond and appeared before the Board of Registration, with a request that he be registered and licensed as a surveyor under the grandfather clause. They rejected his request to be licensed as a surveyor, but said that he could, without doubt, be registered as an engineer based on his record with the United States Engineering Department. He was only interested in surveying, and so he let the matter drop without pursuing it further.

He went back to school and enrolled at Virginia Military Academy, where he earned ninety semester hours of credit in surveying and astronomy. While there, he learned that the Virginia State Board was planning to give a special examination for certification and license in land surveying to any interested members of the graduation class in engineering. He was not a member of the graduating class, but they allowed him to take the examination. Thirty-one people chose to take the examination, only two passed it. Woodrow was one of the fortunate two. On May 18, 1948, Woodrow became certified to survey land in Virginia.

Out of his love for surveying, Woodrow Bedsaul formed his own firm, Bedsaul Surveying Company. He opened an office in Lambsburg, Virginia, employed a crew, and devoted full time to surveying land. Land adjoining the Blue Ridge Parkway was being developed, and Bedsaul Surveying Company located and laid out numerous subdivisions along the Parkway. Included among these subdivisions were Little Waterfalls, Skyline Lakes, High Chaperall, Meadow View, and many others.

Surveying in North Carolina

In 1964, he decided to register in the state of North Carolina. He found that the rules were different in North Carolina. Without a calculator or trigonometry tables—only a slide rule was permitted (he had no slide rule)—he managed to pass the examination. On July 6, 1964, he registered to survey land in the state of North Carolina.

In the early years of surveying, Woodrow used the magnetic compass and staff. Later, he used the surveying transit, which had a magnetic compass and vernier built in. With the transit, angles could be turned and read to a one-minute degree of accuracy. On some transits, degrees, minutes, and seconds could be read. He also used the latest field and office electronic equipment.

Equipment being used at this time was primarily transits and steel tapes. Office calculations were time-consuming. Distance meters and computers would come later. Ray Jones, an engineer with Reynolds Tobacco Company, told him about a little Olivetti computer that could be used to work up closures on field surveys. He said that Niblock Company, in Winston-Salem, had them for sale. Intrigued, Woodrow called Niblock to find out more about the computer. Anxious to show it to Woodrow, Gordon Niblock got a speeding ticket on his way up to Mount Airy. He said that he had sold one to Otis Jones, a surveyor in Winston-Salem. He was the only surveyor, to his knowledge, that had one. Woodrow knew that if he was going to keep up with the Jones boys, he would have to hustle. He bought one and took a step into the future.

The next big advancement in the field of surveying was the distance meter. In the late 1960s, Woodrow purchased a H-P 3800 EDM and brought this technology to the region. He had begun his work with the North Carolina State Park system and knew that the project would require a lot of mapping. Geodetic control would have to be established from Pilot Mountain to the Yadkin River. He believed in the state plane coordinate system and taught his surveyors grid calculations at the same time they were learning latitudes and departures. He tied many transit and tape surveys to grids before any rules required it to be done. He set up twenty-two geodetic stations, which were checked for accuracy and were accepted into the North Carolina Grid System. The only two "toys" in the surveyor's arsenal that Woodrow was not the first to use were the data collector and GPS.

He opened an office in Mount Airy, North Carolina, and employed additional personnel. He spent several years surveying in Mount Airy and the surrounding area. He surveyed the site for Mayberry Mall in Mount Airy and laid out sewer and water lines, buildings, a shopping center, and parking areas. His people left tracks all over the city of Mount Airy. He coordinated his efforts with those of Irvin L. Gentry, a Mount Airy City Engineer. Irvin had previously worked with Ira W. Barber, a famous surveyor whose picture now hangs on the wall in the Surry County Register of Deeds office in Dobson, North Carolina. Mr. Barber had planted numerous property corners and survey markers in the area, and Irvin Gentry knew their locations. This knowledge saved time.

Woodrow said, "In my humble opinion, the most important surveys that I ever did were in the state of North Carolina. When I refer to the surveying that I did, it is with the full realization that no surveyor ever did a survey by himself. The result is the product of team effort. Each member of the team could usually do his part better than I could have done it myself."

Some Members of His Team:
Charles P. (Phil) Wagoner
Oscar K. Merritt
Richard D. Hodges
Damon C. Webb
Donald V. Semones

"Give them the credit that they deserve. They all trained under my supervision and later became registered as surveyors, and they established businesses of their own. After Father Time halted my own activities, they continued to grow, learn, and produce. They are now my superiors in knowledge and skills. I am proud to know, and to recommend, each and every one of them," Woodrow said.

North Carolina Park Surveys

Jonesville Recreation Park
Davie County Youth Park

Yadkin County Recreation Park
Rich Park, Mocksville
Pilot Mountain State Park, Surry County
East Bend Swimming Pool (Loan)
Yadkin/Shore River Access Site, Yadkin County
Kernersville Recreation Park
Hanging Rock State Park, Stokes County
Richmond Hill Law School Park, Yadkin County
Winston Square Park, Winston-Salem
Walkertown Recreation Park
Nature Science Center, Forsyth County
Highway 601 River Access Site, Davie County
Covington Memorial Park, Rural Hall
Boonville Recreation Park
Old 421 Yadkin River Access Site and Park, Forsyth County
King Recreation Park
Yadkin River Section, Pilot Mountain State Park
Donnaha Park, Yadkin River Access Site, Yadkin County

... And Woodrow Bedsaul, with his team, surveyed them all.

In recognition of his work in surveying North Carolina state parks, he received an award from the Appalachian Regional Commission in March 1985. Woodrow noted that he had surveyed more than 5,700 acres of state-owned property, including historical sites as well as recreational areas.

Family-Church

Woodrow was married to Savada Easter Bedsaul for over fifty years. They had one daughter, Ann Bedsaul Hawks, and one son, George Allen Bedsaul. Woodrow and his wife had close ties with, and were active in, the Lambsburg Christian Church, which presented them a plaque in honor of their work in the church and community.

Community Service

Woodrow Wilson Bedaul had a strong sense of, a love of, and dedication to the community. He wanted to make things better. He always placed great emphasis on schools, and served seventeen years as a member of the Carroll County School Board, receiving a Certificate of Merit for his service. He was commended for his service to the Wytheville Community College in Virginia and served as a member of the Engineering Technology Curriculum Advisory Committee.

History was one of his main loves, and he helped found and served as president of the Carroll County Historical Society. The society had a committee that cataloged the cemeteries in Carroll County. Woodrow worked on mapping the cemeteries for them. Through his drawings, Woodrow taught where the boundaries lay when the colonies were first formed under the Virginia Company Charter of 1584 and the London Company Charter of 1606. He showed the original counties of Virginia, the streams and mountains used by the first settlers to determine landholdings, and the location of various Indian tribes who lived in the area.

He served the Boy Scouts of America as Scoutmaster of Troop 81 in Lambsburg, VA. He received the Ruritan National Award as "Most Valuable Ruritan of the Year in 1985" from the Lambsburg Ruritan Club. The club also presented the "Golden Heart Award" in 1987 to him and his wife for their community service.

The Department of Health Emergency Medical Services issued a certificate to him for his training and service as an emergency medical technician in Carroll County.

He received a Fellow Award from the American Congress on Surveying and Mapping, the objectives of which are to advance the sciences of surveying and mapping in the public interest, strengthen programs in education in the technological sciences and professional philosophies of surveying and mapping, and to improve the standards of the profession.

He held lifetime memberships in several surveyors' associations and received an Award of Appreciation in 1977, from the Virginia Association of Surveyors for having served in all offices on the association's board of directors.

He was instrumental in the reorganization of the Piedmont Chapter of the North Carolina Society of Surveyors, Inc. He served two terms as president. He was also a lifetime and fellow member of the North Carolina Society of Surveyors.

He was recognized by the Northwest Piedmont Council of Governments in 1985, for the fact that he had surveyed, and assisted in acquiring, land in excess of 5,700 acres to be incorporated in the North Carolina State Park System.

Woodrow Wilson Bedsaul died on October 20, 1998. He had lived his life, and died, in the same house in which he was born.

Phil Wagoner wrote the following of Woodrow Bedsaul in the May 1998 issue of *The Tarheel Surveyor*:

> "During the 1960s, 1970s, and 1980s, he was the dominant force in the surveying market in the area around Surry County, NC, and Carroll County, VA. He set a standard that the legal community still expects of the ones who came later. Working behind an old Bedsaul survey is as good as it gets in this area. All of his maps were lettered with Leroy templates, corners were always in place at the time of the map. The projects were well researched, and his integrity and reputation in the community has always been impeccable."

North Carolina Society of Surveyors, Inc. History

PART I—THE EARLY YEARS (1939–1956)

There is, and has always been, a great need in North Carolina for closer cooperation and fellowship among the surveyors. The organization of the North Carolina Society of Surveyors is a start toward the needed cooperation and fellowship. The extent to which the society will succeed in this aim is dependent on the surveyors themselves.

We can secure a great many benefits for ourselves if we organize and cooperate. The surveyors are the only professional men who have not organized in sufficient strength to make their influence felt in the state of North Carolina. In addition to the benefits which we can hope to secure by organization, there will be the pleasure of forming new friendships and discussing our work and problems with members of our society from all sections of the state.

Weldon Willis
President, 1942

NOTE: *The following information is a history of the North Carolina Society of Surveyors, Inc. (NCSS), as compiled by Otis A. Jones, PLS, from selected portions of the minutes of meetings from 1939–1956.*

~

Minutes of the Organization Meeting of the North Carolina Society of Surveyors January 31, 1939

The meeting was called to order by Professor C. L. Mann, temporary chairman. Mr. Mann stated that the purpose of the meeting was the organization of a North Carolina Society of Surveyors and stated that the first business would be the election of officers so as to form a permanent organization.

He called for nominations for president. Mr. F. C. Morton was unanimously elected president. Mr. G. S. Harrell was nominated and unanimously elected vice president. Mr.

Mann was nominated for secretary/treasurer. The vote was put by Mr. Ragsdale, and Mr. Mann was elected secretary/treasurer.

Mr. W. J. Lambert and Weldon Willis were elected as members of the board of directors. Mr. Lambert was elected to serve one term and Mr. Willis two terms.

Motion was made that the president appoint a membership committee, the purpose of which would be to secure additional new members to the society. Motion carried. The president stated that he would appoint the committee later.

Mr. Lambert made a motion that the board of directors be a legislative committee whose principal duties for this year would be devoted toward securing legislation requiring registration for surveyors. The motion passed.

Mr. Mann distributed copies of a proposed constitution for the society. This constitution was read and acted upon by sections. The constitution was adopted with a few minor changes, and the secretary was instructed to incorporate these changes.

A motion was also made that drafts of any proposed amendment to the registration law be sent to the present members of the society for their consideration.

A resolution was also made and passed that the members present go on record as favoring compulsive registration for surveyors.

Mr. Ragsdale made a motion that the secretary be requested to keep in touch with the members of the society to the extent of improving surveying methods in the state. This motion passed.

A resolution was passed endorsing the Institute of Engineers and the Institute of Surveyors conducted by the School of Engineering, North Carolina State College, and a vote of thanks was given to Professor Mann and the Department of Civil Engineering for its assistance in conducting the Institute of Surveyors.

There being no further business, the meeting adjourned to meet at the call of the presid ent..C. L. Mann, Secretary

Constitution of the North Carolina Society of Surveyors

ARTICLE I

Name, Location, and Object

Section 1. The name of this organization shall be the "North Carolina Society of Surveyors."

Section 2. The offices of the society shall be located in Raleigh, N.C.

Section 3. The objects to be obtained are the advancement of surveying knowledge and practice; the cultivation of friendly relations with all surveyors; the maintenance of high professional standards; and cooperation with other surveying societies, with a view to promoting the general surveying practice in North Carolina.

Section 4. Among the means to be employed for this purpose shall be meetings for the presentation and discussion of papers, and the encouragement of surveyors who are not members to attend and take part in all features of such meetings.

ARTICLE II

Membership

Section 1. Any man of good standing in his community, who is qualified by law, or by surveying experience, to practice surveying shall be eligible for membership.

ARTICLE III

Dues

Section 1. The annual dues payable by all members shall not be more than one dollar payable in advance on the first day of January, and any member whose dues are more than one year in arrears shall cease to be a member of this society.

ARTICLE IV

Officers

Section 1. The officers of this society shall be a president, a vice president, and a secretary/treasurer, who, with the two latest living past presidents, one to serve one term and one to serve two terms, shall constitute a board of directors, in which the government of the society shall be vested.

Section 2. The terms of office of the president of the society shall be one year, of the vice president, one year, and of the secretary/treasurer, two years. The term of each officer shall begin at the close of the annual meeting at which such officer is elected, and shall continue for the period above named, or until a successor is duly elected. No officer, other than the secretary/treasurer, shall be eligible to serve a succeeding term in the same office, and no vice president may be elected to a succeeding term as president.

Section 3. A vacancy in any office shall be filled by election at the next regular meeting of the society.

Section 4. The officers following those elected at the first organization of the society shall be elected at the annual meetings of the society thereafter.

Section 5. When officers of the society are to be elected, a nominating committee of three shall be appointed and, when available, one member shall be the latest living past president of the society; the other two members shall be appointed by the board of directors at least thirty days before the date of the annual meeting. The nominating committee shall present a list of two names for each officer to be elected, and shall transmit this list to the secretary who shall prepare letter ballots to be sent to the members not later than twenty days before the date of the annual meeting.

ARTICLE V

Meetings

Section 1. The annual meeting of the society shall be held on a date to be fixed by the board of directors. Ten members shall constitute a quorum for business.

Section 2. A regular meeting shall be held at least one time each year at such time and place as may be appointed by the board of directors. At these meetings, the business of the society shall be transacted and the discussion of papers shall be in order.

ARTICLE VI

Amendments

Section 1. The constitution may be amended only by an affirmative vote of not less than two-thirds of the members voting, provided the total number of voters shall be not less than a majority of the whole membership...*January 31, 1939*

A bill to be entitled: An Act to Amend Chapter 21 of the Laws of 1921 Relating to Engineering and Land Surveying

The General Assembly of North Carolina do enact:

Section 1. That Section 15 of Chapter 1 of the laws of 1921, the same being Section 6055 (q) of Chapter 97 (A) of the Consolidated Statutes of North Carolina, be and the same is hereby amended as follows: By striking out all said Section 15 and substituting in lieu thereof the following:

"Section 15. Land Surveying, as covered by this act, refers only to surveys for the determination of areas or for the establishment or reestablishment of land boundaries and the subdivisions and platting of land and making plats, maps, and drawing descriptions of the lands or lines as surveyed, platted, or investigated. Nothing in this act shall be construed as prohibiting a duly qualified registered engineer from making land surveys."

Section 2. That this act shall become and be in full force and effect on and after January 1, 1940.

Section 3. That all laws and clauses of laws in conflict with this act be and the same are hereby repealed.

Members of the North Carolina Society of Surveyors for the Year 1939

NAME:	ADDRESS:
Baker, Golden M.	Pinnacle, North Carolina
Beems, C.	Faison, North Carolina
Cavin, W. Marsh	Stanley, North Carolina
Corey, A.	P.O. Box 441, Williamston,N C
Denney, Gilmer	Pinnacle, North Carolina
Dove, T. C.	Monroe, North Carolina
Dudley, E. R.	Kinston, North Carolina
Ellis, W. O.	Washington, North Carolina
Fisher, Guy J.	Concord, North Carolina
Foy, J. L.	Kinston, North Carolina

Gillespie, R. S.	Elizabethtown, North Carolina
Harrell, G. S.	Shannon, North Carolina
Holmquist, Charles G.	94 Burnell St., Bridgeport, CT
Inscoe, Phil R.	Castalia, North Carolina
Kerr, L. C.	Clinton, North Carolina
Lambert, W. J.	Benson, North Carolina
Lewis, Meriwether	Kinston, North Carolina
McBride, Sam	Marshville, North Carolina
Mann, C. L.	Raleigh, North Carolina
Moore, E. L.	Danville, Virginia
Morton, F. C.	Oxford, North Carolina
Powell, Sam	Garner, North Carolina
Ragsdale, William S.	Smithfield, North Carolina
Robbins, A. A.	Council, North Carolina
Rodman, William C.	Washington, North Carolina
Sharrett, B. B.	Bristol, Virginia
Stell, Pittman	Zebulon, North Carolina
Willis, Weldon	Marion, North Carolina
Wiseman, R. L.	Ingalls, North Carolina
Womble, F. E.	Siler City, North Carolina
Young, O. S.	Angier, North Carolina

Meeting of the Board of Directors of the North Carolina Society of Surveyors State College November 25, 1939

Members present: F. C. Morton, president; W. J. Lambert, G. S. Harrell, P. R. Inscoe, and C. L. Mann, secretary. Mr. Weldon Willis was unable to be present.

It was decided to have the annual meeting on Wednesday, January 24th, this being the day before the beginning of Engineer's Week.

A tentative program as follows was adopted:

10:00 A.M.	Registration at office of registration board.
11:00 A.M.–1:00 P.M.	Business meeting, election of officers, and general discussion on remunerations, mapping and records, etc.
2:00 P.M.	A paper on "City Surveying," by Mr. E. L. Moore of Danville, Virginia. Discussion.
3:00 P.M.	A paper on "Line and Corner Markings," by G. S. Harrell. Discussion.

A paper on "Legal Aspects of Surveying in General," by a lawyer.
Discussion.

The board selected the following as a nomination committee: F. C. Morton, E. L. Moore, and Meriwether Lewis.

Mr. Morton was instructed to call a meeting of this committee as soon as possible, and select the proposed candidates for the various officers to be voted on at the January meeting. Mr. Morton was also instructed to procure the speaker for "City Surveying," and Mr. Harrell, the speaker on "Legal Aspects of Surveying."

The secretary was instructed to include in the program to be sent out to the surveyors a notice, to the effect that instruction courses would be offered by the department of civil engineering to any surveyors who might wish instructions in any subjects pertaining to surveying, such courses to be given during Engineers Week.

The Annual Meeting of the North Carolina Society of Surveyors
Raleigh, North Carolina
April 17, 1940

The meeting was called to order at 11:00 A.M. by Mr. G. S. Harrell, vice president, due to the inability of Mr. F. C. Morton, who was unable to attend because of illness. The chairman noted that this meeting was a deferred meeting from January 24th, which was called off at that time on account of unusually bad weather.

The minutes of the meeting on January 31, 1939, were read and approved. The chairman then called upon the secretary for the financial report. This report was given and is herewith incorporated in the minutes of the meeting today:

North Carolina Society of Surveyors

FINANCIAL REPORT

Receipts:		
Dues—32 members—$1.00 each	$32.00	
Interest—Raleigh Industrial Bank	.36	
Disbursements:		
Carolina Printing Company,		
200—1939 and 1940 membership cards		$4.75
Stamps for F. C. Morton, President		1.00
	$32.36	$ 5.75
BALANCE on Principal,		$26.61
Raleigh Industrial Bank	$32.36	$32.36

The chairman then appointed the Resolution Committee, composed of Meriwether Lewis, W. C. Rodman, and C. L. Mann.

The secretary read the minutes of the board of director's meeting, which met on November 25, 1939, said minutes of which are to be found on pages 11 and 12 of this minute book.

Visitors and new members were then introduced to the society, and the secretary was instructed to write letters soliciting their membership. The names were as follows: Walter P. Bird, Lexington, N.C., recommended by O. S. Young; A. M. Culbreth, RFD, Fayetteville, N.C., recommended by G. S. Harrell; Bruce Pierce recommended by G. S. Harrell; J. W. Blanchard, Rose Hill, N.C., by C. L. Mann; Henry Vann, by C. Beems; John D. Beath, Elizabethtown, N.C., by R. S. Gillespie; Charles A. McCall, Linville Falls, N.C., and E. M. Crawford, Marion, N.C., by Weldon Willis; Don Cromartie, Garland, N.C., by A. A. Robbins; Archie Buie, Pembroke, N.C., and J. C. McAdams, by G. S. Harrell.

Mr. Ragsdale moved that the nominating committee propose three names for the officers and mail to membership, and that officers be elected by vote at the annual meeting. This motion passed unanimously.

Mr. Stell moved that the legislative committee of this society be instructed to promote before the members of the legislature a law favoring a four-year term for county surveyors. This motion was seconded by Mr. Ragsdale and was passed.

The remaining time was spent on the discussion of remuneration for surveyors. Mr. Mann pleaded for a quote of remuneration for surveyors other than the hour or day basis. He suggested, as he has done before, that acre basis is more satisfactory to the client as well as the surveyor. This brought on a good deal of discussion. No definite motion was taken.

A suggestion was made that the time of the annual meeting be held in April instead of January. There was no vote on it, but it was the general opinion that the surveyor's meeting during the Engineer's Institute Week was more desirable.

The chairman appointed a committee to canvas the ballots and the committee reported later as follows:

PRESIDENT:	NUMBER:
William S. Ragsdale	10
Philip R. Inscoe	7
VICE PRESIDENT:	
Sam Powell	7
Guy J. Fisher	10
SECRETARY/TREASURER:	
C.L. Mann	14
DIRECTORS:	NUMBER:
W.C. Rodman, Jr.	9
W. Marsh Cavin	8

OFFICERS FOR 1940 WERE:

President:	William S. Ragsdale
Vice President:	Guy J. Fisher
Secretary/Treasurer:	C.L. Mann
Directors:	W.C. Rodman
	F.C. Morton
	Weldon Willis

(F.C. Morton and Weldon Willis by the constitution remain as directors.)

The Resolution Committee reported as follows:

The North Carolina Society of Surveyors, in regular session, do hereby resolve that the society extend the heartfelt sympathy to the President, Mr. F. C. Morton, now confined to his home on account of illness; that sincere wishes for his immediate recovery are expressed by the society; and that the secretary be instructed to convey this message to Mr. Morton.

In addition, the North Carolina Society of Surveyors expresses their sincere appreciation to Mr. Franklin T. Dupree for his most helpful talk and discussion.

Committee: Meriwether Lewis, W. C. Rodman, C. L. Mann

The meeting adjourned for lunch to meet again at 2:00 P.M. The secretary stated that anyone who did not care to go uptown to lunch could get a very good meal at the college cafeteria.

The meeting met at 2:00 P.M., and a very interesting talk and discussion on "Legal Aspects of Surveying" by Mr. Franklin T. Dupree, Attorney, was enjoyed very much. Mr. E. L. Moore gave a very instructive paper on "City Surveying." This was followed by "Line and Corner Markings" by Mr. G. S. Harrell, which was of most general interest to all the members.

The meeting adjourned to meet again at the call of the president.

April 17, 1940 C. L. Mann, secretary

North Carolina Society of Surveyors
Raleigh, North Carolina

The following surveyors have paid the renewal fee for the year 1940:

NAME	ADDRESS
Baker, Golden M.	Pinnacle, North Carolina
Beems, C.	Faison, North Carolina
Blanchard, Frank	Rose Hill, North Carolina
Blanchard, J. W.	Rose Hill, North Carolina
Cavin, W. Marsh	Stanley, North Carolina
Clements, E. W.	Morrisville, North Carolina
Dudley, E. R.	Kinston, North Carolina

Ellis, W. O.	Washington, North Carolina
Foy, J. L.	Kinston, North Carolina
Gillespie, R. S.	Elizabethtown, North Carolina
Gregory, R. T.	Stovall, North Carolina
Harrell, G. S.	Shannon, North Carolina
Hollowell, A. C.	Corapeake, North Carolina
Holmquist, Charles G.	94 Burnell St., Bridgeport, CT
Inscoe, Phil R.	Castalia, North Carolina
Johnson, Herbert L.	Coats, North Carolina
Jones, Walter T.	Patterson, North Carolina
Kerr, L. C.	Clinton, North Carolina
Lambert, W. J.	Benson, North Carolina
Lewis, Meriwether	Kinston, North Carolina
McBride, Sam	Marshville, North Carolina
McNeill, A. L.	Rockingham, North Carolina
Mann, C. L.	Raleigh, North Carolina
Morton, F. C.	Oxford, North Carolina
Ragsdale, William S., Jr.	Smithfield, North Carolina
Robbins, A. A.	Council, North Carolina
Robeson, W. B.	Red Springs, North Carolina
Rodman, W. C. Jr.	Washington, North Carolina
Stell, Pittman	Zebulon, North Carolina
Thomas, O. T.	Route 2, Jonesboro, North Carolina
Tripp, F. McCoy	Winterville, North Carolina
Tyson, J. Ed	County Surveyor, Robeson County Lumberton, North Carolina
Walker, N. Glen	Brown Summit, North Carolina
White, L. O.	Route 1, Statesville, North Carolina
Williams, E. R.	110 S. Williams St., Goldsboro, NC
Williams, John R.	3218 N. First Pl., Arlington, PA
Willis, Weldon	Marion, North Carolina
Womble, Floyd E.	Siler City, North Carolina
Worthington, Robert	Ayden, North Carolina
Wiseman, R. L.	Ingalls, North Carolina

The following surveyors joined the society in 1939, but did not renew their membership for 1940:

Corey, A.	P.O. Box 441, Williamston, NC
Denny, Gilmer	Pinnacle, North Carolina
Dove, T. C.	Monroe, North Carolina

Fisher, Guy J. (Pd)	Concord, North Carolina
Powell, Sam	Garner, North Carolina
Sharrett, B. B.	Bristol, Virginia (deceased)
Young, O. S.	Angier, North Carolina

A Synopsis and Excerpts of the Minutes 1941–1956

The third annual meeting was held January 22, 1941, in Raleigh, North Carolina. Some were unable to attend due to illness; W. C. Rodman and Meriwether Lewis had gone into the military service. After some recommendations and discussions, the society went on record as favoring compulsory registration for land surveyors, and the Legislative Committee was instructed to proceed, as it thought best, to obtain the necessary legislation that would include a liberal grandfather clause. Officers elected for 1941 were R. S. Gillespie, director; G. S. Harrell, president; P. R. Inscoe, vice president; C. L. Mann, secretary/treasurer.

* WRITER'S NOTE: *At this time, it should be said that the United States was forced into World War II (1941–1945) due to the brutal attack on Pearl Harbor, December 7, 1941. This brought about many changes in the country. One great change was a manpower shortage as many of our own men were serving in the armed forces. Because of this, many women went to work in factories to compensate for this shortage. There were many other shortages as well, such as food, sugar, gas, tires, and scrap metal. Due to these shortages, the North Carolina Society of Surveyors (NCSS) experienced slower growth, but adapted well to all of these changes and shortages.*

On January 13, 1942, the annual meeting was held in Raleigh, N.C. A motion was made that the state be divided into districts in order that the districts might organize and elect officers for the purpose of having meetings to conduct business in advancing the activities of the state society. Motion passed. It was suggested that the districts be formed with respect to the number of surveyors in the locality. Also, the Legislative Committee was instructed to find out what could be done toward abolishing the office of county surveyor in the state. New officers elected were Weldon Willis, president; J. W. Blanchard, vice president; C. L. Mann, secretary/treasurer.

On January 28, 1943, the annual meeting was held in Raleigh, N.C. with Weldon Willis, who complimented those who were present in spite of bad weather and the gasoline and tire shortages. An election of officers took place with the following new officers elected for the year 1943: P. R. Inscoe, president and A. L. McNeill, vice president. It was reported that dividing the state into zones would be postponed until after the war because of gasoline and tire rationing. On the topic of abolishing the office of county surveyor, it was decided that it would be left up to each county to enact its own law.

The next annual meeting was held in Raleigh, N.C. on January 27, 1944. These were the new officers elected for 1944: R. S. Gillespie, president; F. McCoy Tripp, vice president and C. L. Mann, secretary/treasurer. It was recommended that a committee of five be appointed to cooperate and work with a similar group from the N.C. Society of Engineers in connection with any legislative matters affecting both groups. It was the general opinion of the body that no change in the Registration Law helping either the engineers or surveyors could ever be accomplished before any legislature until such changes were backed by the full membership and by the individual members of the North Carolina Society of Engineers (NCSE) and the NCSS.

At the annual meeting on January 25, 1945, the secretary requested permission to pay five dollars to a stenographer from the funds of the society for her services in connection with the operation of the society office. This was approved. The following officers were elected for 1945: Meriwether Lewis, president; Frank Blanchard, vice president; and C. L. Mann, secretary/treasurer. During the meeting, a motion showed that the society approved of compulsory registration for surveyors. A committee composed of Harrell, Mann, and Lambe was named to correspond with a similar committee of the NCSE to study and make a report on the standardization of surveys, descriptions, maps, etc.

The annual meeting in 1946 was held on January 24th in Raleigh, N.C. It was opened by Meriwether Lewis. The Legislative Committee reported concerning the society's Registration Amendment Bill. They stated that a majority of the members of the Legislative Judiciary Committee No. 1 disapproved of the bill and that they would not agree to recommend its passage. For this reason, the committee felt that it should be tabled.

A motion was made that a committee composed of Secretary Mann, Grady Harrell, and P. R. Inscoe be appointed to compile a code of ethics. This code shall also be a code of practice for furthering uniformity in public relations and in the practice of land surveying in general. Such a code should be an official publication of the North Carolina Society of Surveyors, and when completed and accepted by the society in regular session, a copy is to be furnished to all members of the society. Motion carried.

It was brought to the attention of the society's members that unsatisfactory land surveying fieldwork and deed descriptions had been permitted by incompetent surveyors. Therefore, it was resolved that the society approve and recommend that its Legislative Committee be instructed to use its efforts in getting the present registration law amended to require registration of land surveyors.

The following officers were elected: Richard Seawell, president; A. A. Robbins, vice president and C. L. Mann, secretary/treasurer. **Writers Note: This was Professor Mann's final term as secretary/treasurer. He served long and well, from the beginning of the NCSS in 1939, as one of the founding members, to his final year, 1946 (also the year he retired from N.C. State College). He will long be remembered for his tenure. He also served on the North Carolina State Board of Registration for Professional Engineers and Land Surveyors from 1928–1954.*

Outgoing president, Meriwether Lewis, read a prepared address to the meeting's members, which was received with much enthusiasm and favorable comments. His address in its entirety is as follows:

Fellow Surveyors,

It is indeed a pleasure as your president to welcome every one of you here at this meeting. I sincerely hope the good you derive from being here and the joy of fellowship in meeting your fellow surveyors will fully repay you for all the trouble you had in getting here. The North Carolina Society of Land Surveyors was organized a few years ago by the land surveyors of North Carolina interested in the advancement of our profession as practiced in our state. Our membership has not been as large and all-inclusive as we might have wished, but we can look back and see some definite progress in the aim and purpose of our society, both in raising the standard of the work of our profession, and the increase of the respect of the general public for our work. I am greatly encouraged by this progress and feel that we are much more the competent and better surveyor for our annual meetings here, and that we will continue to improve in our profession in the future, and by increasing our own abilities and standards of work we will have advanced the standard of the profession as a whole, which will result in increased respect for our work in the eyes of the general public with which we do business. As one example of the progress of our society, we have been invited to our sister state of South Carolina to assist in organizing a similar society. There are some of us that have been unable to attend the meetings for the past three or four years because of an important duty with our government, and as one of those, I am glad to be back and I give the others a hearty welcome back with us, and I also want to thank those who kept the society going so well during our absence and under such trying circumstances. As a practicing land surveyor of twenty years experience, I want to look back and make a few observations and comments about the land surveyor himself and his relations to the public with which he deals.

Time was when any man with a compass and a chain could hang out his shingle and set himself up as a land surveyor regardless whether he had any of the other qualifications of a land surveyor or not. And this naturally leads us into the question of—"What are the qualifications of a competent land surveyor?"

First among these is equipment—the tools with which he does his work. This includes a correct method of measuring distance, be it chain or tape. Then a compass, be it Jacob staff or transit, and this should be kept in working condition and periodically checked with government markers for accuracy. Then, a proper system of taking notes of work done that lends itself readily to easily filing. Then, the necessary instruments for mapping work done and producing a correct and easily understood plat of the property involved. These are the material equipment of the land surveyor, those things visible that one can see with the eye, that sometimes fools the public into thinking the owner is a good and competent surveyor.

To use this good equipment, the competent surveyor must have that other necessary qualification—technical education in land surveying. And those things a person may acquire through books by studying and application such as: the proper use of the compass and the proper use and application of the importance of magnetic variation; the use of the vernier in the securing of angles; the use of the stadia in the securing of distances; the use of instruments for proper platting and the producing of maps; the technical knowledge necessary to close a survey and to calculate the proper area of a survey. These unseen qualifications a man can acquire through study and application from technical books, and all good land surveyors do acquire them in varying degrees of skill and expertise.

I have spoken of two of the qualifications of a land surveyor, and, as important as these two are, to me, they are not as important in the discharge of the duty of the land surveyor to his public and community as the third qualification, and that is the most important one of CHARACTER—those distinctive qualities or traits that mark or distinguish one man from another in his dealings with his fellow man and in the practice of his profession among them. The watchword of the character of the land surveyor should be HONESTY, honest to himself and to his fellow men, honest in the big things and in the little things, honest in all its other meanings: upright, just, sincere, equitable, fair, righteous, frank or open, trustworthy. Honest in the proper measuring of a line, honest in the proper application of the variation, honest in the selection of a proper starting point, honest in the retracing of an old line, honest in the recording of notes, honest in the closing of a survey, honest in the figuring and recording of the acreage of a survey, honest in your decision as to the ownership of land. You may not always be correct— you will make mistakes, we all do— but let it be an honest mistake. The old saying, "Be true to yourself and you cannot be false to any man," in my opinion, applies more closely to the land surveyor in his daily practice of his profession than to any business with which I am acquainted.

Now, the question arises, "Where does our society come in on all of this?" The answer is that by organizing and banding together we can best advance the practice of land surveying by advancing the individuals engaged in that practice, and this can be done by meeting together and discussing new equipment, new methods, learning from the experience of others, getting answers to problems that need answering, and discussing any legislation that we may deem necessary for our profession. In doing this, we all have the benefit of the others' advice and counsel. Here are some of the questions I would like to hear discussed:

- *How is the best way, method or system, to use aerial survey or maps in land surveying?*

- *Can we set up a uniform schedule of prices? How best can we charge—on a contract, or per-day basis?*
- *Should we endorse a law requiring the compulsory registration and examination of all land surveyors?*

Now, in closing, let me say that any man with the qualifications that I have mentioned can establish himself as a land surveyor, and by diligent practice and performance, he will acquire the fourth qualification which only practice and time can give him—and that is the one of experience, including practical knowledge and woods craftsmanship. He will become acquainted with the laws concerning surveys and surveying and the ownership of property. He will become an expert in the tracing of the path of descriptions of land as given in the recorded records of the county. As time goes on, he will become the judge and jury in land disputes, the arbitrator in question of the ownership of land, and he will grow in status and esteem in the eyes of his fellow men; and through a judicious exercising of his influence, he will rightfully take his place as one of the most honored, trusted, and respected men of the community in which he lives and works.

This address resulted in instructed discussions from the floor, and a copy of this address has been made a part of these minutes.

The annual meeting of January 23, 1947, held in Raleigh, N.C., was called to order by President Seawell. The election of officers for 1947 came next. These new officers were Frank Blanchard, president; Pittman Stell, vice president; and Richard Seawell, secretary/treasurer. The president made a short speech on the need for an established code of ethics and rules of practice.

The Resolution Committee submitted a resolution setting up a "Uniform System of Marking Trees Used to Indicate the Location of Property Lines and Corners." After some discussion, the resolution was passed, and a copy is a part of the minutes. A motion was made and passed that the secretary send all members copies of the following: (1) resolution on uniform system of marking trees, (2) the address made by Mr. McMillan on "How Surveyors and Lawyers Can Be Helpful to Each Other," (3) A paper prepared by the late Hon. James H. Pou on "Land Titles in North Carolina," and (4) a roster of active members of the society. A motion was made and passed that the society hold a meeting the following summer, preferably August.

The annual meeting was held April 16, 1948, in Raleigh, N.C. Mr. Harrell made the motion that E. W. Ruggles, director of the Extension Division of State College, be made an honorary member of the society. The motion was seconded and unanimously approved. Also, Professor Mann extended an invitation to all members to visit the exhibits of the Engineer Exposition. New officers elected were Grady S. Harrell, president; A. B. Hafer, vice president; and E. W. Ruggles, secretary/treasurer.

* WRITERS NOTE: *This was Mr. Harrell's second term as president; his first was in 1941. Also,*

he served on the North Carolina State Board of Registration for Professional Engineers and Land Surveyors (1941–1961). This was the first term for E. W. Ruggles, secretary/treasurer.

The important topic discussed at the meeting was the proposed "Manual for Land Surveying." Mr. R. Getty Browning of the State Highway Commission gave a talk on the manual. The members were urged to submit any suggestions for additions or changes. The society is expected to have an important part in compiling the proposed manual and getting it adopted as a required code of practice for anyone making a land survey to go on record.

February 17, 1949, was the date of the annual surveyors' meeting in Raleigh, N.C., President Harrell presented Mr. Paul Lyman, who explained clearly the requested amendment to the North Carolina License Law for land surveyors and engineers. After this, the following resolution was unanimously passed: "that the society go on record favoring the adoption by the legislature of the proposed changes in the law for registering engineers and land surveyors, and that the society commend the committee of the NCSE for their splendid work in preparing these changes to the law."

Mr. R. Getty Browning presented and explained the proposed manual for land surveyors which had been prepared by a committee of the NCSS. The president instructed the secretary to duplicate the manual and send it to all surveyors in North Carolina.

A motion was made by A. B. Hafer that the chair appoint a committee to poll and receive recommendations of the surveyors of North Carolina on the manual. The committee was instructed to meet to coordinate the suggestions received and decide on further action by the society for the present legislature. The secretary was instructed to write a letter to accompany the manual requesting each surveyor's opinion of the manual.

New officers elected for 1949 were C. B. Fulghum, president; J. Chandler Eakes, vice president; and E. W. Ruggles, secretary/treasurer. The following were appointed by the president to act for the society on the surveyor's manual: A. B. Hafer, C. B. Fulghum, J. Chandler Eakes, Richard Seawell, E. W. Ruggles, Grady S. Harrell, and P. R. Inscoe.

The annual meeting of the society was January 26, 1950, in Raleigh, N.C. Dr. R. E. Fadum, head of the Department of Civil Engineering of the N.C. State College, spoke on codes of practices, ethics, and registration for land surveyors. He said that the licensed surveyor should follow the Golden Rule in applying the codes of practice. He said that relations with clients should be such that charges would be in line with the best of jobs to cover adequate research of a project. Another point he made was that a surveyor should not accept any job unless he is fully qualified to complete it. A strong point was made—that the society should have as many members as possible—there is strength in numbers. If you have a strong society, you can carry out common objectives. This statement was made in connection with the possible future plans for the new Registration Law. He also made suggestions as to how lines may be established.

The Honorable A. Corey, a member of the society and a Representative in the North Carolina General Assembly, spoke on the need to establish a unified (standard) system. Mr. Corey suggested that the society work toward the development of definite and lasting identification of boundary lines and that surveyors work under a definite system and code of ethics. Mr. Corey made a motion that a committee of three be appointed to meet with the Society of Engineers and cooperate with them in drawing up a skeleton for a bill, which would be presented to the legislature. This motion was amended by Mr. Fulghum to the effect that the incoming officers form the proposed committee. The motion was further amended to include the outgoing officers. It was seconded and unanimously approved.

Officers elected for the year 1950 were A. B. Hafer, president; A. Corey, vice president; and E. W. Ruggles, secretary/treasurer. Meriwether Lewis moved that the incoming and outgoing officers form a legislative committee to meet and draft a bill, which would be presented to the 1951 legislature. He further said that the members would be allowed ten cents per mile travel expenses and that mimeographed copies of the proposed bill be mailed to each member of the society. This motion was unanimously passed by the society.

The annual meeting for 1951 was held on February 23rd in Raleigh, N.C. Meriwether Lewis spoke on House Bill No. 98, a bill to be entitled "An Act Rewriting Chapter 89 of the General Statutes for Engineering and Land Surveying." He called attention to Article 3, which stated that the board shall consist of five registered engineers who shall be appointed by the governor, one of whom shall be a registered land surveyor. He moved that they adopt the following resolution and that the secretary mail a copy, along with a copy of the bill, to each member of the General Assembly. Grady Harrell suggested that each member should do what they could to get the bill changed. He also moved that the president appoint a committee to go before House Judiciary Committee II to let the society's wishes be known regarding the change. The society considered the new constitution, and on a motion that was properly seconded, it was adopted unanimously. Also, after considering the code of ethics prepared by the committee, there was a motion made, and seconded, to adopt it. A motion was then properly seconded that the manual be adopted by the society and it passed unanimously.

A. Corey then moved that all three of the documents mentioned, along with a list of the society's membership, be printed on suitable loose-leaf notebook paper so that changes could be added from time to time.

Professor C. L. Mann and Professor Ralph Fadum were unanimously elected honorary members of the society. Officers elected for the year 1951 were J. Chandler Eakes, president; J. C. Currin, vice president; and E. W. Ruggles, secretary/treasurer.

In 1952, the annual meeting was held on March 7, 1952, in Raleigh, N.C. Many ideas and concerns were brought up and discussed during this meeting:

1. Membership Committee—There was a suggestion that the state be divided into districts and a chairman be appointed to each district.
2. Publication and Public Relations Committee—This would be headed by the vice president.
3. Professional Development Committee—An important part of this committee would be to assist in the formulation of the plans for the annual school at MCTI.
4. Legislative Committee—Follows legislature and their enactments that are important, and they correspond and cooperate with the NCSE.

5. Constitution and Bylaws Committee
6. Necrology Department
7. Grievance Committee
8. Program Committee

These committees were recommended by the board of directors.

Another item of importance that was discussed was the publishing of a paper by the Geodetic Survey that would fit in the notebook and would contain the constitution and bylaws. Also discussed was whether the publication is wanted every three months, and, if so, should twenty-five cents a year be added to the dues to cover it.

The society presented R. C. Holton with a lifetime honorary membership. The secretary was instructed to print the paper on "Magnetic Declination" by E. A. Kramer that was presented at the 1951 meeting. Johnnie Currin was elected president for 1952; T. Berry Liles was vice president and E. W. Ruggles remained as secretary/treasurer.

The next year, the annual meeting was held in Raleigh, N.C. on January 14, 1953. The date decided on for the annual business meeting was April 17, 1953, in an effort to avoid conflict with the date of the annual Engineer's Fair. M. C. Adams moved that a request be made that N.C. State College provide a school in two sections—five days and three days. This would allow students to attend the full five-day course or only the three-day program with a joint social for both groups at the end of the course. This motion was seconded and passed.

A motion was made that the dues be raised to three dollars as of the beginning of 1954. It was seconded and passed. It was also decided that the society should apply for incorporation to the Secretary of State. The motion was seconded and passed. Officers nominated and elected for the year 1953 were A. Corey, president; B. W. Paschal, vice president; and E. W. Ruggles, secretary/treasurer.

The annual meeting for 1954 was held on April 9th in Raleigh, N.C. The secretary was asked to send copies of today's minutes, statement of dues, and short course program to all surveyors in the state of North Carolina. A motion was made and seconded that the Membership Committee of 1954–1955 send a letter to all registered and nonregistered surveyors in the state in an effort to bring in more members.

After some discussion, the society agreed to support a request to the Division of College Extension of N.C. State College to offer a short course in surveying at Morehead City, in June of 1954. A list of courses was suggested: (1) General Practice of Surveying, (2) Night Problem on North Star, and (3) Legal Aspects of Surveying.

Officers elected to represent the society in the year 1954 were B. W. Paschal, president; E. P. Fritts, vice president; and E. W. Ruggles, secretary/treasurer.

On April 8, 1955, the annual society meeting took place in Raleigh, N.C. A motion was passed that the president write the attorney general and indicate that the society supports the bill to delete paragraph G. S. 89–14 Section I, of the Act to Regulate the Practice of Professional Engineers and Land Surveyors, as passed in 1951. A motion was made, seconded, and passed that the society request that the North Carolina Board of Registration for Engineers and Land Surveyors support the above resolution. Another motion was made and seconded that the NCSPE (North Carolina Society of Professional Engineers) be asked to support the resolution also. Motion was passed. A motion was also made and unanimously passed to make Grady Harrell a lifetime honorary member of the society.

According to a resolution that was passed, the Board of Registration of Engineers and Land Surveyors was to notify the Register of Deeds and Clerk of Court in each county of North Carolina to inform them of the law requiring that all surveyors be registered before recording surveys. The 1955 short course was set to be held at Morehead City. Newly elected officers for the year were E. P. Fritts, president; J. A. Whitman, vice president; and E. W. Ruggles, secretary/treasurer.

On May 4, 1956, the annual meeting for the NCSS took place in Raleigh, N.C.

J. Atwood Whitman was elected as the new president and Moses Farmer, vice president with E. W. Ruggles remaining as secretary/treasurer. A. Corey and J. W. Ivey were made honorary lifetime members.

The North Carolina Board of Registration for Engineers and Land Surveyors was instructed by the last General Assembly to write a manual of instructions to govern the practice of land surveying in North Carolina. Mr. J. Atwood Whitman gave a report to the society on the progress made by the Board of Registration concerning the writing of the manual. Mr. Whitman is one of six members who have the responsibility of writing the manual of instructions.

A motion was made by Moses Farmer that a committee be appointed to have the responsibility for making recommendations for a manual of instruction similar to the manual reported on by Mr. Whitman.

The years 1939 through 1956 were most important in the history of the society as shown by this brief account of the minutes. They were the foundation on which the profession was built. It was an era of searching and beginning for engineers and surveyors, an era of seeking to build a better professional image.

These years produced the "growing pains" for the years that were yet to come. Even with the interruption of World War II and the problems it brought with it, the profession improved and a period of growth took place in the ensuing years.

Moses Farmer, who became president in 1957, helped to bridge the society and profession from that era into the years that followed. He was instrumental in the beginning of continuing education.

North Carolina Society of Surveyors, Inc. History

R. Larry Green, PLS

PART II (1957–2003)

January 1, 1957, dawned upon a far different world than the one we live in today. The threat of terrorism did not exist in the United States in those days, though we did have other concerns. It was a time of peace and prosperity in many respects, but we also lived under the fear of communism. Although drugs were a problem in large cities, in small towns they were something you only read about. Jerry Lee Lewis, Little Richard, Buddy Holly, and Elvis Presley were delighting teenagers and making parents nervous.

It was a far different world of surveying as well. I had no idea I would someday become a professional land surveyor, but if you lived in the country and your family owned any land, you learned a little something about surveying. I had already accompanied Lawton Haney, registered land surveyor (RLS), on several surveys around my grandfather's property. Mr. Haney was typical of surveyors of that day in the foothills of western North Carolina. Surveys were conducted using a shiny, brass compass mounted on a Jacob' s staff. Measurements were taken with a steel tape, but were slope rather than horizontal. When the woods were thick and the helper lazy, a few "bends" in the measurement were acceptable. That's where I came in. The surveyor came alone and a fifteen-year-old boy held the other end of the tape. Measurements, both angular and linear, were crude, but I was uncritical. In fact, I was utterly fascinated with the skill of the man. He set the declination, allowed for variation, read the needle and, invariably, seemed to come out close to the next corner. If he missed by more than a little, he would adjust the variation and run it back marking the line as he went. This was essentially the only kind of surveying being conducted in McDowell County in the 1950s. Magnetic compass surveys would continue to predominate into the early 1970s.

Upon entering college en route to a degree in forest management, I was introduced to more sophisticated surveying procedures in class during the regular semester. Additionally, we received training on the compass during the mandatory ten-week summer camp between our sophomore and junior years. While working for the U.S. Forest Service during three summer vacations, I helped retrace property lines on a number of occasions. These retracements were invariably conducted using a Jacob's staff and a surveying compass.

The surveying history for most of the rural counties in North Carolina and for the outlying portions of the more-densely populated counties is one of compass surveying. I would later become somewhat critical of the practitioners of the art of compass surveying, but as I gained experience, I came to appreciate the fact that they helped preserve a lot of lines and corners. I also came to appreciate the difference between being precise and being accurate. I have often said, and sincerely meant, that if one doesn't know how to survey with a compass, one does not really know how to survey at all. I will leave that for the reader to interpret for himself.

Significantly, in 1957, the Registration Law (GS 89-C) was amended, and the legislature mandated that the Board of Registration for Professional Engineers and Land Surveyors "prepare, or have prepared, a Manual of Practice for information and guidance of those engaged in the practice of land surveying." As noted elsewhere, the manual was completed in 1960, and became the first successful attempt to establish recognized standards for good practice in these United States. North Carolina may have lagged behind in some areas over the years, but in surveying matters, we have been consistently at, or near, the front.

The North Carolina Society of Surveyors (NCSS), was founded in 1939 with thirty-one members. It had grown to 115 members by 1957. Moses Farmer was president with Gerald H. Ehringer serving as vice president (he would serve as president the next year). Edward W. Ruggles was secretary/treasurer. Education had always been a high priority for the North Carolina Society of Surveyors. The College Extension Division of North Carolina State College conducted a weeklong short course in land surveying that year. The course took place in Morehead City, and Dr. Michael V. Smirnoff, who for years taught surveying in the civil engineering department at North Carolina State College, instructed along with Professor Claude Lambe. Twelve students attended. Education is a constantly recurring theme in the minutes and publications of NCSS. Surveyors seem to have a genuine thirst for knowledge. They want to be "the best that they can be."

One of the goals of the North Carolina Society of Surveyors over the years has been a Uniform Mapping Law. Earliest references to a Mapping Law (in GS 47-30 footnotes) date back to 1911, but nothing like the Uniform Mapping Law was ever produced. The year 1958 saw a renewal of the effort. The commission for the study of a Uniform Mapping Law, which the General Assembly had established by resolution in 1957, issued a final report. NCSS passed a resolution endorsing the recommendations of the commission.

The Tarheel Surveyor had made the scene by the late 1950s, but it was a shaky publication at best. It was published on a variable basis with lapses, sometimes measured in years, occurring between sporadic efforts. Discussions were held in 1958 concerning whether to continue publishing this newsletter and about the possibility of selling advertisements to support it. The decision was made to continue publishing for at least a few more issues, but discussion about allowing advertising was tabled. A surveying short course was again taught in Morehead City, utilizing the same instructors who had conducted the 1957 course.

There is a dearth of information available about the North Carolina Society of Surveyors from 1959 through 1962. *The Tarheel Surveyor* was not published during these years, and apparently no minutes of the meetings of the period exist. A very significant event did take place in 1960, however, when the Division of Geodetic Survey in North Carolina was established. The division has provided an invaluable and indispensable service to surveyors and the public for its entire existence. It is hard to imagine what life would be like without it.

Suffice it to say, not a lot changed at the individual practitioner level during this interval. McDowell County had surveyors familiar with the use of a transit and, upon rare occasions, these surveyors actually utilized one. For the most part, surveys continued to be conducted with a compass and tape. This was not unique to one county. It was the same throughout the mountains and foothills and, I suspect, across the vast majority of the state. To make matters worse, North Carolina was rife with unregistered individuals who owned, or had access to, a surveying compass and who regularly conducted surveys. For the most part, real estate attorneys were too busy with matters they considered more important than the quality of surveys, and they regularly made deeds from the work turned out by those bogus surveyors. Indeed, some often encouraged their clients to use these "cheap" surveyors rather than waste money on a real one. Leadership at the state level continued to be in the good hands, however, of the following presidents: W.J. Outlaw (1959), C.W. Russum (1960), E.C. Smith (1961) and Gerald H. Ehridge (1962).

Upon taking my first college course in surveying in 1960, I was amazed at the accuracy the professor expected of us. In the lab portion of the class, we conducted actual surveys around campus and the required closure, at first glance, seemed unbelievable. My first impression was that this was going to be incredibly hard. Indeed, most students taking this course considered it one of the more difficult courses they experienced during their college career. I was really impressed, however, with the information my instructor imparted as to the pay a surveyor received. He reported that they were regularly charging the enormous sum of $10.00 per hour. I quickly calculated $400.00 per week earnings, which seemed a fortune to me. To say I was a bit naive is an understatement. Even though my father was a small businessman and I knew something about overhead, I failed to see that as a significant factor in surveying. After all, I had accompanied a surveyor whose investment in equipment seemed minimal and who worked out of his home. Of course, I allowed for no idle time in my calculations nor any "difficult clients" who might not be satisfied and perhaps not willing to pay.

Payment-in-kind (bartering) was still practiced occasionally in my section of the state during those years, though it was no longer common. It was not uncommon to be offered "white liquor" on a survey job in my part of the state. I, myself, had received such an offer in the early years of my career, though it was always stipulated "only after the job is finished." Not being a connoisseur of white lightning, I never took a client up on such an offer.

Surveyors could also be confronted with disconcerting or dangerous situations as well. One day, as I stepped out of my truck, I was approached by a client with, "are you the one I am going to have to whip?" "I hope not," I replied. I then managed to talk this individual, whom I had never seen before, into letting me proceed. He accompanied me all day long. I also remember standing nose-to-nose with a drinking adjoiner trying to calm him while telling my mouthy client, who was at my back, to "get in the jeep," while I watched the adjoiner's son-in-law inch toward the house. This same son-in-law had, two days earlier, been shooting a pistol on the property in an obvious attempt to intimidate. In my working lifetime, a surveyor and an attorney were killed in one of the far western counties while walking a property line in preparation for a land lawsuit. These examples may sound like the distant past, but all occurred in the 1960s, '70s, and '80s. Thankfully, such incidents are largely behind us now, although we still occasionally must deal with an irate landowner.

Land surveyors have always had a more contentious relationship with the Board of Registration than have engineers. There have been many reasons for this, I suppose. One is clearly the frustration surveyors felt at being underrepresented on the board. The pure-and-simple fact is that, for many years, the surveyor got only what the engineer was willing to let him have. Therefore, many of the goals and aspirations of surveyors went unmet. Another factor is probably the disparity in education required for entry into the two professions. In some minds, the native ability and intelligence required by the two professions were not the same. Some engineers, though certainly not all, felt themselves superior to the land surveyor.

Conversely, some surveyors, whether they cared to admit it or not, felt inferior to engineers. In 1963, matters came to a head when NCSS pushed for, and nearly got, a separate board. Details of this incident are contained in the Board of Registration chapter of this book and will not be repeated here. Suffice it to say, surveyors are probably better off that the effort was unsuccessful. As a long-time member of the National Council of Examiners for Engineering and Surveying (NCEES), I have generally viewed these separate boards as being too poor to enforce effectively the laws of their state and too weak to have much influence at the national level. There are some boards that are stronger than others, but even they fit this mold to some degree. The society, after failing to establish a separate board, tried to get more representation on the combined board. They also wanted the board to employ a full-time executive director rather than continue to utilize the services of a sitting board member. They would wait a year before making a formal recommendation to that effect, because they did not want to jeopardize their chances of getting more surveyors appointed to the board. The General Assembly did respond by increasing the surveyor members of the board from one to two in 1965.

Chapter presidents first became members of the board of directors of NCSS in 1963. There were only two chapters in the state at that time. As time went on, the number of chapters increased. This has done much to make individual members feel a part of the process, since all would know a director very well or even stand a good chance of being one themselves someday.

Apparently, some surveyors were chafing under the new requirements mandated in the Manual of Practice that, as mentioned earlier, was completed in 1960. They were attempting to have the Board of Registration interpret the manual as being for information and guidance only, rather than as actual rules and regulations. NCSS went so far as to seek legal opinion to that effect. If there is any ambiguity in the law at all, you can usually get an opinion to support any reasonable interpretation. While I have the utmost respect for the law as a professional and hold most of its practitioners in high esteem, I cannot help but remember the time I asked an attorney for an interpretation of a law pertaining to surveying. He replied, "What do you want it to mean?"

Ed Little served as president of the society in 1963. Dissatisfied with the board's enforcement of the surveying laws, the society appointed June Lineback to receive information concerning malpractice and violations. He was instructed to "investigate and consider the complaints and, where proper, to present them to the officers of the society for further handling." If officers found it necessary, they were to present the information to the board. Further, all surveyors in the state would be notified of Mr. Lineback's appointment. It is important to remember that the board would not create a position of board investigator until 1972, and even then, it was a part-time position, so the society's action made a lot of sense.

The Tarheel Surveyor, following several years of idleness, resumed publishing in 1964, under the leadership of President Theodore Rondthalder. It fell the duty of the secretary of NCSS to oversee the publication, to distribute the newsletter, and to accept any advertising.

There are many references to legislation and the General Assembly in the early records of the society. The main emphasis was always on being vigilant of the General Assembly that it did not pass legislation detrimental to the surveying profession. Secondary to that was the desire to support legislation that might be beneficial.

One of the things that struck me when reviewing the minutes of meetings and thumbing through old issues of *The Tarheel Surveyor* was the emphasis placed on religion. Churchmen often spoke, prayed, and opened the meetings. Meetings were sometimes held in church buildings (example: The summer meeting of 1965 was held in Reynolda Presbyterian Church in Winston-Salem). *The Tarheel Surveyor* often had a passage of scripture or a religious thought on the front page. I believe several inferences can be drawn from this. One is that surveyors spring from the land and the people of the land. In this part of the world, people of the land have traditionally been devout people. Not necessarily "saved" people in their own eyes, but deeply believing. A second inference is that surveying is a difficult profession. This is to say, it is a profession that has seen its share of hardships and setbacks. When a person has to claw and scratch for recognition and respect, for status commiserate with his importance to the community, and for enough money to keep body, soul and family together, then that person, many times, tends to rely more upon the strength and comfort of a Supreme Being.

The year 1964 marked the First Annual Convention of the North Carolina Society of Surveyors, which was held in the YMCA Building on Hillsboro Street in Raleigh. Not a lot of information was available on that meeting, but the Second Annual Convention held in the same building in 1965 was well recorded. The morning session of that meeting was devoted to a talk by Professor John B. Shuler on modern methods of surveying. Topics covered were "electronic and light-beam methods of measuring distances, use of computers, aerial photography, and two-way radios." Also on that year's program were discussions on urban development and community planning, and the surveyor's role in these activities, as well as a session on the legal rights of a registered land surveyor. Several other educational talks were given, and a film was shown along with the normal business sessions. The convention continued to be held at the YMCA for the next two years.

The practice of holding a weeklong, intensive short course for surveyors continued with a session at Brevard College in July 1965. As always, it was of the highest quality, and was taught by some of the most qualified professors in the state.

Apparently, the society suffered from a decline in membership during this period. A count of the members in good standing revealed 102 individuals as of June 30, 1965, down from 115 in 1957.

The "loan survey," a term some surveyors refuse to use because of the negative connotation they feel is attached to it, has been a sore spot for surveyors for many years. It has always been the policy of the Board of Registration (now Board of Examiners) that a survey is a survey is a survey. Nevertheless, the loan survey became, in many parts of the state, nothing more than a map of the property taken from a recorded plat or deed description with the house and drive sketched thereon. What this, many times, amounted to was a visual inspection of the property made by a single individual, with perhaps a check of distances between found corners. It was not an actual survey. When a surveyor in Asheville, Mr. W.G. "Hutch" Hutchinson, produced a map (1965) showing an actual survey of a lot, which contained a description not exactly matching the recorded deed, the attorney in the case accused him of being too honest. The board cracked down on this loan surveys practice, and finally, after decades, this fight has largely been won. Title insurance companies do not always require a current survey these days because the cost involved in obtaining a real survey is much greater than the old survey used to be.

The 1965 president of the society was Mr. Paul Ward, of Southern Pines. President Ward and others expressed concern over the number of surveys being performed by unregistered persons. He reminded the society that all complaints should be turned in to June Lineback. He stated that he had been assured that all malpractice complaints coming to the board would be checked.

There was also concern about competitive bidding among surveyors. It has long been the custom, sometimes bolstered by law, that government agencies obtain professional services through negotiation, rather than by a bidding process as with goods and nonprofessional services. Part of the struggle to be recognized as a profession involved arriving at the point where surveying was treated as a profession by the various branches of government. The fact that surveyors, anxious to obtain work, often participated (some willingly, some reluctantly) in the bidding process did not help matters. A letter was sent to all surveyors, to the Board of Registration, and to all school boards, informing them that the society was not in accord with competitive bidding in any surveying and mapping work.

Two professional societies for surveyors actually existed in North Carolina in 1965. In addition to the North Carolina Society of Surveyors, a separate group, the North Carolina section of the American Congress on Surveying and Mapping (ACSM), was also active. Meriwether Lewis introduced a resolution (which passed) for NCSS to look into the possibility of a merger of the two organizations so that only one surveyors' group would exist in North Carolina. A study of such a merger was made, but no immediate action was taken. The Western Chapter and the Guilford Chapter joined the Eastern and Southern Chapters during 1965, bringing the total chapter memberships to four. Finally, legislation was passed increasing the number of land surveyors on the Board of Registration from one to two, as reported earlier. This was not all that surveyors had been hoping for, but it must have been like manna from heaven to a starving profession. At least now, there was more than a lone voice in Raleigh. William M. Turner joined Meriwether Lewis on January 1, 1966.

The society continued to place a strong emphasis on continuing education and, once again, held a weeklong short course at Brevard College in 1966. Joe Hardee was president of the society that year, which saw the addition of the Albermarle Chapter. Speaking to the membership in September of that year, in a joint meeting between the North Carolina Society of Surveyors and the North Carolina section of the American Congress on Surveying and Mapping (ACSM), President Hardee recommended that NCSS affiliate with ACSM. This affiliation would create a single united voice for the surveyor in North Carolina. He likened it to the political structure of precinct, county, state, and national parties, each handling problems at the appropriate level.

The year 1966 saw the largest growth in membership, as well as in the activities of the society, that had taken place in many years. A grateful membership reelected Joe Hardee for a second term, making him the only president to serve two consecutive terms. The January 1967 edition of *The Tarheel Surveyor* commented on the effective leadership Joe had provided. That issue also mentioned an initial meeting to mark the beginning of a new chapter in the Winston-Salem area, which went on to become the Piedmont Chapter. President Hardee identified the consolidation of efforts within the state for the betterment of the profession and its service to the public, producing a standard of practice. This consolidation continued to build membership and develop new chapters, with emphasis on education as the major issues facing the society in 1967. In keeping with the emphasis on education, a short course was held again. This time, the W.W. Holding Technical Institute at their facility in Raleigh conducted the course. Seventeen surveyors and engineers attended.

Sometimes we forget the effect inflation has had on our businesses. Here are a couple of reminders. Fees in 1967 ranged from $10.00 per crew hour to $15.00 per crew hour, with the average "mortgage" survey bringing $35.00 to $50.00, according to *The Tarheel Surveyor*. The society voted to pay the expenses of the secretary/treasurer, not to exceed $100.00, to attend the National Convention of the American Congress on Surveying and Mapping in Washington, D.C. Simpler times, to say the least.

A vote of the membership was held concerning the society becoming an affiliate of the American Congress on Surveying and Mapping with a 213 majority required to effect such a union. Only eight votes were cast in opposition and, in 1967, NCSS did, indeed, become an affiliate of ACSM. This action effectively left the state with one viable professional surveying society.

The year 1968 saw the convention move away from the Raleigh YMCA for the first time. It was held at the Hilton Inn in Raleigh, where A.J. (Jimmie) Davis was installed as president.

A chapter called the "Lumber Chapter" was chartered. This was probably the forerunner of the Southern Chapter, but no mention of its demise, or of any name change, was found.

The 1968 surveyors' short course moved to Wilmington, North Carolina. NCSS, in cooperation with Cape Fear Technical Institute and Wilmington College, sponsored it. A hydrographic course was included among the many subjects. These short courses, the forerunner of today's NCSS Institute, provided high-quality continuing education to those surveyors who took advantage of them. North Carolina has always been up front in continuing education. We have a legacy of which we can be proud. As will be seen later, surveyors led the way in the enactment of continuing professional competency requirements, which exist today and apply to engineers and surveyors alike.

Violations and ethics have been a constant concern of NCSS over the years. In 1969, the society developed a four-step procedure for handling violations: (1) the individual detecting a violation should approach the violator and attempt to solve the problem, (2) if not successful, it should be taken before the local chapter, (3) all findings should be presented to the board of directors if the chapter is unsuccessful, and (4) if the board of directors cannot handle the violation, all findings would be turned over to the North Carolina Board of Registration for Professional Engineers and Land Surveyors. This policy, or some form of it, was used for a number of years. As late as the early 1980s, the policy of the Western Chapter still was to attempt to handle violations at the chapter level as an initial step.

Mr. Louis Smith was installed as 1969 president of the society by his father, Mr. E.C. Smith, who had served as president in 1961. The convention was held at the Hilton Inn in Raleigh for a second year.

Perhaps the most significant event of the year was Governor Robert Scott's request on November 3rd for the resignation of the entire Board of Registration, effective December 15, 1969. This incident is covered in some detail in the chapter on the history of the board and will not be rehashed here. Suffice it to say that this act reshaped the board and altered its method of operation.

The society submitted a list of six men to the governor for consideration of the two land surveyor slots. Three of these men went on to be presidents of the society. Three would serve on the Board of Registration—two at that time and one later on. The men were Clarence H. Blue, Otis Jones, Maurice Seaver, Robert Inman, Howard Loughlin, and W.C. Rodman, Jr. On March 5, 1970, Robert Inman and C.H. "Pat" Blue took the oath of office, along with four engineer members. On August 4th, B.A. Soholsky became the first executive secretary of the board who was not a board member. Robert Inman prepared and graded the land surveyors' examination for the board, beginning in 1970. An engineer had handled this duty prior to this time.

The convention was held at the Hilton Inn in Raleigh, where Willard Hintz was sworn in as president. The emphasis of the society for 1970 could be summed up in one word: legislation. For several years, there had been a push to effect changes in GS 89-C as it governed land surveying. As 1970 drew to a close, land surveyors had united behind the latest proposed version:

(1) Division of the board should be in two sections: an engineering section and a surveying section, both having five members;
(2) Two of the surveying members must be certified for subdivision work;
(3) The governor would be required to pick from a list of not more than three, submitted by NCSS;
(4) Matters of a purely engineering nature or surveying nature would be decided by the members of the section rather than the whole board. Any disputes between engineers and surveyors, or any matter involving an engineer or surveyor practicing outside their area of expertise (engineer practicing surveying or surveyor practicing engineering), would be decided by the full board with the chairman having two votes in the case of a tie;
(5) A minimum of one joint meeting per year would be required;
(6) The executive secretary could not be a member of the board or be registered to practice engineering or surveying in any state;
(7) Each section would have its own code of ethics; and
(8) Land surveyors passing an additional examination would be able to perform the following tasks within a subdivision:
    (a) Design public roads and streets;
    (b) Prepare plans and profiles for the roads, streets, culverts, curbs and gutters, ditches and drainage swales;
    (c) Prepare plans for storm sewer extensions; and
    (d) Prepare plans for sanitary sewer collector lines using prescribed local, state, or federal standards where such work was incidental to the design of a subdivision.

These radical changes would have greatly altered the surveying landscape. By May of 1971, this legislation had been introduced in the General Assembly. The 1971 Convention was held at the Sir Walter Raleigh Hotel, where Robert E. Wilson of Greensboro, North Carolina, was installed as president of the society. Moses Farmer, the outgoing secretary/treasurer, suggested that the NCSS think seriously about obtaining the services of an executive secretary to handle the day-to-day business of the society. Mr. Farmer suggested that this be accomplished before the year was out, but it was another five years before it actually happened.

The proposed rewrite of GS 89-C came to naught. There were no changes to the law in 1971 or 1972. Significant events did occur in 1972, however. That was the year Howard Loughlin, RLS, of Wilmington, North Carolina, invited the Board of Registration to charge him with violating GS 89-C in that he had performed many of the acts the proposed rewrite would have codified, specifically the design of streets and storm drainage within a subdivision. This incident is dealt with in some detail in the chapter on the history of the Board of Registration. Mr. Loughlin was tried, found not guilty, and declared competent to practice in those areas. For a time, he was the only surveyor in the state legally qualified to provide these services. This led to a change in the law in 1973, which gave those privileges to all registered land surveyors, as long as the design was incidental to a subdivision. The exact meaning of "incidental drainage" would provoke much debate and more than a little acrimony in the years to come.

The 1972 Convention was held outside Raleigh for the first time, at the Holiday Inn Four Seasons in Greensboro, North Carolina. Hoyt Bradshaw was installed as president that year. The 1973 Convention was again at the Holiday Inn Four Seasons when Mike Donovan became society president.

The North Carolina Society of Surveyors has always had an ambitious legislative agenda. At times, the efforts of the members have been like a cat gnawing away at a grindstone: much effort, with little or no progress. Nevertheless, like water wearing away at a rock, surveyors kept on trying. No matter how hard they were slapped down, they always seemed to be back the next session with renewed effort. The year 1974 was no exception. This was a short session of the General Assembly, meaning no new legislation could be introduced. Much time was spent preparing the next year's agenda and lining up sponsors and supporters in the legislature. The result was that in 1975, several long-term goals were realized. For many years, surveyors had objected in vain to engineers being allowed to survey, no matter what their disciplines. The 1975 rewrite required, for the first time, that engineers pass the Principles and Practices exam for land surveying to obtain a Certificate of Registration. For just as long, if not longer, land surveyors had sought more representation on the Board of Registration. They had succeeded in getting a requirement for at least one surveying member in 1951. In 1965, the number was raised to two, and in 1975, to three. At last, the profession was approaching parity in that respect.

The leadership of the society in the pivotal years of 1974 and 1975 fell to President Marvin Borum (1974) and President Howard Loughlin (1975). Both of these men had been active in their efforts to achieve passage of legislation favorable to land surveyors, with Howard Loughlin chairing the Legislative Committee for several years.

The society's efforts, in 1976, to prevent engineers with no land surveying background from obtaining a license to survey by virtue of the grandfather clause are discussed in the chapter on the Board of Registration. It is mentioned here, merely to bring attention to the fact that there was a grandfather clause, and of the new requirement for an engineer to obtain a separate registration to survey. It resulted in the first registration of a woman in North Carolina. Incredibly, no women were registered before 1976. Our profession has been overwhelmingly white and overwhelmingly male throughout its history. Even in 1998, the Register listed only twenty-four women. While not as easy to trace in this era of political correctness, I know of but one Native American (1973 registrant) and two or three individuals of African-American descent who are professional surveyors licensed in North Carolina today. I do not believe history will continue to repeat itself. As time goes on, expect a significant number of women and minorities to enter the profession. There is too much talent and too much diversity of interest among all North Carolinians for it to be otherwise.

The year 1976 marked the first time a land surveyor held the office of chairman of the North Carolina Board of Registration for Professional Engineers and Land Surveyors. As noted in the chapter on the history of the board, Robert Inman was accorded that honor by his fellow board members and went on to bring honor to himself and his profession by the leadership he demonstrated as spokesperson for ESJAC (Engineering and Surveying Joint Action Committee) in front of the Sunset Commission. That same year, Robert's wife, Lucille Inman, became the first executive secretary of the North Carolina Society of Surveyors. She would go on to serve for twenty-one years in that capacity, and for twenty of those years, she was also the editor of *The Tarheel Surveyor.* Lucille put in countless hours, and the society owes her a great debt of gratitude for her dedicated and faithful service over the years.

The president of the society in 1976 was Paul Lawson. He visited the Western Chapter in the course of that year, which marked my first encounter with a NCSS president. As a new registrant in 1975, I made it my first order of business to join NCSS, but at this time, I had never attended a convention. I attended my first one in Charlotte, North Carolina, in February of 1977, and have never missed one since.

Late 1977, and much of 1978, was largely consumed with preparing for the Sunset Commission Hearings, which are covered in more detail in the chapter on the Board of Registration. As mentioned before, Robert Inman led the way from the board. Richard Biggs, NCSS president in 1977, and Pat Blue, the 1978 president, led the way from the society. Many surveyors were foot soldiers in this battle, and as reported in the chapter on the board, were successful in continuing the existence of the Board of Registration. The actual hearings in front of the commission took place late in 1978.

Perhaps the most significant event of 1978, when viewed from today's perspective, was one many surveyors have little, or no, knowledge of. For as long as surveying had been a licensed profession in North Carolina, there had been a significant problem with unregistered practitioners. This problem was exacerbated by the willingness of attorneys to prepare deeds and rights-of-way from maps produced through these illegal acts.

The Western Chapter had an associate member by the name of Ed Krause, who was, and is, a practicing attorney in Asheville, North Carolina. Fed up with seeing illegal maps, Mr. Krause wrote the North Carolina State Bar Ethics Committee for an opinion concerning the use of such maps by an attorney. A ruling was issued, and published, stating that it was unethical for an attorney to rely on a survey prepared by an unregistered individual. When the ruling appeared in print, it had an immediate and dramatic impact in my area of western North Carolina. Never again did I encounter much of a problem with respect to an attorney using the work product of an unregistered individual.

The work of the ESJAC with regard to the Sunset Legislation did not end in 1978. A final hearing was held by the commission in February 1979, followed by a hearing in the Senate and two in the House. Robert Inman made the ESJAC presentation for each of these hearings. The new Registration Act, which came about as a result of the Sunset Commission report, was passed into law in 1979.

Once the dust from the Sunset Commission hearings settled, 1979 President Robert Stephenson placed his emphasis on improving the everyday operation of a surveying business and on continuing education for surveyors. He especially deplored the low fees charged by some practitioners in the state. According to his figures and those of his accountant friends, the fees charged by some surveyors were guaranteed to keep them at the poverty level. He suggested a fee-and-wage survey at the chapter or state level.

Competitive bidding again became a topic of discussion in 1979. The United States Forest Service and other governmental agencies were securing surveying services on a competitive-bid basis, even though the Brooks Bill required them to select professional services on a negotiated basis. The problem was that surveying was not listed as a profession by the General Accounting Office. This problem occupied the attention of the society for some years to come.

A Loan Survey Committee had been appointed in 1979 to wrestle with the continuing problem of surveyors preparing maps purporting to depict an actual field survey when, in fact, no such actual survey had been conducted. In the spring of 1980, the committee, consisting of Chairman Robert Inman and members Ferd Hobbs, W.G. Hutchinson, and Robert E. Stephenson, issued their report. This report, which is well worth reading in its entirety, appeared in a special edition of *The Tarheel Surveyor* in March of 1980. It identified the problem, condemned the practice, and called for the prosecution of guilty individuals before the Board of Registration. The entire report occupied two-and-one-half pages and was forwarded to the Board of Registration for their approval. The board did approve it, and over the years, has reprinted an article concerning loan surveys in the board newsletter. The board has also vigorously upheld the principle that all surveys are "equal," and that no special status is accorded the "loan survey." All surveys must be actual surveys.

George T. Paris became president of NCSS at the February 1980 Convention held at the Royal Villa Hotel, Raleigh, North Carolina. The issue of mandatory continuing education began to move toward the front burner of the society's stove in 1980. Recommended, but not mandated by the Sunset Commission, the idea had been rejected by the Board of Registration. The position of the engineers, both those on the board and the vast majority of the registrants, was that mandatory continuing education was neither necessary nor desirable. Surveyors, as a group, were much more open to the idea, but it was, by no means, a universally held position that it should be required. Few members were lukewarm on the subject. They were either totally in favor of it, or thought it was a terrible idea. This issue would lead to one of the biggest crises the society ever faced.

Errors and omissions insurance was also on the minds of many surveyors in 1980. This was a coverage most surveyors were in favor of, but few had it. The reason was the cost involved in obtaining adequate quality coverage. Victor O. Schinerer had long been the leader in errors and omissions coverage. Coverage was expensive, in part, because surveyors were lumped with engineers. In September of 1980, a new plan was introduced by American Centurion Insurance, thanks to the efforts of the society's Insurance Committee. This "plan" would be the first of several to be approved, as each failed from lack of participation or flagging interest on the part of the insurer.

The year 1981 saw Billy M. Duncan installed as president of the society at the annual convention, which was held at the Mission Valley Inn in Raleigh, North Carolina. A highlight at the installation banquet was the presentation of an "engineer's" cap to Howard Loughlin. The actual cap was a train engineer's, but the implication was that Howard had won us the right to practice minor engineering within a subdivision, when he had offered himself as a sacrifice for us all in 1972.

President Duncan appointed two special committees that year, in addition to the standing committees. The first was the committee studying mandatory continuing education. The second was the committee to work on a revised GS 47-30 (Mapping Law). Both of these committees were destined to have a big impact on the society and surveyors alike. The Mandatory Continuing Education Committee consisted of George Paris, R. Larry Greene, C.H. Blue, and Howard Loughlin. The Mapping Law Committee consisted of Dan Collier, Sam Marlowe, R. Larry Greene, Robert D. Inman, John W. Parker, William Shaw, and Ronald Scott (advisor).

The winter 1981 issue of *The Tarheel Surveyor* contained a two-page article entitled "Proof of Continued Competency or In What Form and by Whose Hand Will Your Destiny Be Shaped?" by Robert D. Inman, a strong proponent of mandatory continuing education. This article was well written, persuasive, and thought provoking. That same issue contained a quote from a letter sent to the society by the Board of Registration, stating their opposition to mandatory continuing education and their rationale behind that opposition. Many in the society, including some of the leadership, were not in favor of the idea. The battle lines were beginning to form around each group. The committee met twice during 1981. The first meeting took place in Southern Pines in May, and the second in Winston-Salem in August. The committee considered three issues:

(1) Mandatory continuing education as a requirement for re-registration as a land surveyor in North Carolina,
(2) A separate Board of Registration for land surveyors in North Carolina, and
(3) Minimum education requirement for registration of land surveyors.

It was the recommendation of the committee that these three issues be placed on a ballot, with a 60% favorable majority being required for passage. If such a majority was reached, the society would push for passage before the legislature.

The year 1982 was the year I, Larry Greene, served as president of NCSS. The primary emphasis of the society in 1982 was the beginning of an effort to get a two-year degree requirement for surveyors. Calling for the establishment of a scholarship fund and finishing the rewrite of GS 47-30 in time for introduction during the 1983 legislative year was equally important. Also, bringing some structure to the continuing education program, so that basic educational needs were addressed on a regular basis, was stressed that year.

In June of 1982, the municipal engineer of Winston-Salem, North Carolina, issued a policy letter based on his interpretation of what "incidental drainage and street design within a subdivision" meant. This interpretation severely limited what the city would accept from a land surveyor and precipitated a mini-crisis. In essence, a surveyor could design streets of a ribbon-pavement type, not exceeding twenty-five feet in basic section. Drainage was limited to prefabricated pipes laid in natural drains and at intersecting streets and driveways, as long as such streets were not a part of any street system plan designated by official governmental or planning bodies.

As a result of this proposal, the Board of Registration issued a policy on incidental drainage. While couched in largely negative terms, the policy did leave intact the surveyors' right to design streets and drainage incidental to a subdivision. The city of Winston-Salem backed off its earlier position and stated it would accept whatever the board decided. This action cooled the issue of incidental drainage for a while, but it still left a lot of room for doubt as to just what "incidental to a subdivision" really meant. Before many years passed, the issue would come to the forefront once more.

Larry Akers became president of the society in 1983. The year would bring passage of the revised Mapping Law and, for the first time, all counties in North Carolina would fall under one law. The year would see an anonymous donor contribute $100.00 to jump-start the scholarship fund. The society had authorized the fund and was prepared to allocate $10,000.00 to it but was waiting for passage of a two-year degree requirement before actually appropriating any money. The $100.00 represented a tangible beginning. John W. Parker was appointed chairman of the newly established Scholarship Screening Committee. The first task of this committee was to explore the best methods of setting up the fund.

The year 1983 was also the year the Fellow Member classification was established to honor those persons who had toiled long and well in service to the society. In the years since, only a few have been elected to this category of membership. Currently, sixteen persons hold that status of membership.

There was a good deal of dissatisfaction within the society in those years with the way the North Carolina Board of Registration handled complaints and dealt out penalties. In 1984, this dissatisfaction reached a level that resulted in the society asking for, and being granted, an audience with the board to discuss the problem. It was generally felt that investigations were often inadequate because the investigator did not know enough about surveying to recognize a violation, or if it was recognized, the investigator did not know enough to ask the right questions. Beyond that, the society felt that when a person was found guilty of a violation, the penalty levied for essentially the same violation was often inconsistent from one case to another and, many times, inadequate for the gravity of the offense. The meeting ended with little resolved, but most people attending felt better about the sincerity of the board and had a better understanding of the difficulty the board faced when trying to come to a just verdict from the evidence presented.

Larry Ritter was president of the society in 1984. It became a running joke that your given name must be Larry (Greene, Akers, and now Ritter) before you could hold that high office. An effort was also under way to get a two-year degree requirement for registration as a land surveyor in North Carolina written into GS 89-C. Billy Duncan chaired the committee; the other members included Gary Moore, Pat Hutchinson, and Larry Greene.

The Standards of Practice Committee was also very active during this period of history, as surveyors tried to come to grips with a written set of standards all surveyors should abide by. Charles O. (Hamp) Hampton chaired the committee for several years, and he, and other members, spent countless hours on this project. Many of the standards developed by this committee eventually found their way intact into the official Standards of Practice published by the Board of Registration. Even those standards that did not find their way into that document exerted a heavy influence on its overall content.

Early in 1985, the society published the Standards of Residential Surveys. These standards comprised a small, but significantly important, part of the standards as a whole, but they had much more significance given the problems inherent in loan surveys over the years. They stated that all residential surveys would be Class A urban surveys, as defined in the North Carolina Board of Registration Standards. They went on to list nineteen specifics as to the information to be contained on such a survey. Progress was slow in this area, but gains were being made.

Sam T. Marlowe became the newest president of NCSS in 1985, ending the reign of the three Larrys (Greene, Akers, and Ritter). As he began his term of office, he called for better attendance by chapter presidents at board meetings and pledged to meet with each chapter at one of their local meetings during the course of the year.

Representative Richard Wright introduced House Bill 1007 in May of 1985. This bill, as introduced, would have established a two-year degree requirement to obtain a surveyor's license. It also would have established experience requirements of two years with a B.S. degree in surveying, four years with an associate degree in surveying, and twelve years with a high school diploma. Resistance was encountered in the State Government Committee chaired by Foy Hightower. Representative Hightower, and others, felt that no impediments should be put in the way of a high school graduate obtaining his or her license to survey. It was difficult to convince these legislators that surveying was a real profession requiring an education. They had soon pared the bill down to a six-year education requirement, which would have represented no change. The House passed the bill unanimously. Chairman Larry Greene, of the Legislative Committee, was out of the country with his church on a youth mission tour when all the trouble was encountered. Larry Ritter, and others, gathered in Raleigh on short notice, to see what could be done to salvage the bill. It was finally decided to delay the bill to give time to rally support for its passage in its original form, or at least affect some increase in the amount of experience required. Representative Wright singled out Mr. Ritter for special commendation for his efforts to keep the bill alive.

Representative Wright, a gifted and able legislator, introduced a number of bills on behalf of the profession of surveying over the years. He commanded much respect in the legislature, and it was definitely a plus to have him for a sponsor. A grateful society made him an honorary member in 1989, one of only four such persons to be elected to this category of membership.

The society continued to express its concern over what it saw as a lack of understanding on the part of the Board of Registration of the true nature of individual land surveying violations brought before it. They felt this resulted in inappropriate discipline. They lamented the fact that the investigator was neither a land surveyor nor engineer, feeling that each was needed in order to develop a good case in their respective areas. The board's position then, as now, was that they wanted persons experienced in investigations, not in surveying or engineering.

Finally, in the year 1985, the first scholarships were awarded from the Scholarship Fund. A long-standing dream was at last a reality.

In 1986, the germ of an idea that had originated in the mind of NCSS President Otis Jones began to take root and spring to life. This idea was for a weeklong NCSS Institute dedicated to the continuing education of practicing professional surveyors. It would be held at North Carolina State University's McKimmon Center for Continuing Education and would be a joint venture with North Carolina State University. Otis served as chairman of the NCSS Institute for as long as it remained a joint venture. He has continued in a leadership role as Institute director and as a teacher after the society took over its management in 1995. Eventually, it would become the premiere continuing education program for surveyors in the nation. Many have contributed much to this endeavor over the years. Special kudos go to Thomas Reynolds and Ken Suttles, among others, for their role as directors of the Institute. Most of all, however, the credit goes to Otis. He made it happen.

In June of 1986, H.B. 1007 passed the House and the Senate and was ratified into law. Gains were modest compared to what had been hoped for, but the experience requirement for sitting for the land surveyor's exam was increased to seven years with a high school diploma. The two-year degree requirement in surveying technology passed, and engineers had to sit for the full sixteen hours of examinations to obtain a surveying registration. Sometimes, you have to get your salami in slices, rather than the whole loaf at one time.

The surveying and engineering professions lost a true giant in 1986 with the unexpected death of Chappell (Chap) N. Noble, North Carolina Board of Registration member and Southern zone vice president of the National Council of Engineering Examiners, as it was previously called. He is still remembered for his outstanding leadership and compassionate concern for his fellow man.

In October, a joint meeting of representatives of the North Carolina Community College Systems, the Board of Registration, and NCSS met to formulate plans for instituting a two-year degree program in surveying technology at several community colleges statewide. This would quickly lead to the establishment of an Education Task Force, which would establish the curriculum for such a program. Overall, 1986 was a good year for surveying education in North Carolina.

In 1987, GS 47-30 was once again on the agenda, and the special Legislative Committee appointed by NCSS to rewrite the Mapping Law was busy coordinating with the Register of Deeds Association Liaison Committee, without whose support the bill stood no chance. Among changes being sought were more uniformity across county lines in the sizes of the plats Register of Deeds would accept, more assurance that the copies obtained of recorded plats would be legible, the requirement that plats be archival, and recognition of the North American Datum 1983, in addition to NAD 27.

The NCSS Institute was held for the first time in January of 1987, with forty-three registered land surveyors in attendance. The Institute consisted of three separate sections dealing with different subject matter, each lasting one week. It would take three years to complete the Institute and "graduate." The Institute was later expanded by a fourth section. While on the subject of education, it serves well to remember the passing of Moses Farmer in April of 1987. Moses was a leader in every area of NCSS life. He was president, vice president, and secretary/treasurer for eight years and served in legislative matters, but nowhere was his influence more felt than in the field of surveying education. It was he who organized the weeklong surveyor's short course held for many years in the '50s, '60s, and early '70s. By the time I joined NCSS in 1975, Moses was no longer as active as he once had been, but I had the privilege of meeting him and observing some of his accomplishments. His influence was everywhere. He had put his stamp on the organization.

The often-debated meaning of "incidental drainage within a subdivision," a term about which engineers and surveyors had largely different concepts, was about to hit the front burner again. The Division of Environmental Management (DEM) had issued regulations that allowed only professional engineers to do drainage design in the twenty coastal counties of North Carolina that fell under its jurisdiction. A series of hearings were held in the eastern part of the state, and they quickly became a battleground of opposing views. Culmination came in a well-attended and emotion-filled meeting of the Board of Registration in September of 1987. For a time, it appeared the board would side with the engineers' position as presented by Professional Engineers of North Carolina (PENC), rather than the surveyors' position as presented by NCSS. In the end, however, the board asked that NCSS and PENC representatives get together and work out wording that would be satisfactory to both sides for a definition of "incidental drainage." In the meantime, the board issued a statement supporting DEM's proposed changes with respect to system design, "provided that provisions are incorporated in these rules to allow registered land surveyors to do incidental drainage within subdivisions as permitted by GS 89-C."

While a crisis was averted for the time, it still left unanswered what the board considered "incidental drainage" to be. As a result, a committee of two (one engineer and one surveyor) was to meet and report to the full board their recommended definition of incidental drainage, and just what it included. Charles A. Rawls was the leader in the fight to get the surveyors' legal role clarified with DEM. He and his committee worked hard to effect this recognition. It is a hallmark of the surveying profession that surveyors have worked with no pay and little recognition throughout the latter two-thirds of this century to save, to protect, and to gain back traditional surveying tasks. Without this fierce dedication, we could not have survived as a force to be reckoned with. When I think of it, I am sometimes literally in awe of what these men have accomplished, and it still goes on today.

Derward Baker was our president in 1987. In June of that year, a lady who helped lead us over the years, Sally Hutchinson, wife of surveyor W. G. (Hutch) Hutchinson, and mother of Patricia Hutchinson, RLS, died after a courageous bout with cancer. She was one of the founders of the Ladies Auxiliary, which has contributed so much to the society since its founding in 1982. She was also a lady of high integrity and a member of a family of high integrity. Patricia Hutchinson was president-elect of the society at the time of her mother's death and became the first, and thus far only, female president in its history. She was also its youngest.

Of significance in the year 1988 was the formation of the Political Action Committee (PAC), to accept donations for use in making contributions to candidates for office who favored legislative needs of the society. Larry Greene, chairman of the Legislative Committee at the time, made the suggestion at the April 30th board of directors meeting in Hickory, North Carolina. A special committee was appointed to make a feasibility study, with the results being reported to the Executive Committee. The report was delivered to the full board of directors on August 5, with the recommendation that a PAC be formed. The vote to form a PAC was unanimous, and Alex Rankin was selected to be its treasurer. Within ten days, the Political Action Committee of the North Carolina Society of Surveyors was a reality.

The North Carolina Board of Registration for Professional Engineers and Land Surveyors had worked throughout 1988 to formulate a Standards of Practice, which would replace the Manual of Practice, which had been in existence for about twenty-seven years. The new standards would be a part of the board rules, and, as such, legally enforceable. In January of 1989, the board approved the new standards, which were distributed to all registrants shortly thereafter. Those sections of the old manual, which were considered mandatory, were retained with some revision and additions. The standards developed by the society, under the leadership of Hamp Hampton and his committee, were heavily relied upon in formulating the new board rule (Rule 1600). The document consisted of a single sheet at that time. It has since more than doubled in size, and is due for another revision based on the new definition of surveying contained in the 1998 revision of GS 89-C.

The year 1989 marked the 50th anniversary of the North Carolina Society of Surveyors, the second-oldest state surveying organization in the nation. President Al Frieze presided over the birthday bash, as he was sworn in at the convention in Raleigh. During the convention, a time capsule was buried on the campus of North Carolina State University, to be opened on the society's 100th anniversary. The spot was monumented with a horizontal station disk by North Carolina Geodetic Survey (NCGS), and contained maps and instruments in common use at the time.

Several bills affecting surveying and surveyors were introduced in the 1989 Session of the North Carolina General Assembly. A Condominium Bill was passed, requiring certification of a registered land surveyor on plats and plans of condominiums. The maximum fine that could be levied by the Board of Registration was increased from $500.00 to $2000.00. A bill to add a fourth surveyor member to the Board of Registration failed. A Procurement Bill, that amended the statutes regarding the procurement of architectural and engineering services by state and local governments to include surveying services, passed after some initial opposition. The proposal to add a fourth surveyor member to the Board of Registration drew so much interest, both pro and con, that the legislature drafted a bill entitled, "A Joint Resolution Authorizing the Legislative Research Commission to Study the Desirability and Feasibility of Creating Separate Licensing Boards for Professional Engineers and Land Surveyors." In other words, if you can't get along without constant bickering, we will just separate you. While many surveyors would have welcomed a separate board, many others saw strength in a combined board and believed the two groups could work together in harmony. The controversy subsided over the next year, and the study never took place. The Board of Registration removed much of the impetus for a separate board with the issuance of "Guidelines for Interpretation of Incidental Streets and Storm Sewer System Designs." Initially hammered out by Dana Rucker, PE, and Larry Greene, RLS, this document was first reviewed and approved by the Engineering and Surveying Committees of the board, and then approved unanimously by the full board. With this document, "incidental drainage" was at last defined and the rights of surveyors protected. In the years since, the board has consistently upheld the right of surveyors to perform these services within a subdivision of their own design.

The year 1990 opened the last decade of the twentieth century (I know, the first year is really 1991). My, how the profession has changed since 1957! It has progressed from transit and tape to theodolite with top-mounted electronic distance meter (EDM) to total station to global position system (GPS). And from slide rule to battery-operated calculator with trig functions (who could believe it?) to fully electronic calculator to data collector to computer. And from draftsperson to computer drafting to AutoCad. The ensuing ten years saw even more rapid advances from three or four dependable satellites for GPS to twenty-four, from computer-assisted drawing to actual transmission of those drawings over telephone lines. These same years would see the elevation of the surveyor from the status of a tradesman to one of a professional! But are we truly professional? Well, we are close. We drew even closer in the 1990s, but we realize we still lack full status as professionals, if we are honest with ourselves. What will it take? I believe it can never happen until a college degree in surveying is a requirement for licensure. This is not the only step we must take, but it is, in my opinion, the biggest and the most essential. There are no true professions that lack this requirement.

Our leader to begin the decade was Charles A. Rawls, who had so ably led the fight to preserve our rights with respect to "incidental drainage" in 1987. "Incidental drainage" again became a topic of discussion as the City of Wilmington, North Carolina, proposed regulations which would have prevented the surveyor from doing any storm water design. Although the Board of Registration has settled the question, it seems to rise again city-by-city and county-by-county. This time, however, the board was on our side from the beginning, making the battle a much easier one.

Another hot topic was the time involved in getting the United States Army Corps of Engineers to inspect a site for wetlands. At that time, the corps insisted that only they had the authority to determine wetland involvement, and they were taking up to six months or longer to make those determinations on private lands. The Coastal Chapter of NCSS became quite involved in attempting to solve this problem through contact with North Carolina's congressmen and senators. Senator Helms promptly responded with promises to contact the Army Corps of Engineers and see what could be done to alleviate the problem. Senator

Helms generally evoked a strong emotion, either pro or con, with most people throughout the United States. Regardless of how he is viewed, however, he was undeniably one of the most responsive members of the United States Senate when it came to his constituents.

The year 1990 also marked the first time the Board of Registration took a position on the use of GPS equipment. They ruled that control survey work performed using GPS equipment was a function of land surveying and could only be done by a surveying registrant of the board. Finally, 1990 was the year surveyors took control of ACSM. Without stepping on too many toes, or at least not on the ones with corns, it is no stretch of the truth to say that land surveyors made up 70% of the membership and exerted 30% of the influence. Robert Inman was the ACSM delegate from North Carolina during this time and exerted much influence in what occurred. ACSM had, in effect, gone broke in 1990. The organization had spent all the money at its disposal. The National Society of Professional Surveyors (NSPS) voted to incorporate, to strengthen its position, to open its own bank account, and generally exert the influence its membership numbers warranted. While some predicted the demise of ACSM, the result was its rescue from the brink of disaster. Would it be enough for its ultimate salvation? That question has yet to be answered. Two things are certain, however: (1) surveyors need a strong national voice and, (2) traditional land surveying is inextricably entwined with geodetic surveying, photogrammetry, cartography, and remote sensing.

The year 1991 was not good for many people in the surveying profession. For many, problems actually began in 1990. For others, it might have been delayed a few months beyond 1991, but for most, it was a trying time financially. Jobs were scarce as interest rates hit a record high, and not much land was changing hands. But as *Tar Heel Surveyor* editor, Lucille Inman, said in the March issue of 1991, "Surveyors are survivors." And we are. And we did.

We were saddened with the death of long-time secretary/treasurer Bill Shaw in February of that year. Bill served quietly and with dignity. If you attended a society meeting, a convention, or a seminar, all you had to do to see Bill was to look around. He was always there. We need to remember the Bill Shaws, the Moses Farmers, and the Woodrow Bedsauls of our world. These are the men (along with countless others) who have laid the foundation and built the walls. Sometimes, we don't stop to think of the work and sacrifice these men made, and for what? They did it for the love of a profession and the people they associated with, and for reverence of the past, and hope for the future. For you and for me.

Gary Thompson, arguably the best-known surveyor in North Carolina, was the 1991 president of NCSS. Of all the surveyors I have come in contact with in my years as a practitioner, NCSS officer, and Board of Registration member, Gary Thompson has been the most helpful to me personally. I have never called on him when he did not respond in a positive manner. He has consistently worked for the welfare of the public (first) and for the profession of land surveyors (second). I received a good deal of credit for my work in developing a professionalism and ethics course for surveyors, which is now used throughout the United States. Without Gary Thompson, the money to fund such a course would have been much slower in coming, or it may never have been fully raised at all. As ACSM area director, Gary kept the issue at the forefront at NSPS and NCSS meetings.

He was also instrumental in the development of the proposed "Standards of Practice for Photogrammetrists," and in formulating guidelines governing Land Information System/ Geographic Information System Surveys (LIS/GIS) as they apply to surveyors. How many of you, dear readers, have called on Gary for his help, and received it over the years? Another treasure among many. Another in the long line.

As far as surveyors were concerned, 1991 was a very active year in the legislature. The GS 47-30 rewrite, Johnie Garrason's pride and joy, was introduced, as was a bill establishing a statute of limitations on surveyor liability. On the negative side, two bills that were introduced would adversely affect the way employees of state boards were treated, and how the funds generated by those boards would be handled. One of the strengths of the board over the years has been its autonomy. The board has been able to exert influence in many matters because it has had the freedom and the funds to send all its board members, and any staff it felt necessary, to the NCEES annual meeting and to Southern Zone meetings. As a result, North Carolina has been a leader in getting continuing education into the Model Law, and in getting LIS included in the definition of land surveying; in making sure the "land" was not dropped from land surveyor; in seeing that a professionalism and ethics course for surveyors was developed, and in many other achievements. Now, one of our own, Mr. Dick Cottingham, PE, PLS, was in line to be president of NCEES in the 2000–2001 administration. Thanks to the efforts of surveyors and engineers, we were successful in passing all the positive bills and defeating the negative aspects of all other bills affecting the profession. This included the defeat of a bill that would have allowed subdivisions to be recorded prior to the setting of any interior corners.

The society was once again working on the concept of mandatory continuing education. A committee created in 1990 was busy studying the issue and forming several proposals for consideration by the membership. The idea was voted on by the membership in the fall of 1991, and 62% of those voting were in favor. This information was relayed to the Board of Registration, along with the recommendation that mandatory continuing education be made a condition of renewal of licenses for surveyors in North Carolina.

Montgomery T. Speir, who had served as executive secretary to the Board of Registration since January 10, 1977, resigned effective December 31, 1991, and was elected an honorary member of NCSS in February 1992. Monty had served not only long, but well, in that position and had earned the respect of surveyors and engineers alike.

William R. (Bill) Coleman assumed the presidency of NCSS with a call to "get down to business," which was the theme of that year's ACSM meeting. The two-year controversy between ACSM and NSPS seemed finally resolved with surveyors having a much larger voice in ACSM than they had ever enjoyed before. Likewise, the on-again/off-again controversy that had plagued NCSS and the Board of Registration had largely been resolved, with surveyors feeling they had a much better relationship with the board than they had enjoyed in many years.

It was time to concentrate on some of the important objectives for surveyors, such as continuing professional competency (formally known as "mandatory continuing education"). The newly appointed chair of the committee to study a continuing education requirement, Larry Greene, met with members of the NCSS Mandatory Continuing Education Committee in the spring of 1992, to discuss the issue with regard to common ground. At that time, surveyors and surveying board members were generally in support of the idea, while many engineers and most engineering board members were not. It was generally felt that while the most-desirable scenario would be a requirement covering both professions, surveyors would not attempt to force the issue on engineers, if they could not be convinced of its desirability. The board had the power to require it of both professions or of either profession alone. This was only one of many issues the board and NCSS would work on in a new spirit of cooperation.

Surveyors lost a contemporary and a friend with the sudden death of Earl Smith in early June 1992. I will digress with a personal word about Earl, if I may be indulged. Many may not know that Earl was a cancer survivor, having beaten malignant melanoma a good many years before. I will never forget the support Earl showed my family when my own father was diagnosed with the disease in 1979. He offered encouragement and advice that led my father to treatment at Duke Hospital. While my father did not survive the disease, Earl's unwavering support was a source of strength for me, my mother, and my brother, who attended the same church as Earl. Johnie Garrason and I taught the seminar that Earl attended the day before his death, and he appeared in good health. I spoke with him briefly, never suspecting it would be for the last time. He was faithful in all of his obligations to the end.

Legislatively, it was a year of preventing harmful legislation from passing more than making any new progress. Several bills to alter GS 47-30 were impeded and eventually defeated.

The year 1993 began with the notification that Johnie Garrason had been selected to receive the 1993 NSPS Surveying Excellence Award, the second North Carolina surveyor to be so chosen. Larry Akers, former president of NCSS, had received this award a number of years earlier. The 1993 president of NCSS, Charles O."Hamp" Hampton got off to a busy start. One of his first opportunities came as he was able to discuss mandatory continuing education with engineers at PENC's Annual Convention. As might be imagined, it was the hot topic at that time.

On July 9, 1993, the Board of Registration held a hearing on the subject of continuing professional competency. This hearing was well attended and was held at the McKimmon Center for Continuing Education, at the North Carolina State University campus. A great many people spoke, some in favor and many opposed. Most of the speakers were individual engineers and surveyors. By this time, the concept had the support of NCSS, PENC, and Consulting Engineering Council (CEC) of North Carolina, all but assuring its passage. Representatives from these organizations were present to voice their support.

For some time, a proposal to require recordation of all survey plats called for in deeds had been discussed within NCSS. Linda Edmondson chaired the committee that studied this proposal, and in September of 1993, a copy of their report was submitted to *The Tarheel Surveyor.* The proposal was well thought-out and was founded on some real concerns. Support for the proposal proved spotty, however, and after several months of debate and revision, it was finally abandoned. NCSS did go on record as supporting a four-year degree requirement for registration of land surveyors in North Carolina.

The year 1994 was a very significant year for surveyors in North Carolina. A number of events have been chronicled in the chapter on the Board of Examiners (formerly Board of Registration), and while they may be recapped here, it is recommended the reader review that section. Johnie Garrason, 1994 president of NCSS, wrote in the March issue of *The Tarheel Surveyor* of the enormous increase in membership of several sister societies, with the advent of mandatory continuing education in their states. He called on NCSS to be prepared to accommodate an expected increase in membership should continuing education be mandated as expected. Such a requirement was, in fact, mandated by unanimous vote of the North Carolina Board of Registration on May 12, 1994. It applied equally to land surveyors and engineers and would, when fully implemented in 1998, require fifteen hours of continuing education per year. The long struggle for surveyors was finally over, and an important landmark reached. If you own a surveying firm, as so many land surveyors do, 1994 marked the year that you had to register that firm.

In 1994, five people met in the office of Webb Morgan in Asheville, North Carolina, to discuss a subject that started out as controversial, but which would eventually change the face of surveying in North Carolina forever. The five were Webb Morgan, Charles O. (Hamp) Hampton, Charles Bemhardt, Carol Bernhardt, and Larry Greene. The subject was the regulation of the profession of photogrammetry. Surveyors had long felt that photogrammetrists were practicing land surveying when they produced topographic maps. More recently, they had ventured into the more traditional areas of land surveying with the advent of more sophisticated and accurate technology. Now, GPS units are being utilized on board some of the planes obtaining the data. Webb reported that at a recent meeting of the North Carolina section of the American Society of Photogrammetry and Remote Sensing (ASPRS), he had broached the subject of regulation and found them receptive. Many of them knew of poor practice among so-called professionals, but no governing body existed to rein them in. Both members of ASPRS and Webb agreed that the Board of Registration was the logical regulatory body to take on this task. The subject of the meeting on this day was to explore the means whereby that might be brought about.

At first the discussion centered on photogrammetry as a separate profession, but it was soon the consensus that this was not the tack to take. As the only Board of Registration member present, Larry Greene suggested the logical course, and the easiest to implement, would be to take photogrammetry in as a separate discipline with no difference in the license required. The board could handle any issue of straying outside one's area of discipline just as they had historically handled it in the case of engineering.

This was thought to be the best approach by all present. Everyone also agreed it would take a major education effort to convince traditional land surveyors that this was the proper approach. Many obstacles lay ahead. So many, in fact, that they must be overcome one at a time, through separate efforts, to accomplish this seemingly impossible task. First, people who saw this as a positive action for the two disciplines must convey that belief to others and win converts. Second, the Board of Registration must see this as a logical and natural extension of their jurisdiction. Third, the North Carolina General Assembly must pass legislation enabling the board to assume jurisdiction. Finally, the board must come up with standards, grandfathering provisions, and examinations that would be fair to the professionals, and at the same time, protect the safety and welfare of the public. The people gathered in that room knew the odds, but there was an excitement, an anticipation, a knowledge that the profession could take a giant step into the future. Without this kind of willingness to adapt and grow, professions can die or wither away to positions of less importance. The year 1994 was a year to file away and remember.

As 1995 began, the licensing of photogrammetrists was the issue before NCSS. It would be an understatement to say it was viewed with skepticism by many and with outright hostility by others. A panel discussion with surveying members of the Board of Registration was held at the Annual Convention on February 9, 1995, and it was well attended. Supportive views were aired by board members Anders, Long, and Greene, but it was obvious that many hurdles must be cleared. Members of both professions must be convinced of the wisdom of such an attempt before any move to actually license photogrammetrists was initiated. Board members, and other supporters of the concept, had met earlier with the North Carolina section of ASPRS at their annual convention to discuss the issue and to answer questions. Both meetings ended with most of those present willing to approach the idea with an open mind.

Webb Morgan, a staunch supporter of including photogrammetry as a surveying discipline, was sworn in as president of NCSS at that convention. His first message emphasized how important he felt the licensing of photogrammetrists was to assuring the surveying profession assumed its proper role in GIS. Larry Greene was asked to participate in a panel discussion on the licensing of photogrammetrists at the annual ACSM-ASPRS Convention held in Charlotte, North Carolina. The effort was off and running.

Photogrammetry was, by no means, the only significant issue in 1995. Legibility of plats obtained from the Register of Deeds office was of major concern. Surveyors are required by GS 47-30 to submit legible plats, but legibility is always compromised in the reproduction process. Most plats were now being put on microfilm, further reducing legibility. How much responsibility should the surveyor bear in preparing his or her map in such a way that legibility was insured given these reproduction problems, which were beyond the surveyor's control? How much responsibility should lie elsewhere? Wherever responsibility lay, the public deserved to be able to obtain legible copies from the public record.

Another issue also was how the NCSS Institute should be administered, which was debated for several years. Some felt the Institute should be under the complete jurisdiction and control of NCSS. In fact, it was set up as a semi-autonomous organization in 1986, closely affiliated and co-sponsored with North Carolina State University Office of Continuing Education and Professional Development. The decision to let North Carolina State University continue to administer the NCSS Institute caused more debating in 1995. This was shortly resolved with the merging of the Education and Institute Committees, with NCSS assuming all administrative duties for the Institute.

A four-year degree requirement continues to be discussed. A minority of states has such a requirement at this time, but the number is growing. North Carolina, a leader in many respects, lags behind in this area.

In March of 1995, the surveying profession lost another giant with the death of Walter G. (Hutch) Hutchison. Hutch was a leader in the state but especially in the Western Chapter. He, and a few like him, literally pulled the western part of the state into the twentieth-century. The Western Chapter became the third chapter in the NCSS. The closeness and support that developed among surveyors in that region was a wonder to behold. Hutch was also a fine Christian man who lived his religion. He was famed for his ministry to prisoners, taking seriously the call to "do unto others." I saw Hutch in the Asheville Airport not too long before his death. His memory fading, he did not recognize me. I told him who I was, and that I was a surveyor. He spoke glowingly of his pride in his daughter, Pat, who he reminded me, was the only female president in NCSS history. I never saw him alive again after that day.

Webb Morgan's final article as president appeared in the January 1996 issue of *The Tarheel Surveyor.* He reported, among other things, that registration of photogrammetrists as surveyors appeared to be a bitter pill for some to swallow, indicating the size of the hurdles yet to be cleared.

C. Wayne Hyatt, Jr. was the 1996 president of NCSS. In his first message, he acknowledged that the biggest question before NCSS was the registration of photogrammetrists. Ballots with several options had been distributed to all members. Of significance is a letter appearing in the March issue of *The Tarheel Surveyor,* written by Johnie Garrason. Johnie expressed his support of regulation of photogrammetrists by the Board of Registration and acknowledged this represented a change in his thinking. This sentiment is indicative of what took place in many surveyors' minds and shows the willingness of members of the profession to listen to arguments, be open-minded, and, if the arguments are convincing, to change their mind.

Results from the balloting were published in the May issue of *The Tarheel Surveyor*. Of the 459 ballots cast, 154 people voted against registration of photogrammetrists as surveyors, and 290 people voted for registration by the North Carolina Board of Registration for Professional Engineers and Land Surveyors under the surveying profession. Most still felt it should be a registration separate and apart from surveyors. The support of the society was then conveyed to the Board of Registration, which was in the process of formulating a GS 89-C rewrite. North Carolina ASPRS likewise proposed that the current RLS license be modified to include photogrammetrists and proposed the requirements be close to, or identical with, those for traditional land surveyors. The only exception would be in the test on Boundary Law. They also recommended criteria for grandfathering those currently practicing photogrammetry in North Carolina.

Throughout the latter part of 1996 and into 1997, a controversy arose over an audit of the society's accounting records by the IRS. The officers and directors worked diligently with the auditor to satisfy the IRS's requirements. At the suggestion of the auditor, the NCSS, for the first time in our history, hired an accountant to check our accounting methods and to prepare our yearly income tax returns. Considering the number of members in the society, over 1200, the officers and directors considered it an excellent idea.

During the same time, the society's office was moved to the Raleigh area. This placed the office in a central location so that committees could easily meet at the office and have access to any records they might require during their meeting. Formerly, the committees would meet in different locations around the state, which cost the society for the rentals of meeting rooms. Since the move, most committee meetings occur at the office, saving the society important funds.

Another reason for the move of the office was NCSS' active participation in the legislative process in Raleigh. Many times, senators and legislators told members if NCSS wanted to have a greater influence in the legislature, it needed a presence in the Raleigh area—an office where members could invite senators and legislators to meet to discuss upcoming bills important to the society.

William C. "Bill" Owen was installed as president of NCSS at the February 1997 Convention in Winston-Salem, N.C. The actual move of the society's office fell on the capable shoulders of the new president. Darlene H. Johnson assumed the duties of executive director of NCSS in mid-year, and the new offices of NCSS were opened July lst in Cameron Village, Raleigh, North Carolina. Past Presidents Joe Hardee and Derward Baker and Executive Director Darlene Johnson did a magnificent job in moving and quickly establishing the new office and transforming it into a beautiful meeting place. By the summer meeting in August, the new office was in full operation.

The year 1997 brought yet another revision to GS 47-30. The most objectionable change was the establishment of a review officer in each county to review a surveyor's compliance with the Mapping Law before a plat could be recorded. A change not considered objectionable was the elimination of the requirement that a surveyor's signature be notarized.

The NCSS Museum of Archives and Preservation of Surveying, Inc. (NCSS Maps, Inc.) and the NCSS Historical Committee were significant accomplishments for the NCSS. Together, they focused efforts on formulating plans to preserve the documentary heritage of surveying in North Carolina from the late 1700s through the year 2003. Under the leadership of Otis Jones, president/chairman, from whose mind the idea sprang, 27,000 maps, thus far, have been archived in the North Carolina Cultural Resources Archives and History. Many books, papers, and other records also have been collected from former times. The committee also collected, and continues to collect, surveying artifacts, such as surveying and drafting instruments and equipment. Last, but not least, the committee is responsible for the writing of this book and has plans for creating a museum of the history of surveying in North Carolina.

In 1998, President Kenneth T. Mills, of Asheville, North Carolina, began the year with a call for surveyors to "toot their own horns." He pointed out a number of accomplishments surveyors could be proud of, gave credit to all who had helped gain this ground, and called on surveyors to let the public know about their contributions.

The much worked on and long-debated GS 89-C rewrite had been introduced in 1997 and passed by the North Carolina House. It contained a number of significant changes and additions, not the least of which was the inclusion of photogrammetry as a discipline of surveying. Additionally, the definition of surveying was rewritten to recognize and accommodate new technology including GIS. It was the most sweeping and significant legislation affecting surveying since enactment of the law in 1921. The year 1998 saw the passage of the bill by the Senate, but changes necessitated a House-Senate Conference to resolve differences. Finally, in September 1998, Governor James Hunt signed the bill into law. What had seemed, at one time, to be an impossibly high mountain had been scaled.

On June 29, 1998, Governor James B. Hunt, Jr. appointed C. Phil Wagoner, PLS, to the Board of Examiners to fill a position that had been held by Ray Anders. Ray's term had expired on December 31, 1997, but he had continued to serve beyond that time while the governor's appointment was pending. The profession owes much to Mr. Anders for his long and dedicated service. Having served with Ray for over nine years on the board, I can truthfully say a more honest and dedicated individual would be hard to find. In addition, Helen Merritt, public member, resigned because of a move out of state. Ms. Merritt, who served on the Land Survey Committee for most of her tenure, was a very fine member of the board who took her duties seriously.

Linda Edmondson, Professional Education, Planning and Development (PEPD) administrator and chairman, did her usually fine job of overseeing the society's continuing education course offerings. Linda has been tireless in her efforts for NCSS over the years. She is especially dedicated to education, both primary and continuing.

North Carolina lost two more leaders in 1998, with the passing of Woodrow W. Bedsaul, PLS, and Sam T. Marlowe, PLS. These men, like many before them, stood tall and never shirked their responsibilities—true professionals in every sense of the word. With the last hours of 1998 came yet another loss. Albert (Al) Frieze, who served long and ably as officer, committee chair, and ACSM representative, died of a massive heart attack on December 31st, while preparing to go to Blowing Rock to celebrate the coming of the New Year. Al had been in poor health for several months, but his sudden death came as a shock to all who knew and loved him. It is up to all of us to take up the slack when a person of such stature is lost. Traditionally, surveyors have been up to that task.

The Thirteenth Annual NCSS Institute was held in March of 1999, a testament to the dedication North Carolina surveyors have for continuing education. We, as a profession, have a hunger for knowledge. The time has come to translate that desire into a four-year degree requirement for the profession of surveying in North Carolina. Few in the profession would dispute that the field is too complex to base licensure on experience in lieu of education. North Carolina, long a leader in our field, is woefully behind a number of states in this area. The trouble lies not with the profession, but rather with a legislature that does not appreciate the need. It is up to us to stand shoulder-to-shoulder in a show of solidarity, in order to convince others of the legitimacy of this need.

I believe the greatest challenges to our survival and growth as a profession are (1) guarding against the loss of an essential role in the development of GIS and (2) obtaining full professional status with the requirement of a four-year degree in surveying. We have a great history. We face a challenging future. It is up to us to see that our heritage continues.

Martin L. Barrow, Jr., who served as president of the society in 1999, worked for the establishment of a four-year degree program in surveying for North Carolina. In April, Governor James B. Hunt appointed William C. Owen as a surveying member of the Board of Examiners, replacing R. Larry Greene, who had served ten years and four months.

The year 2000 ushered in J. Dean Slate as the new president of NCSS. It also saw Lucille S. Inman, long-time executive secretary of the society, honored at the Annual Convention held in Asheville, North Carolina. She served from 1976 to 1997 and oversaw tremendous growth and change during her tenure. The society owes much to Ms. Inman for her dedicated service.

Richard P. Bennett served as president of NCSS in 2001. That year saw the establishing of the NCSS Education Foundation. The purpose of the foundation is to solicit donations for the establishment of a four-year surveying degree program in North Carolina. North Carolina A&T University agreed to establish a program in their engineering department, and enthusiasm for such a program within that department was very high. However, as time passes, with no imminent adoption of a four-year degree program, this enthusiasm may be waning. The establishment of a four-year degree program would fulfill a long-standing objective of NCSS. It could also ease the way in the State Legislature for the passage of a four-year degree requirement. Money is tight with the state at present, and none is available for the establishment of new programs. This means the foundation must raise $150,000 or more if the dream is to become a reality. John Furmage was the first chairman of the foundation, and a number of directors serve staggered terms.

The year 2001 saw the passing of James W. Bailey, Sr., who was a long-time friend and business associate of many in the profession. For many years, he was involved in the aerial mapping of North Carolina and surrounding states, both as an employee and as a business owner. When the photogrammetrists were brought into the profession in 1998, James became a professional land surveyor and joined ranks as one of us. James was a husband, a father, a land surveyor, a valued member of his community, and a friend.

No one living in these United States will ever forget what happened on September 11, 2001. I am sure all of us remember exactly where we were and what we were doing at the time. North Carolina land surveyors are no exception. I had gone to the dentist that morning and sat in the chair in disbelief as news rolled in over the radio, one tragedy followed by another.

Mark R. Seffels served as president of the society in 2002. Mark placed a good deal of emphasis on education and professionalism. He saw a danger in our slipping from a profession to a trade. He dwelt on the obligations inherent in being a professional and how one learned those obligations. Another hot topic was the physical relocation the society would take when the building is to be vacated. The building in Cameron Village is scheduled for demolition in the near future. Two ad hoc committees were established, one looking at Wake County and the other at the Asheboro area. This will be a critical decision that will affect much more than may be evident on the surface. Location will have much to do with the direction the society takes as we march into the future.

The NCSS Convention was held in Sunset Beach, North Carolina, in 2003, where Richard M. Benton placed his main emphasis on membership development, wanting to give members "more bang for their buck." As a part of this, a $10,000 life insurance benefit for each paying member was purchased at no cost to the member. An option to increase to $50,000 was made available with no medical exam. This benefit could also be purchased for spouses who were members of the Ladies Auxiliary.

Melissa Beard became the new executive director of the society in December of 2002. While technically a 2002 news item, Melissa's history with the society really begins in 2003. She has been actively visiting all of the chapters statewide and is already getting her feet wet down at the legislature as our lobbyist. She is an energetic person with a can-do attitude. We can look forward to many positive accomplishments with Melissa in this position.

The former policy of a one year's free membership for new registrants is being reinstated under President Benton's leadership. Statistics show the society has retained about 60% of the members who have received this benefit over the years. Other changes include updating and improving *The Tarheel Surveyor* by Executive Director/Editor Beard. *The Tarheel Surveyor* will be published four times a year rather than six. The new look is a good deal more professional and represents another forward step by the society.

The history of the profession is long and distinguished. The future looks bright and promising, though pitfalls are inevitable. The society must build on that history and make some history of its own if the profession is to continue its growth.

North Carolina Society of Surveyors Institute
"A Unique Experience in Continuing Education"

Otis A. Jones, RLS
Chairman, Institute Committee

We are born into this life as distinct individuals with different natural talents and instincts. From the time we breathe our first breath of life until we breathe our last breath at death, we are constantly in a learning process. Each of us being different, we naturally take different paths in this process to satisfy our individual desires in learning. So it is of little wonder that in the pursuit of our formal and continuing education we differ in how to attain it.

For the past two decades, the rise of the level of education in the surveying profession has been tremendous! Formal education resulting in two-year and four-year degrees in surveying is becoming commonplace. Structured continuing education, such as the North Carolina Society of Surveyors' Institute, is becoming a model for others to follow. The progressive experience required and needed by a surveyor is on a higher level than ever before.

The present generation of professionals on the scene is instilling into those being trained a strong desire to excel in their personal and professional life. Due to our quest for excellence as surveyors, public respect for and confidence in surveyors has shown much growth in recent years. This trend is reflected today by businesses, individuals and other professionals when they have surveying needs. We respond with a surveyor and/or a high tech team of surveyors meeting their needs.

In surveying in the past, we have used the surveyor's compass (during the eras of Washington, Jefferson, and Lincoln). Soon after that period, the transit came into wide use. In recent years, we have used the optical micrometer theodolites, electronic distance meters (EDM), handheld calculators and computers (mostly used individually). Now all are combined into a total station and data collector performing these functions simultaneously. The total station, at the present, is the predominant piece of field equipment in use. Innovative development of the total station/data collector will continue.

New and changing surveying technology will change our mode of practice. The use of hightech automated field and office equipment, along with the hightech team of surveyors, will make our management and production more efficient. Our work load will be greater, but it can be accomplished with fewer employees producing a higher financial return with a lower liability risk. Many subjects in the NCSS Institute deal with these new and changing concepts.

The NCSS Institute was founded in 1986 for the purpose: "To provide continuing education to develop a better understanding of the many important aspects of surveying." Also included is the opportunity to share experiences and to have fellowship with participants from many parts of the country. A supportive membership and a dedicated Institute Committee working together toward a common goal of excellence have created an institute of learning of which we can be proud! Seven years of continuing success with the Institute has "lit the fire" in a great number of surveyors. Their desire for our profession to excel will make surveying of the future exciting and truly something to look forward to!

The improved techniques and modern state-of-the-art equipment and software can only mean one thing—that surveying has nowhere to go but forward. The "appetite" of many young surveyors has been whetted by continuing education and by the Institute to the extent that their desires and dreams are only beginning to be attained.

The Institute is helping all present and future surveyors attain their goal for excellence and desire to perform as top quality professionals. The success of the Institute is an indication that the students and graduates have a genuine interest in what we are accomplishing together. There is excitement over what is transpiring in continuing education and this is assuring the surveyors of today and tomorrow that, with their continued interest and positive sharing of ideas, their hopes and dreams will, indeed, be fulfilled!

At the time the Institute was organized, the North Carolina Society of Surveyors was holding two or three seminars a year in furnishing continuing education to surveyors in North Carolina. Many seminars were being held by outsiders for profit. The Institute changed this! Now most of our continuing education comes from within and is not being done for profit, but out of our desire to control our own destiny individually and collectively.

The 1993 NCSS Institute (March 3–6) was held at the Jane S. McKimmon Center. It was co-sponsored by the NC State University Office of Continuing Education and Professional Development and supported by the NC State Board of Registration for Professional Engineers and Land Surveyors.

This year's Institute is the result of experience gained in the six previous Institutes and was our finest yet. The four sections in the Institute offered twenty-nine subjects in business management/marketing, time management, the environment, drainage/erosion control, land planning, legal aspects of the profession, astronomic direction/polaris observation, GPS/GIS/LIS, adjustments and professional ethics/image. All instructors are educated and experienced in their chosen fields. Many of them have been teaching in the Institute since its beginning. Their teaching is dynamic and appreciated by attendees.

With the emergence of a new conscientious generation of professionals blending with the present generation, we are quickly coming together, united in our purpose to find solutions to our needs in our personal, business and professional life. These generations will set the standards for future generations in the twenty-first century. The Institute has had a part in bringing about these changes and has "stood the test of time." At the Institute, the doors are open to all, providing freedom to enjoy and share in the pursuit of our aspirations.

WRITER'S NOTE: The NCSS Institute is now in its eighteenth year, offering the finest in continuing education to the surveying profession.

Reprinted by permission of *The Professional Engineer*/March–April 1993, page 10

From left, Steve Mullins, Gary Thompson, Owen Osborne and Randy Noland discuss data collecting in a recent Institute class.

Lincoln Statue—New Salem.

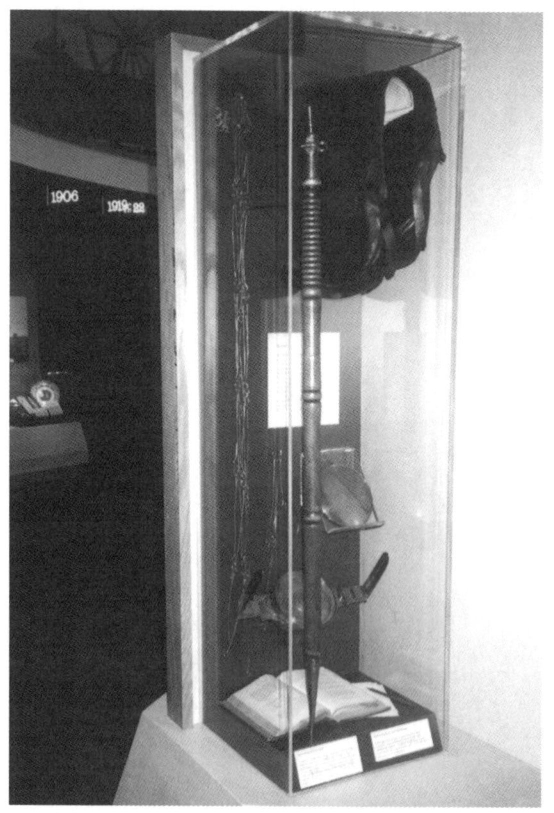

Lincoln's Compass, Jacob Staff, Chain, Saddle Bag, and Book.

Statue of Abraham Lincoln surveying, and other pictures taken by Otis A. Jones. Used by permission of Lincon's New Salem State Historic Site, Petersburg, Illinois.

North Carolina Board of Examiners for Engineers and Surveyors Years 1921–2003

R. Larry Greene, PLS

The State Board of Registration for Professional Engineers and Land Surveyors, as it has been known through most of its history, was created by an act of the North Carolina General Assembly on February 25, 1921. The bill was entitled "An Act to Regulate the Practice of Engineering and Land Surveying in the State of North Carolina," but is better known by its General Statute designation, GS 89-C. From its inception, the board was charged with safeguarding the life, health, and property of the citizens of North Carolina. This is, in fact, its only reason for existence. The second paragraph of the original act specifically stated that anyone could practice engineering or land surveying without being registered to do so, "unless the same involves the public safety or health."

The first board consisted of five members, at least one of whom had to be appointed from the engineering faculty of North Carolina State College, and at least one from the engineering faculty of the University of North Carolina. Not more than three members could be from the same branch of engineering. While land surveyors could serve on the board, there was no requirement that one be appointed. Toward the end of the act, after all the fine-sounding legal language had been put to paper, it was stated that " nothing in this act shall be construed as prohibiting any person from doing land surveying, provided he does not represent himself to be a registered land surveyor."

The first meeting of the new board was held in Governor Cameron Morrison's office on May 23, 1921. Governor Morrison instructed the members of the board as to their duties and advised them he was ready to assist them in any way that he could in carrying out the provisions of the law. The oath of office was then administered to each of the five appointees, whereupon they promptly adjourned for lunch at the Yarborough Hotel.

All five members of the original board were trained engineers, and all took the title of professional engineer (PE). Three of the five also chose to add the designation, registered land surveyor (RLS). The first chairman of the board was Charles E. Waddell, PE, RLS, of Asheville. Gilbert C. White, PE, of Durham was vice chairman, and Harry Tucker, PE, RLS, of Raleigh was secretary/treasurer. Other members were Park H. Daggett, PE, of Chapel Hill, and N.S. Mullican, PE, RLS, of Durham.

That first meeting of the board was largely occupied with the business of getting organized, designing a suitable certificate for professional engineers, designing an official seal for the board and selecting appropriate stationery. It was decided to communicate with existing boards in other states to obtain copies of their rules and regulations. The board did adopt one bylaw before adjourning. It provided that "special meetings shall be held at the call of the chairman of the board or at the request of any member of the board." The entire meeting lasted two and one-half hours, lunch included.

Two other meetings of the board took place in its first year of existence. The O' Henry Hotel in Greensboro hosted a meeting in July, and the other was held in October at State College Station, Raleigh. Several matters of substance were decided at these meetings. It was decided that all applications for registration approved prior to January 1, 1922, would bear the January 1, 1922 date. The protection of the name "engineer" was addressed, and it was decided to ask the American Radiator Company to refrain from calling plumbers "heating engineers." It is interesting to note that the board never received a reply to its request. The American Radiator Company simply ignored it.

The first granting of registration took place in October 1921, with fifty-one individuals receiving the designation "professional engineer" or "registered land surveyor." Of these fifty-one, twelve were registered as both engineers and land surveyors, and only one, Mr. K.C. Elkin, was registered only as a land surveyor. He thus became the first registered land surveyor in the state of North Carolina.

At the first meeting of 1922, the board discussed and approved a salary for the secretary of the board. It is interesting to note that while the secretary was, for a time, the equivalent of what is now titled executive director of the board, the salary he received was only $600.00 per year. Out of this handsome sum, he was to pay for stenographic and other office assistance.

By February 25, 1923, the board had registered 450 individuals. No breakdown of the registrants by profession was contained in the minutes of that meeting, but it was noted that of the sixty new applications that had been received since the prior meeting, forty were engineers, and twenty were land surveyors. Probably some of the twenty, perhaps the majority, were also counted among the forty.

In December 1924, the board sent out a questionnaire to all registered professional engineers. Among the questions asked were two pertaining to the registration of land surveyors. One asked for comments on the advisability of requiring the registration of all land surveyors. The other asked for an opinion on registering all land surveyors aged forty years or more, based on experience alone. Many years later, the question of the registration of all land surveyors was still being debated. In 1937, the board sent out 350 questionnaires to registrants selected at random, the vast majority of whom were engineers. The first question on this survey asked, "Do you favor required registration for surveyors?" Within two weeks, 250 questionnaires had been returned. The results on the registration question were 240 "yes" votes. There were nine "no" votes and one "no answer." The board then voted unanimously to ask the sitting legislature to amend GS 89-C to include mandatory registration to practice land surveying. It would be more than twenty years before such legislation would be introduced and passed.

The 1951 rewrite of GS 89-C required, for the first time, that a land surveyor be included on the Board of Registration. Mr. Grady S. Harrell, RLS, was a sitting board member at that time, having been appointed in 1941 as the first, and only, pure land surveyor to be chosen. He continued to occupy that position for another ten years, serving through 1961. In 1962, Mr. Merriwether Lewis was appointed by Governor Terry Sanford to the vacated position, and so became the second surveyor in the board's history. Other changes mandated by the 1951 rewrite provided for examinations for land surveyors, allowed registration without examinations for those persons having ten years of lawful experience and who were over the age of thirty years. It also allowed an eighteen-month grandfather period during which all such persons could obtain registration without meeting the qualifications set forth in the act. It still contained the clause that allowed anyone to survey as long as he did not represent himself to be a registered land surveyor.

In 1957, the Registration Law was amended to require the board to prepare, or have prepared, a Manual of Practice for the information and guidance of those engaged in the practice of land surveying. This manual was known as the " blue book" by most surveyors. From these beginnings evolved the Standards of Practice for land surveying in North Carolina as we know them today. The manual, completed in 1960, became the first successful attempt to establish recognized standards for good practice in land surveying in the United States.

In 1963, there was a nearly successful attempt to establish a separate Board of Registration for land surveyors. This effort grew, at least to a degree, out of the frustration of land surveyors in dealing with a board composed of four engineers and one land surveyor. The bill to establish a separate board passed the House with no dissenting votes and was sent to the Senate. The Senate referred the bill to the Committee on State Government. Supporters of the bill expected no opposition, but at the committee hearing, they were blind-sided by a large group of surveyors who attended and were opposed to a separate board. Most of these surveyors were engaged, either directly, or indirectly, in work involving state and local government or federal government departments and agencies. As a result, the bill was reported out of committee unfavorably and was withdrawn. A substitute bill was prepared which would have increased the number of surveyors on the combined board from one to three, a change supported by the sitting members of the board. Legislation increasing the board from five to six members by adding one additional land surveyor was passed in 1965, and the appointment was made effective January 1, 1966. The length of a board member's term was increased from four years to five at that same time. William N. Turner was appointed to the new position.

The longest serving member in the history of the board was Carroll L. Mann, who was appointed in 1928, and served until 1954. In terms of power and influence, however, none could compare with Robert B. Rice, Professor of Diesel Engineering at North Carolina State College. First appointed in 1948, Professor Rice served continuously until 1969. By the 1960s, it would not be much of a stretch to say he was the board, serving both as a member and as its executive director. He largely wrote, or influenced the writing of, the requirements for surveyors (1960 Manual of Practice). He wrote the examination that surveyors had to pass to become registered. He likewise exerted a heavy influence over engineering requirements and decisions.

By 1968, other board members were chafing under his rule, and in 1969, matters came to a head. Board members voted 4–2 to remove Professor Rice from his position as executive director of the board.

When the board met next, the members arrived to an empty conference room. All the chairs and the conference table had been removed. The board attorney was contacted and the furniture retrieved. During the ensuing days, Governor Scott was contacted by factions of both camps with complaints and charges against the other faction. Governor Scott concluded that the only thing he could do was dismiss the entire board and start over. He wrote each board member asking for their resignation. Gone were board members Rice and Little, along with George S. Rawlins, PE; Chilton R. Jones, PE; William N. Turner, RLS; and Ernest Elsevier, PE, RLS. The appointments of Clarence H. (Pat) Blue, RLS; Lambert T. Gibbs, PE, RLS; Robert D. Inman, RLS; Richard H. Moore, PE, RLS; and Robert F. Ruffner, PE, became effective January 1, 1970. In addition, the governor reappointed former board member John D. Watson, PE, who had served from 1958 through 1966. B.A. Soholski was hired as the first independent executive secretary of the board in 1970, and Robert Inman, RLS, took over writing the land surveyor's examination for the board and did so for the next thirteen years. For the first few years following Professor Rice' s departure, Mr. Inman wrote and graded the entire sixteen hours of examination. He continued to write and grade the state portion of the exam, first as a board member, and then, after his appointment expired in 1978, as a consultant until 1983.

Several other significant events took place in the early 1970s that changed the way the board interpreted GS 89-C, in regard to certain activities most surveyors now take for granted. The first of these involved Robert Wilson of Greensboro, North Carolina. Mr. Wilson had been awarded the stakeout contract on a large construction project in the Greensboro area. This apparently did not sit well with some registrants, as charges were filed with the board against Mr. Wilson for practicing engineering. No hearing was ever held because the board ultimately decided that this type of work required neither a PE nor a RLS to be in charge. During the course of the investigation, however, a good many professionals came to Mr. Wilson' s defense. He particularly remembered Marvin Borum and Howard Loughlin as being supportive. Mr. Loughlin, it seems, was particularly outspoken in his defense of Mr. Wilson.

During the annual question and answer session with the board held at the NCSS Convention that year, Mr. Loughlin let it be known that he not only routinely performed construction stakeouts, but that he also designed his own storm drainage and street grade and alignment within the subdivisions he surveyed. Going a step further, he invited the board to visit his office where he would be happy to pull his originals and provide them with copies of his designs. A number of board members felt they should take him up on his invitation. Since the position of board investigator had just been established, the board voted to send newly hired investigator, Mr. John Laws, to Wilmington to look into the matter. When Mr. Laws arrived, the executive secretary, B. A. Soholsky, was with him. Mr. Loughlin informed them they would have to wait for his attorney to arrive. When the attorney arrived, Mr. Loughlin pulled from his files a number of examples of profiles, alignments, grades, and storm water designs and proceeded to make copies.

Mr. Laws returned to Raleigh with an abundance of evidence with which to prepare a case against Mr. Loughlin. Charges were eventually brought. Two hearings were held. The first hearing took place on October 19, 1972, and was mostly taken up with testimony from an expert witness for the board and testimony from Mr. Loughlin. The second hearing, about a month later, was held in the Wake County Courtroom, to accommodate the expected crowd. Approximately thirty to forty surveyors appeared in Mr. Loughlin's defense, testifying that they performed essentially the same services for their clients. After a while, it was reported the board simply would ask the witness before them if the testimony they were about to give would be essentially the same as those who had gone before. Upon receiving an affirmative answer, they would dismiss that witness and proceed to the next one. Lonnie Williams, the defense attorney for Mr. Loughlin, summed up his case with the assertion that surveyors had been performing these tasks, "since the mind of man runneth not asunder."

The board found Mr. Loughlin not guilty and, as a result, the law was changed in 1973 to allow "alignment and grades of street and incidental drainage within the subdivision" be performed by a registered land surveyor.

The spring of 1974 was the first administration of the fundamentals examination as prepared by the National Council of Examiners for Engineers. The second day's examination was still prepared by the board, and both had to be passed separately to obtain registration. That same year, Howard McCaully became the newest surveyor member of the board, replacing Pat Blue.

In 1975, GS 89-C was amended to require separate registration as a surveyor for a professional engineer performing land survey work. Engineers were given one year to grandfather as surveyors. After the grandfather period expired, they would have to sit for the principles and practices portion (second day) of the examination in order to obtain registration as a land surveyor. Other changes enacted into law that year included: provisions for surveyor-in-training status, an additional land surveyor member to the board (now four engineers and three land surveyors), and a limit on the number of five-year terms a board member could serve. James R. Burrow was appointed as the new land surveyor member of the board. Also passed was legislation allowing a surveyor or engineer to file a mechanics lien to collect unpaid fees. The Uniform Mapping Law, GS 47-30, was first passed into law in 1911. It allowed counties to exempt themselves if they had their own law. As of 1975, forty-two counties remained exempt from the Mapping Law and attempts were underway to amend the law to cover all one hundred counties.

As a result of separate registration for professional engineers and land surveyors, the board registered its first female surveyor in 1976. Emily Blount, who was also the first female professional engineer in North Carolina, grandfathered (grandmothered?) as a registered land surveyor and took her place in history for a second time. The first female to become a registered land surveyor by examination was Jane Ferguson who attained that honor in 1977.

The year 1976 saw a lawsuit filed against the Board of Registration by the North Carolina Society of Surveyors in an attempt to prevent professional engineers who could not demonstrate experience in land surveying from becoming registered surveyors by grandfathering. The society carried this case through the appellate courts, but lost at every level.

In 1976, one other significant achievement for land surveyors occurred. Robert Inman was elected chairman of the board and became the first pure land surveyor to serve in that capacity. Mr. Inman served with distinction and did much to raise the status of land surveyors on the board.

In 1977, Sunset Legislation was passed which eliminated virtually all regulatory boards by a given date. This elimination varied according to the function of the board. For the North Carolina Board of Registration for Professional Engineers and Land Surveyors, that date was July 1, 1979. The only way the board could continue past that date was for the General Assembly to enact a new Registration Law prior to the deadline. It might seem ludicrous to younger professionals, who did not live through this time, that this would ever be a worry. It was very serious to those who went through it.

Robert Inman was a forceful and effective speaker whose thoughts were well organized and logically presented. Because of his obvious ability in this area, he was chosen to chair the Joint Action Committee consisting of representatives from NCSS and the engineering societies. He also agreed to be its spokesman at the various hearings held throughout the state. It was with an enormous sense of pride that I attended some of these hearings and watched a land surveyor lead the way. As we all know, the Registration Act was renewed and the professions were saved.

In another significant move, Montgomery T. Speir replaced B.A. Soholsky as executive director of the Board of Registration. He would go on to serve fifteen years in that capacity. He also is an honorary member of the North Carolina Society of Surveyors.

Phil Stanley replaced Robert Inman as a surveyor board member in January of 1978. Mr. Stanley was a professional engineer, as well as a registered land surveyor.

The enactment of the amended Registration Law, as mandated by the Sunset Commission, occurred in 1979. As a result, the Board of Registration was increased to nine members by adding two public members for the first time. There was much wailing and gnashing of teeth when this law was first passed. What could a non-professional possibly add to a professional board? The answer was not long in coming. Public members have, from the outset, been a valuable component of the board. Almost to a person, they have served with distinction, and they have added a dimension and a perspective not possible without them.

The 1979 version of the law also gave the board the authority to require continuing education for registrants, and mandated that they consider the matter. The board took no action to actually implement continuing education at that time, but it enabled a later board to do so.

Jack Thomas was hired to replace the retiring John Laws as board investigator, and that position became a full-time job with this appointment. Howard Loughlin, who had been tried by the board in 1972, became its newest surveyor member in 1979, replacing Howard McCaully.

In 1980, the board considered, and then declined, to place a limit on the number of individuals a single registrant could supervise. The board felt, and rightly so, that supervision depended upon the ability of the registrant, the abilities of those being supervised, and the nature of the work being supervised. Mandatory continuing education, which the board had been instructed to consider, was rejected.

In 1981, Phillip Stanley was the second surveyor member to serve as chairman of the board. He was elected by his fellow members to fill that capacity. George T. Paris, RLS, already the mayor of Red Springs, North Carolina, was appointed to the board as a surveyor member; and the first two public members, Marvin Roper and Charles B. Langstrom, were also appointed.

Ronald H. Carpenter, RLS, was appointed to the board in 1983, replacing the outgoing Philip Stanley. Also, 1983 was the year the long-awaited rewrite of GS 47-30 became a reality. This was the culmination of nearly two years of work by the NCSS Rewrite Committee consisting of Ron Scott, David Campbell, David Shaw, Robert Inman, Sam Marlowe, John Parker and Chairman Larry Greene. The bill was introduced into the House on March 31, 1983, by Representative Richard Wright, now an honorary member of NCSS. By mid-summer, it had been enacted into law and North Carolina had, for the first time, a truly Uniform Mapping Law.

Ceremonies honoring new registrants and their families were initiated in 1984. While sponsored by Professional Engineers of North Carolina (PENC) and NCSS, the Board of Registration has played a significant role in these ceremonies by furnishing speakers and by presenting certificates to the new registrants. This has proven to be a meaningful event for those new registrants who choose to participate.

A significant hire was made by the board in 1984, when Jerry Carter replaced Jack Thomas as board investigator. No one knew it then, but Mr. Carter would go on to play a huge role in the board's history.

In 1985, George Paris became the third surveyor member to chair the board. This is the first of three straight years a surveyor would occupy that position.

In 1986, more substantial changes occurred in the Registration Law. An AAS degree in engineering technology was no longer recognized as a degree leading to registration. The amount of experience required to sit for the fundamentals of surveying examination was increased to five years for applicants whose formal education ended with a high school diploma. To sit for the principles and practices examination would now require passing the fundamentals exam and having a total of seven years experience for the applicants with only a high school diploma. Additionally, professional engineers would henceforth be required to pass the fundamentals of surveying examination before sitting for the principles and practices examination just as all applicants do. Bobby Long was appointed to the Board of Registration replacing George Paris, and Howard Loughlin was elected chairman of the board.

In 1987, the principles and practices examination, which had been a four-hour national examination and a four-hour state specific examination, became a four-hour national examination and a three-hour colonial states examination. Both would be prepared by the National Council of Engineering Examiners. The state specific examination went from four hours to one hour at that same time, with emphasis placed on state law and storm water drainage. All three examinations had to be passed separately to obtain registration. That year, Ronald Carpenter became the third land surveyor in many years to chair the board.

Board member Al Bass wrote his "Treatise on Responsible Charge" in 1988. This paper, prepared at the request of the board for North Carolina registrants and appearing in the newsletter, listed eleven attributes associated with responsible charge. This was, and continues to be, a document of enormous importance. It provides guidelines for the registrant who might be tempted to stretch the envelope or who is earnestly searching for the right mix. It has aided the board in evaluating whether responsible charge was being exercised. It is as applicable today, as it was the day it was written.

Ray Anders was appointed to the board by Governor James Martin, replacing Ronald Carpenter. He would go on to serve almost ten and one-half years with distinction.

The Standards of Practice were written into the board rules in 1989, replacing the old Manual of Practice. This was a significant event in the history of the board. These standards would be strictly enforced. These standards, together with a rise in the maximum civil penalty the board could impose (from $500.00 to $2,000.00), put some teeth into the law.

R. Larry Greene began his first term of service on the North Carolina Board of Registration for Professional Engineers and Land Surveyors on January 1, 1989, after being appointed by Governor James Martin.

Big events happened at the National Council of Engineering Examiners level as well. The National Council is made up of seventy jurisdictional boards from the fifty states and five territories. Much significant work goes on at this level, not the least of which is the preparation of examinations for engineers and surveyors. After much debate over a period of years, the name of the organization was changed to the National Council of Examiners for Engineering and Surveying (NCEES). On the surface, this may seem cosmetic, but NCEES has since moved from being primarily an engineers' organization to one of equality between surveyors and engineers.

Global positioning system (GPS) surveys were addressed in the Standards of Practice for the first time in 1990, joining topography as a recognized function of surveying. This was the beginning of a trend to recognize other disciplines of land surveying besides boundary creation, retracement, and geodetic surveying.

The volume of complaints against registrants rose to such a level that a second investigator position was added to the board staff in 1990. Louis Buonpane was hired to fill that position. Also, in that year, Geraldine A. Overby was appointed to the board as a public member but resigned before the first meeting took place. Helen Merritt was appointed to fill her unexpired term, and served for a number of years as a valued member of the surveying committee.

Bobby Long, RLS, was reappointed to a second term beginning January 1, 1991, after serving as chairman for 1990.

The board became more pro-active at that time, occasionally initiating its own investigations, instead of waiting for charges to be filed by someone. One such investigation saw the board hire a consultant to inspect three randomly selected subdivisions in the Charlotte area to determine if all corners had been monumented as required by the Standards of Practice. Charlotte was not singled out without a valid reason. Allegations had been made to the board on a number of occasions that plats of subdivisions were being recorded in Mecklenburg County, showing that all corners had been set, as required by law, when, in fact, they had not been. Of the three subdivisions inspected, two were found to be in compliance, while one was not. A letter was sent to all surveyors in the Charlotte area cautioning them to be certain that they met all the requirements of the Standards of Practice, and particularly reminding them to monument all corners. This letter was reproduced in the newsletter so that all surveyors in the state were made aware of the board's pro-active nature. A program was also initiated, about this time, to have the investigators visit all Register of Deeds offices and Planning Departments in the state over a period of time to check for compliance with board rules.

Loan surveys had been, and continued to be, a source of concern for the board. Periodically, over the years, including 1991, an article was reprinted that emphatically emphasized the ruling that a loan survey was to be a complete survey in every way, no less carefully conducted than the most complicated boundary survey.

Montgomery T. Speir, known to all as "Monty," announced that he would retire on December 31, 1991, after fifteen years as executive secretary of the board. A committee screened candidates for the position from over a hundred applications. Many of these applications were from highly qualified individuals. When all was said and done, the committee felt, and the full board agreed, that Jerry Carter, who had filled the positions of chief investigator and assistant executive director, was the most qualified candidate. Jerry became the new executive secretary on January 1, 1992. This was a decision the board has never regretted. Like Mr. Speir before him, Jerry Carter is a man of utmost ability and utter integrity. The board has fared well under his leadership.

Before leaving 1991, it should be noted that GS 47-30 (the Mapping Law), as rewritten, was enacted into law, and became effective in March of that year. At the end of that year, the board began a study on mandatory continuing education. This was an idea whose time had come, but in 1992, was far from a sure thing. Larry Greene was appointed chairman of a board committee to study continuing professional competency and to make recommendations to the full board. At the outset, the notion had the outright support of one engineer, one land surveyor and one public member. All board members were open-minded people, who were willing to listen to arguments pro and con. Eventually, all came to support the concept.

The 1993 renewals went out with a different twist than usual. Included was a simple test on board rules that had to be successfully completed and sent in with renewal applications. A second requirement was for the registrant to place his or her seal on the renewal form. Almost everyone passed the test, but many engineers had never obtained a seal because they were not required to use it in their particular job. Again, almost everyone complied, but the seal works were kept hopping filling all the new orders.

The board developed guidelines for continuing professional competency in 1993, and scheduled hearings. R. Larry Greene was elected chairman of the board, and Ray Anders was reappointed to a second five-year term, which began on January 1, 1993. The principles and practices examination was again changed that year. The colonial states exam was dropped and the national exam was expanded to six hours. The state specific exam went from one hour to two hours.

In 1994, Larry Greene began his second term, becoming the first member to be appointed once by the governor of one political party, and the second time by the governor of the other party. He would not be the last, however. Governor James Hunt made several appointments to the board from members of the other party over the next few years.

Firm registration practices started in 1994. Previously, only corporations had to be registered with the board. This made it extremely difficult to trace the activities of a business should the need arise. Continuing professional competency took effect, the board hired its own full-time attorney, David Tuttle, and discussions began on the registration of photogrammetrists as surveyors. All in all, 1994 was a very eventful year.

In 1995, Jo Robinson, who had been Director of Administrative Services, retired after twenty-five years of service. To many people, Jo was the board. She dealt with everyone: board members, staff, and the public, with a quiet and dignified respect that invited the same treatment in return. She was a true asset to the board.

In 1995, the State Bureau of Investigation (SBI), assisted board investigators with two investigations; one dealing with a non-registrant, and one dealing with an individual who had obtained a fraudulent registration in another state and was attempting to practice in North Carolina. Together, the board and the SBI conducted a sting operation to catch the fraudulent "engineer," and he ended up spending several months in jail.

Land Information System/Geographic Information System (LIS/GIS) requirements were added to the Standards of Practice and the board issued a ruling that seals and signatures had to be removed before electronically transmitting a drawing. A statement to be inserted in place of the removed signature and seal was approved and published in the board newsletter.

The board went online in 1996 under the able leadership of Ray Anders, who spent countless hours aiding in the upgrading of the board's computer system. You might say Mr. Anders conducted the board into the 1990s. In other developments, Kenneth D. Suttles was appointed to the board, replacing Bobby Long.

More changes were made to the Mapping Law in 1997, but they were not initiated by surveyors or by the board. The Register of Deeds Association pushed for, and was successful in passing, amendments deleting the notary seal. This created the position of review officer in each county, to review plats submitted for recording to insure compliance with certain requirements of the Mapping Law.

In the history of the board, the most important changes to GS 89-C were enacted in 1998. Not since the original bill was passed in 1921, had legislation been passed that was so significant.

Among the more important changes were:

1. Photogrammetry became a discipline of land surveying. Photogrammetrists would initially be grandfathered in, but in the future, they would have to pass the national examinations all surveyors take, plus a state specific photogrammetry examination.
2. LIS/GIS functions were added to the list of activities which could be performed only by a land surveyor.
3. The Board of Registration became the Board of Examiners for Engineers and Surveyors.
4. Registered land surveyors became professional land surveyors.
5. Registrants became licensed professionals.
6. The definition of land surveying was rewritten to include photogrammetry, as well as the new technologies of LIS/GIS.

R. Larry Greene served a second term as chairman of the board that year, C. Phil Wagoner was appointed to replace Ray Anders, who retired, and Doris Rogers, public member, became a member of the Surveying Committee after replacing Helen Merritt, who resigned because of a move out-of-state.

The end of 1998 saw the assembling of a task force drawn from across the state and nation to address the issues of grandfathering of photogrammetrists, writing a Standards of Practice for photogrammetry and defining the surveyor's role in LIS/GIS. This task force met in 1999, with Larry Greene chairing the two meetings and all land surveying committee members taking part. The task force developed a comprehensive statement on LIS/GIS and produced a proposed set of standards for photogrammetry. William Owen replaced Larry Greene on the board in late April, and approximately fifty new surveyors were added from the field of photogrammetry before the July 1 deadline.

In the December issue of the North Carolina Bulletin, a publication of the board; George Freeman, PE, PLS, chairman of the Continuing Professional Competency Committee, expressed concern over some of the "marginally or questionable" courses being offered. Apparently, the board may be moving toward a core course requirement, something the surveyors have supported all along.

In 1999, the presidency of NCEES went to a North Carolina board member, J. Richard Cottingham, PE, PLS. While chosen in 1999, Dick actually assumed office in August 2000. Emeritus member, R. Larry Greene, received the Distinguished Service Award by NCEES, after being nominated by the North Carolina Board of Examiners for Engineers and Surveyors. He was recognized principally for his work in the area of professionalism and ethics.

The year 2000 brought changes to the rules of professional conduct. Some of these changes simply involved updating the language, but others dealt with matters of substance. They provided a clearer picture of what constituted indiscriminate criticism of a fellow professional, and added language concerning prohibitions against fee bidding on public projects. They also provided for the appointment of a consultant to the Review Committee in cases where an active board member is involved as a complainant, witness, or respondent.

Johnie C. Garrason, PLS, was appointed in March of 2001 to a seat on the board by Governor Easley. Johnie replaced Kenneth Suttles whose term expired at the close of the year 2000.

Board Chairman George E. Freeman expressed further concern about core courses as a part of a continuing education regime. The board began to attend and monitor more courses with an eye toward determining the suitability of content, sponsoring, monitoring procedures, and other possible problem areas.

Jerry Carter, long-time board employee and executive director of the board, resigned to accept a position with NCEES. Mr. Andrew Ritter, a former head of investigations for the board and current executive director of the Mortuary Board, was hired to replace him.

Toward the close of 2001, Glen Haynes, of Asheville, was appointed to fill the unexpired term of C. Phil Wagoner who had resigned earlier in the year. George Freeman, PE, PLS, was appointed for a second term.

Board member William C. "Bill" Owen, PLS, became board chairman on January 1, 2002, replacing George Freeman, PE, PLS, who had served ably in 2001. In his "View from the Chair" article in October of 2002, he announced that the Surveying Committee was preparing a rewrite of the licensure requirements for land surveyors to include a bachelor of science degree in surveying. This rewrite would, of course, have to be introduced and passed by the North Carolina General Assembly and signed into law by the governor before becoming effective.

Henry V. Liles, Jr., PE, was elected chairman of the board for the year 2003, with David Peeler, PE, vice chairman and J. Glenn Haynes, PLS, secretary. At the February board meeting, the board endorsed the development and implementation of a bachelor of science in surveying program. At the March board meeting, the board provided a $45,000 grant to North Carolina A&T University to help establish and develop a four-year degree program at that university.

The April exam for 2003 announced the following results:

*fundamentals of engineering	60% pass rate
*fundamentals of surveying	38% pass rate
*principles and practices of engineering	53% pass rate
*principles and practices of land surveying:	
Part A	56% pass rate

Part B	82% pass rate
Part C (state portion)	27% pass rate

These results are fairly typical, and are mentioned here because they seem to indicate several things:

1. The lack of education (degree) probably is the greatest drawback to passing the fundamentals exam for the land surveyor applicants.
2. The more qualified (i.e. educated) candidates, who take the principles and practices exam (they have already passed fundamentals), perform quite well on the national part of that exam (Parts A & B).
3. Drainage is still tripping up the majority of the applicants taking Part C.

A four-year degree requirement would certainly go a long way toward solving this problem. It would give candidates a more realistic chance to realize their dream of becoming professional land surveyors, and it would give the public better protection by providing totally qualified land surveyors to serve their needs.

While this chapter is a history of the board, if this history is to continue on a positive note for land surveyors, it is probably imperative they join all other professionals in the requirement of a four-year degree.

PART III

The Electronic Age of Surveying

North Carolina Geodetic Survey
The First State Agency Dedicated to the Coordinate System

Gary W. Thompson, PLS
NCGS CHIEF

The State Coordinate System was initiated by two North Carolina State Highway Engineers: George F. Syme, senior highway engineer; and O. B. Bester, engineer for Permanent Surveys and Records. In early 1932, they presented their idea to the U. S. Coast and Geodetic Survey. By 1933, the U.S. Department of Commerce, at the insistence of the U.S. Coast and Geodetic Survey, adopted the State Plane Coordinate System for all of the forty-eight states.

In 1939, House Bill 603 became Chapter 163, adopting the North Carolina Coordinate System, designating the administrative agency for the system and defining the powers and duties of the agency. The Department of Conservation and Development was named as the administrative agency, but no appropriate division was set up at that time.

By 1958, a group of professional engineers realized the need for more accurate surveys. They wrote a bill for the legislature, which led to an agency being set up for the establishment of needed control. This led to the passage of Senate Bill 66 in 1959, and the amendment of General Statute 102, establishing the Geodetic Survey Agency. North Carolina became the first state to have an agency dedicated to providing high order geodetic surveys within the national control network for general usage on a statewide scale. The agency was created "to make, or cause to be made, from time to time, such surveys and computations as are necessary to further, or complete, the North Carolina Coordinate System."

In July of 1960, the agency was activated under the Department of Conservation and Development. A first duty of the agency was to make county maps for each of the one hundred counties showing the location of all first and second order U.S. Coast and Geodetic Survey triangulation stations. Maps were created and sent, along with descriptions of the stations, to each of the Register of Deeds in each county, as set forth in Chapter 102, Section 12.

The director of the new agency, Philip C. Doran, was a retired captain from the U.S. Coast and Geodetic Survey. He had the technical experience and management skills needed to make a successful beginning for the agency. He was followed in 1965, by his assistant, Wilbur C. Fuller, who desired to expand the network across the state as much as possible. The department name changed from "Conservation and Development" to "Natural and Economic Resources"; to "Natural Resources and Community Development"; and later to "Environment, Health, and Natural Resources." However, "Geodetic Survey" remained intact. It has always been a small agency of only around twenty-two positions (field and office personnel).

According to the statute, "all monuments established shall be in conformity with the standards adopted by the Coast and Geodetic Survey for first and second order work." The agency's work was accepted for final adjustment and inclusion in the National Network as long as it met the accuracy requirements. By using this standard, any survey properly tied to the markers can be re-established exactly as the original.

The agency's first surveys depended on a series of backsights and foresights from some known position to another known position. The sophisticated equipment and procedures helped to ensure the accuracy of the surveys. Citizens often questioned the agency's work, much of which was done at night. The angle observations were done after sundown using a theodolite. Also, Polaris observations were done on every fifteen or more stations.

Until the 1970s, the agency only established "horizontal" control, meaning the results of the surveys were precisely positioned markers for latitude and longitude, or "x and y" information. "Vertical" control surveys were begun to establish elevation above sea level for existing marks or for new bench marks established within counties.

Larry W. Akers assumed command from 1976 until 1994. He was dedicated to the basic policy as previously stated by Captain Doran: "We stand ready to consult with any community, engineer, surveyor, or individual about surveying matters and to furnish the basic geodetic data which exists throughout North Carolina." He followed the lead of Mr. Fuller in the densification of control throughout the state. Also, he realized the importance of sharing the data with the users and maintaining existing control within counties that were rapidly developing. During his tenure, cooperative agreements were signed between North Carolina Geodetic Survey and the National Geodetic Survey. This was to ensure that existing monuments be maintained and that information about monuments be provided to users as needed.

A computer database of geodetic control for North Carolina was set up around 1987 and 1988. Randy Dillard, an in-house programmer, set up a program called "SEARCH," to access data by station name and county as information to be provided for users. This advancement enabled users to purchase maps of entire counties, if needed, on computer disks. With the Internet, Geodetic Survey has established a website including SEARCHER, and the maps of counties to allow on-line searching for control.

In the late 1980s, a revolution in surveying methods occurred. With the development and use of Global Positioning Systems (GPS) technology, the surveying world changed forever. No longer do points in a survey have to be intervisible. Using receivers to gather satellite signals, correction factors, and programs designed to interpret and calculate the data, monuments can now be established in any area that has accessibility and clear visibility.

Since 1994, I have led the Geodetic Survey. The agency is now under the Office of State Planning within the Office of the Governor. The Raleigh headquarters office is located in the Elks Building at 121 West Jones Street. There are currently field offices in Asheville,

Mooresville, Washington, and Morehead City. The Morehead City office specializes in estuary surveys, adding another dimension to the agency.

I, as NCGS Chief, am active in North Carolina and the United States in extending GPS education opportunities to surveyors and engineers on new methods and procedures. My hope for North Carolina is for us to continue being a leader in the field of geodetic surveying.

North Carolina Geodetic Survey 1959–2002

Curt D. Johnson, NCGS Technicial Writer

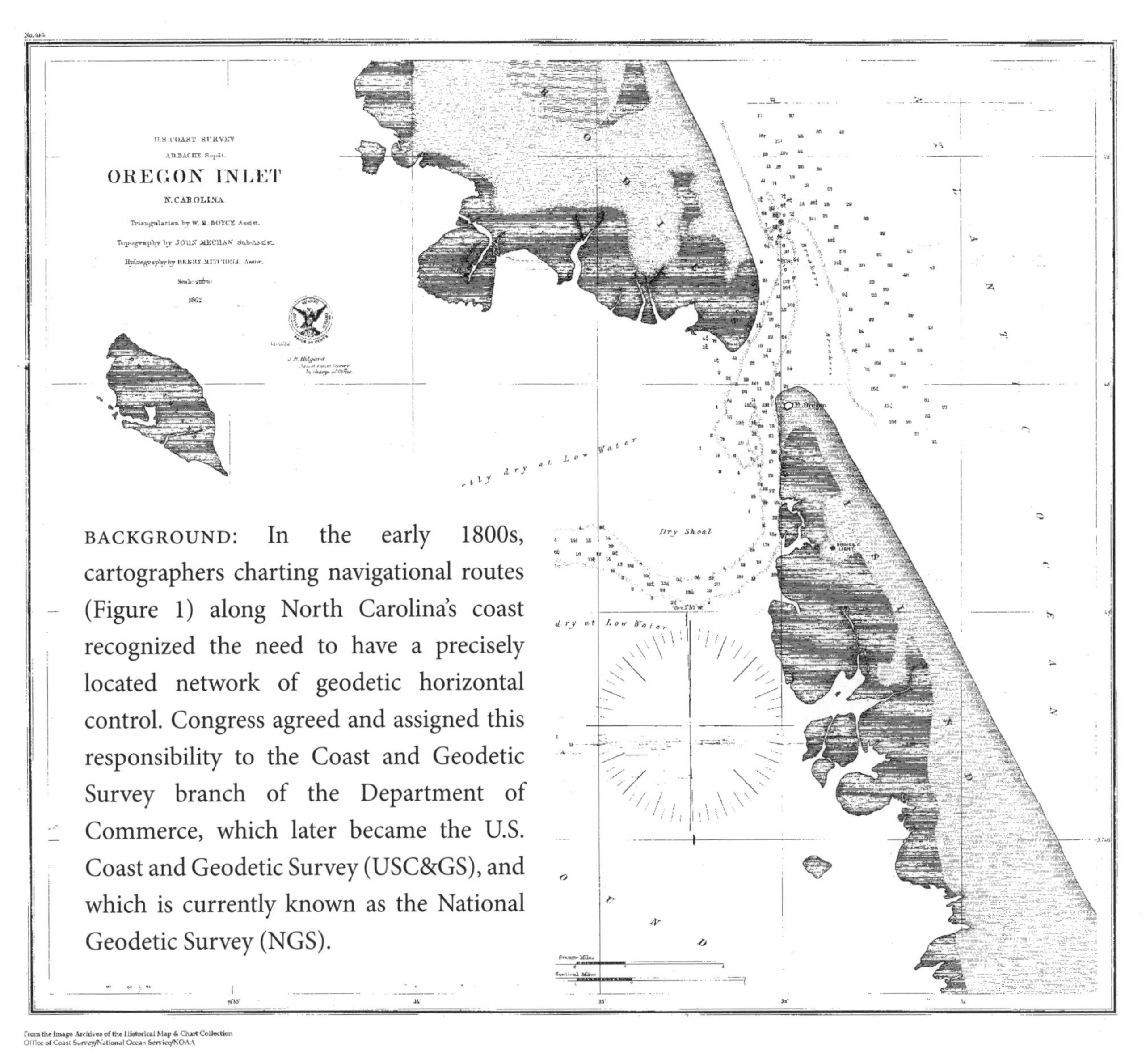

BACKGROUND: In the early 1800s, cartographers charting navigational routes (Figure 1) along North Carolina's coast recognized the need to have a precisely located network of geodetic horizontal control. Congress agreed and assigned this responsibility to the Coast and Geodetic Survey branch of the Department of Commerce, which later became the U.S. Coast and Geodetic Survey (USC&GS), and which is currently known as the National Geodetic Survey (NGS).

From the Image Archives of the Historical Map & Chart Collection
Office of Coast Survey/National Ocean Service/NOAA

FIGURE 1. *An 1860 U.S. Coast and Geodetic Survey nautical chart of Oregon Inlet, North Carolina (Image source: National Oceanic and Atmospheric Administration Office of Coast Survey).*

FIRST HORIZONTAL CONTROL MONUMENT: In 1849, the Coast and Geodetic Survey established the first geodetic horizontal control monument in North Carolina and named it, "BODIE ISLAND NORTH BASE" (Figure 2). Today, the mark is still in good condition. As with most other monuments in the 1800s and early 1900s, the Coast and Geodetic Survey utilized triangulation to establish this monument's horizontal control. Although these early monuments were beneficial to cartographers, the monuments were too far apart to be used by local surveyors.

The NGS Data Sheet

```
EX0456 ***********************************************************************
EX0456  DESIGNATION -  BODIE ISLAND NORTH BASE
EX0456  PID         -  EX0456
EX0456  STATE/COUNTY-  NC/DARE
EX0456  USGS QUAD   -  ROANOKE ISLAND NE (1983)
EX0456
EX0456                         *CURRENT SURVEY CONTROL
EX0456
EX0456* NAD 83(1986)-  35 53 57.55300(N)    075 35 51.23026(W)    ADJUSTED
EX0456* NAVD 88     -          0.9    (meters)       3.     (feet) VERTCON
EX0456
EX0456  LAPLACE CORR-          0.67  (seconds)                     DEFLEC99
EX0456  GEOID HEIGHT-        -38.99  (meters)                      GEOID99
EX0456
EX0456  HORZ ORDER  -  SECOND
EX0456
EX0456;                    North         East     Units   Scale      Converg.
EX0456;SPC NC       -   243,693.206   916,687.173   MT  0.99993634 +1 57 49.6
EX0456;UTM  18      - 3,972,946.588   446,074.300   MT  0.99963583 -0 21 01.4
```

FIGURE 2. *The first geodetic control station established in North Carolina, "BODIE ISLAND NORTH BASE" as described on its NGS Data Sheet (Image source: National Geodetic Survey) and presented on the NCGS control map for Dare County (Image source: North Carolina Geodetic Survey).*

FIGURE 3. *A high Bilby tower (circa 1930s) built over ground stations from 1 to 20 miles apart by the U.S. Coast and Geodetic Survey (USC&GS) (Image source: National Oceanic and Atmospheric Administration Photo Library).*

WORKS PROGRESS ADMINISTRATION: By the 1930s, the Coast and Geodetic Survey had been renamed USC&GS and was establishing most of the horizontal control monuments set in the United States utilizing triangulation and high Bilby towers (Figure 3). Another Federal agency that set marks during this time was the Depression era Works Progress Administration (WPA). During the Depression, the U.S. Congress sought to utilize the unemployed workforce of the WPA to increase the density of the horizontal control monuments throughout the U.S. beyond what could be established by the USC&GS alone.

Unfortunately, these WPA workers-turned-surveyors were not properly trained in surveying. Some workers received only limited training in surveying and others received no training. Therefore, these novice surveyors could not conduct triangulation with high bilby towers, but only low accuracy transit and tape traverse surveys. Furthermore, electronic distance meters (EDMs) had not yet been developed.

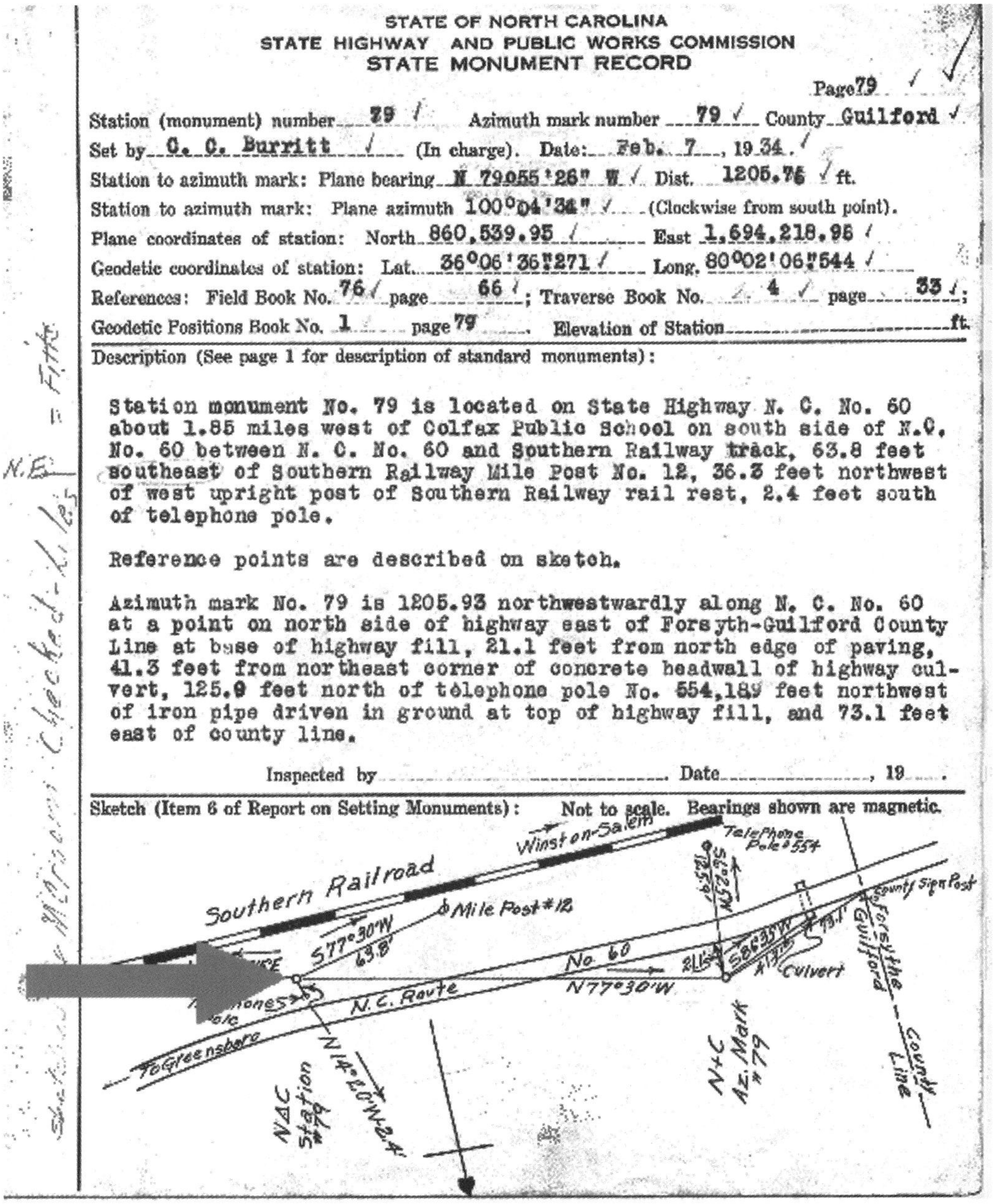

STATE OF NORTH CAROLINA
STATE HIGHWAY AND PUBLIC WORKS COMMISSION
STATE MONUMENT RECORD

Page 79

Station (monument) number 79 Azimuth mark number 79 County Guilford
Set by C. C. Burritt (In charge). Date: Feb. 7, 1934.
Station to azimuth mark: Plane bearing N 79°55'26" W Dist. 1205.76 ft.
Station to azimuth mark: Plane azimuth 100°04'34" (Clockwise from south point).
Plane coordinates of station: North 860,539.95 East 1,694,218.95
Geodetic coordinates of station: Lat. 36°06'36".271 Long. 80°02'06".544
References: Field Book No. 76 page 66; Traverse Book No. 4 page 33;
Geodetic Positions Book No. 1 page 79 Elevation of Station ft.

Description (See page 1 for description of standard monuments):

Station monument No. 79 is located on State Highway N. C. No. 60 about 1.85 miles west of Colfax Public School on south side of N.C. No. 60 between N. C. No. 60 and Southern Railway track, 63.8 feet southeast of Southern Railway Mile Post No. 12, 36.3 feet northwest of west upright post of Southern Railway rail rest, 2.4 feet south of telephone pole.

Reference points are described on sketch.

Azimuth mark No. 79 is 1205.93 northwestwardly along N. C. No. 60 at a point on north side of highway east of Forsyth-Guilford County Line at base of highway fill, 21.1 feet from north edge of paving, 41.3 feet from northeast corner of concrete headwall of highway culvert, 125.9 feet north of telephone pole No. 554, 189 feet northwest of iron pipe driven in ground at top of highway fill, and 73.1 feet east of county line.

Inspected by Date , 19 .

Sketch (Item 6 of Report on Setting Monuments): Not to scale. Bearings shown are magnetic.

Southern Railroad
Winston-Salem
Mile Post #12
No. 60
N.C. Route
To Greensboro
Culvert
Forsyth - Guilford County Line
N&C Az. Mark #79
N&C Station #79

FIGURE 4. *The State Monument Record for monument "79", which was established by a Works Progress Administration (WPA) survey crew in 1934 (Image source: North Carolina Geodetic Survey).*

As a consequence of the training and techniques, WPA's survey work lacked accuracy and volume. In addition, not all of the WPA monuments were actually positioned. The program was disbanded shortly after it began.

Interestingly, some of the WPA monuments established in North Carolina can still be found. These monuments can be located from their original typed descriptions (Figure 4), which are on file at the North Carolina Geodetic Survey in Raleigh.

STATE PLANE COORDINATE SYSTEM: Despite the short-lived WPA surveying program, the 1930s were important to the advancement of land surveying with the development of the state coordinate system, which is now utilized in all 50 states. Interestingly, this coordinate system was initiated by two North Carolina State Highway Engineers: Mr. George F. Syme (senior highway engineer) and Mr. O.B. Bester (engineer for permanent surveys and records). In 1932, these two engineers presented the idea to the USC&GS that a state grid system would eliminate the large amount of computations needed to make accurate surveys of large areas. The USC&GS further developed this idea by creating a State Plane Coordinate System for not just North Carolina, but for each of the then 48 states. The resulting collection of State Plane Coordinate Systems was so well conceived that the U.S. Department of Commerce, at the insistence of the USC&GS, adopted the State Plane Coordinate System for each state in 1933.

In 1939, the North Carolina General Assembly adopted the "North Carolina Coordinate System" as the State's official survey base with the passage of House Bill 603, which became Chapter 163 as described in North Carolina General Statute (GS) 102-1 (http: //www.ncga.state.nc.us/statutes/generalstatutes/html/bychapter/chapter%5F102.html). This legislation defined the duties and powers of a geodetic survey agency (GS 102-9) and designated the Department of Conservation and Development as the administrative agency (GS 102-8). However, the legislation did not define a division for the agency and thus the intended agency was not established.

The Birth of the North Carolina Geodetic Survey

In 1958, a group of professional surveyors and engineers in North Carolina submitted a bill to the North Carolina General Assembly proposing that the State of North Carolina establish an agency to provide geodetic control in the state. This grass-roots effort led to passage of Senate Bill 66 in 1959 and the resulting amendment of General Statute 102, which established the Geodetic Survey Division under the Department of Conservation and Development in July 1960. Consequently, North Carolina became the first state to have an agency dedicated to providing high order geodetic surveys within the national control network for general usage on a statewide scale. Although this agency was defined in the legislation as the 'Geodetic Survey Division', it has always been referred to as the 'North Carolina Geodetic Survey' (NCGS).

NCGS was mandated (GS102-9) "*...to make or cause to be made from time to time such surveys and computations as are necessary to further or complete the North Carolina Coordinate System. The agency shall endeavor to carry to completion as soon as practicable the field monumentation and office computations of the coordinate system.*"

The Agency's First Chief, Philip C. Doran

The first chief of NCGS was Captain Philip C. Doran (Figure 5), who brought over 33 years of leadership and technical experience from the USC&GS. His career with the USC&GS began on a leveling party in northern Minnesota in 1923 and ended as Chief of the Geodesy Division in Washington, DC in 1956. During those years, Captain Doran "surveyed the world" with hydrographic surveying operations along the Gulf coast, Alaskan coast, and the coasts of the Philippine islands; through military service in the U.S. Army Air Force during World War II in Canada, South America, and China; and via liaison duty with the Inter-American Geodetic Survey in South America.

FIGURE 5. *The first Geodetic Survey Division chief, Captain Phillip Doran, while on a USC&GS hydrographic operation in the Philippines in 1932 (Image source: National Oceanic and Atmospheric Administration Photo Library).*

Captain Doran's tenure with NCGS (1960 – 1965) established the agency not only as a technical service to surveyors, but also as the premier state geodetic control agency serving the public.

GEODETIC CONTROL MAPS: As the first chief of NCGS, Captain Doran had no time to gradually build the agency, but was under pressure to complete a state-wide mapping project before July 1, 1962. This project was to produce a geodetic control map for each of the state's 100 counties showing the location of all first and second order U.S. Coast and Geodetic Survey triangulation stations. Remarkably in less than two years, these county maps and their respective set of station descriptions were sent to the Register of Deeds in each county.

BENEFITS OF GEODETIC CONTROL: Captain Doran understood how geodetic control benefited the people of North Carolina and conveyed this importance to the public. He explained that as the geodetic monuments "*...are established, they will furnish the basic framework for all engineering projects whether they be laying out city boundaries, county lines, State boundaries, hydroelectric projects, highways, dams, railroads, sewer systems, water systems, drainage systems, topographic maps, State maps, sub-divisions, park boundaries, forest boundaries, farm acreage, or individiually owned property lines.*"

APPLICATION CATEGORIES: Captain Doran classified the applications of the agency's service into the following three categories: public works, private and industrial development, and certainty of ownership. As to public works, Doran stated, "*...it is recognized that all public works must be preceded by surveys to gather information about the land and that this information is usually presented in a most compact way upon maps.*" He explained that the efficiency and speed "*...of performing these preliminary surveys is a major factor in the final cost of such public works...*", and that this "*efficiency with which such preconstruction surveys can be made is very decidedly a function of the availability of accurate preexisting surveys and maps.*"

Private and industrial development benefits of geodetic control, as explained by Captain Doran, related to the managerial decisions that commit large amounts of capital. Therefore, "*If a State is to experience vigorous industrial development...*", stated Captain Doran, "*...it must provide adequate knowledge about the land upon which can be based bold and sound managerial decisions.*"

As to the certainty of ownership benefits from geodetic control, Captain Doran explained this concept by its absence with, "*Uncertainty in the location of land boundaries eats at the core of business confidence and slows private development.*" Therefore, as North Carolina's population grows and the land becomes more extensively used, there will be an increased need for certainty in ownership of land.

TECHNOLOGY: The circumstances of geodetic technology during Captain Doran's tenure required that most distances be measured at night. During the 1960s and the 1970s, the long-range distance measuring instrument called a "Geodimeter™" (Figure 6) was compromised by heat waves reflected from the ground during the day. Thus, distances could only be measured with these instruments during periods of darkness.

FIGURE 6. *GeodimetersTM (distance measuring instruments) used by NCGS in the 1960s and 1970s. Left image: NCGS surveyors, Doug Felts and Durwood Barbour, shown using a GeodimeterTM in Raleigh, North Carolina (Image source: North Carolina Geodetic Survey). Right image: NCGS surveyor, Doug Felts, shown looking at a GeodimeterTM next to a bank of prisms (Image source: North Carolina Geodetic Survey).*

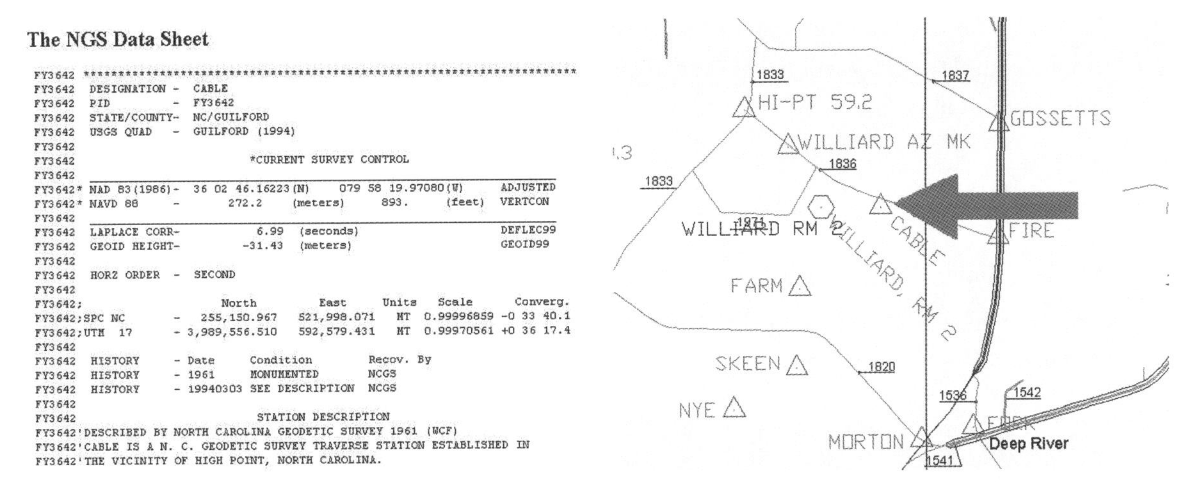

The NGS Data Sheet

```
FY3642 ***********************************************************************
FY3642  DESIGNATION -  CABLE
FY3642  PID         -  FY3642
FY3642  STATE/COUNTY-  NC/GUILFORD
FY3642  USGS QUAD   -  GUILFORD (1994)
FY3642
FY3642                         *CURRENT SURVEY CONTROL
FY3642  ___________________________________________________________________
FY3642* NAD 83(1986)-  36 02 46.16223(N)    079 58 19.97080(W)     ADJUSTED
FY3642* NAVD 88     -       272.2    (meters)     893.      (feet)  VERTCON
FY3642  ___________________________________________________________________
FY3642  LAPLACE CORR-           6.99  (seconds)                     DEFLEC99
FY3642  GEOID HEIGHT-         -31.43  (meters)                      GEOID99
FY3642
FY3642  HORZ ORDER  -  SECOND
FY3642
FY3642;                   North         East     Units  Scale      Converg.
FY3642;SPC NC       -   255,150.967  521,998.071   MT  0.99996859 -0 33 40.1
FY3642;UTM  17      - 3,989,556.510  592,579.431   MT  0.99970561 +0 36 17.4
FY3642
FY3642  HISTORY     - Date     Condition        Recov. By
FY3642  HISTORY     - 1961     MONUMENTED       NCGS
FY3642  HISTORY     - 19940303 SEE DESCRIPTION  NCGS
FY3642
FY3642                          STATION DESCRIPTION
FY3642'DESCRIBED BY NORTH CAROLINA GEODETIC SURVEY 1961 (WCF)
FY3642'CABLE IS A N. C. GEODETIC SURVEY TRAVERSE STATION ESTABLISHED IN
FY3642'THE VICINITY OF HIGH POINT, NORTH CAROLINA.
```


Figure 7. *One of the first horizontal monuments established by the North Carolina Geodetic Survey station "CABLE" as displayed on its NGS data sheet (Image source: National Geodetic Survey) and shown on the NCGS geodetic control map for Guilford County (Image source: North Carolina Geodetic Survey).*

FIRST HORIZONTAL CONTROL PROJECT: Captain Doran did not thrust the agency's surveyors into the first surveying project without practicing night observations. He established a test site in Raleigh where NCGS had set marks along Creedmoor Road. Once the surveyors were proficient with working in the dark with geodimeters™ and theodolites, they began their first project in the vicinity of High Point setting their first horizontal control monuments. Twenty stations were set in that first project including station "CABLE" (Figure 7).

The instruments used in the High Point project included a Geodimeter™ Model 4 to measure distances. NCGS surveyors measured horizontal and vertical angles using three different theodolite models: Kern DKM3, Wild T-2, and a Wild T-3 (Figure 8).

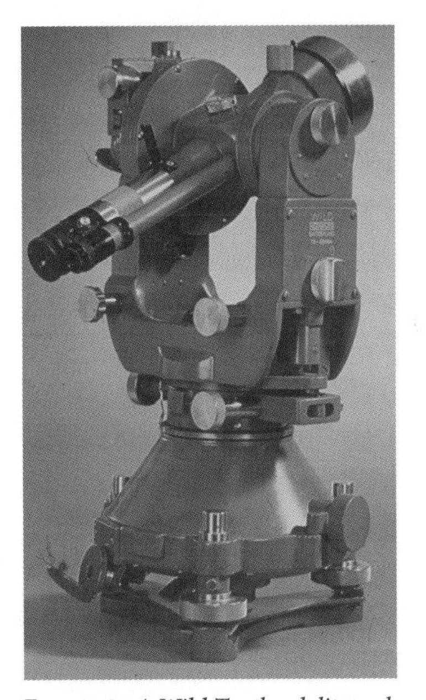

Figure 8. *A Wild T-3 theodolite such as one used by NCGS to measure horizontal and vertical angles during the 1960s (Image source: National Oceanic and Atmospheric Administration Photo Library).*

SMALL AGENCY LIMITATIONS: Throughout the agency's history, NCGS has always remained small being staffed with less than 20 employees. During Captain Doran's tenure, the agency was staffed with only the following ten employees: Wilbur C. Fuller, Helen Brothers, Johnnie Cockrell, David Scott, Charles Scallon, Emory Lashmit, Billy Murray, John Dodson, Doug Felts, Red Harris, and Danny Boykin. As a consequence of having few employees, the agency did not conduct any 1st or 2nd order vertical control projects albeit some lesser order vertical projects were conducted. Yet, there was a great need for accurate vertical control, because the North Carolina Division of Mineral Resources and the U.S. Geological Survey were working together on a topographic mapping project of the state.

The Agency's Second Chief, Wilbur C. Fuller

Wilbur C. Fuller (Figure 9), the former principle assistant to Captain Doran, took over the reins of the agency in 1965 until 1976. His goal was to expand and densify the geodetic network as much as possible.

FIGURE 9. *The agency's second chief, Wilbur C. Fuller (shown front-center) with the NCGS staff. Back row: Dwayne Millard, Fred Seymour, Johnnie Cockrell, Aubrey Darr, Don Satterwhite, and Walker Crump. Middle row: Helen Brothers, John Garner, Wayne Brantley, Sally Jones, and Larry Akers (Note: Larry Akers later became the agency's third chief) (Image source: North Carolina Geodetic Survey).*

GEODETIC NOT GEOLOGICAL: When Mr. Fuller became chief, NCGS was 5-years-old. Unfortunately, the general public was still confusing this agency with the North Carolina's Geological Survey. Although this problem has persisted, the most humorous example of this confusion occurred early in Mr. Fuller's tenure when he received the following letter (Note: The county and the person's name have been omitted):

"Our county does not have a set of rocks for surveyors to set up their instruments by, and I was talking to one of the county commissioners recently and it was difficult for him to see that such a set of rocks would be of much value to the county."

"I would like ever so much for us to have a set in our county and I intend to talk to the county commissioners the first Monday in March to try to get a set."

"Will you please write me a letter telling how useful a set of rocks would be. And if the State furnishes, or where they can be bought."

Unfortunately, the letter writer had to purchase a set of rocks elsewhere. Meanwhile, the agency plunged ahead with more surveying.

FIRST VERTICAL CONTROL PROJECT: In 1971, the agency began its first leveling project in Lenoir, Wayne, and Johnston Counties. Although the agency's survey crews had conducted leveling projects before, this vertical control project was the first project performed to 1st and 2nd order standards of the National Geodetic Survey. At that time, the work was performed with a Wild N-3 geodetic level and Wild invar rods with struts.

TECHNOLOGY: During Mr. Fuller's tenure, the agency saw advances in geodetic technology. One such advance was the laser geodimeter, which could measure distances during the daytime (Note: earlier geodimeter models were limited to night observations). The agency's survey crews used this instrument in 1972 to provide an important role in the building of the state government mall complex north of the Legislative Building. This instrument helped set the geodetic monuments, which were used in the mall's pre-construction survey. Today, these geodetic monuments near the mall complex offer the public an excellent example of applying accurate surveying techniques and instruments to the construction of inspiring public structures.

The Agency's Third Chief, Larry W. Akers

Larry W. Akers (Figure 10) was the agency's third chief from 1976 until 1994. He had previously worked with the United States Geological Survey (USGS) and then started at NCGS as the assistant director during Wilbur Fuller's tenure.

Mr. Akers continued the agency's basic policy, which was formulated by Captain Doran's statement, *"We stand ready to consult with any community, engineer, surveyor or individual about surveying matters and to furnish the basic geodetic data which exists throughout North Carolina."* He continued Mr. Fuller's goal of densifying control throughout the state as well as initiating a more service-oriented approach of providing data to the surveying community and general public. In addition, he sought to maintain existing control within rapidly developing counties. He formalized these new goals for the agency by signing cooperative agreements with the National Geodetic Survey to insure that information on existing monuments be maintained and updated and that this information be provided to users as needed.

FIGURE 10. *The agency's third chief, Larry Akers (Image source: North Carolina Geodetic Survey).*

The advent of desktop computer technology during Mr. Akers' tenure greatly assisted the maintenance and dissemination of information. Previously, information was maintained with typewriters and disseminated by mail or picked-up by the requesting surveyor. In addition, desktop computer technology greatly assisted the computation process, which had previously been conducted by mechanical adding machines and by mainframe computers via keypunch cards.

In 1987, the dissemination of information took a great leap forward with the SEARCH computer program, which was written by the agency's computer programmer, Randy Dillard. This program allowed users to access geodetic data by station name by county. What was even more ingenious was that a users could purchase the database for entire counties and conduct searches on their computers.

TECHNOLOGY: During Larry Akers' tenure, the agency's surveyors were assisted by technological advances in surveying equipment. NCGS purchased its first direct read Electronic Distance Meter (EDM), the "Ranger I", which was made by K&E. This EDM used visible light and could measure distances up to 7 miles. Later, in the early 1980s, the agency purchased a Ranger V. This more advanced model could measure distances up to 17 miles and was purchased for use in western North Carolina. In addition to advances in distance measuring instruments, the agency upgraded its leveling equipment from spirit levels (Wild N-3) to fully automatic levels with compensators (Zeiss Ni-1 and Zeiss Ni-2) and from heavy Wild Invar rods to the light-weight Kern aluminum rods with invar strips.

The greatest advancement in surveying technology used by NCGS surveyors occurred in 1987 when NCGS ended the era of traversing at night to establish horizontal geodetic control and started the era of establishing horizontal geodetic control with the Global Positioning System (GPS). NCGS switched to this satellite-based, U.S. Defense Department (DOD) maintained, navigation system, because GPS surveying greatly reduced the time needed to determine a monument's position and was not restricted by traversing's requirement of setting monuments to be intervisible (i.e. within sight of another monument).

FIRST GPS PROJECT: The first GPS project that NCGS performed was in the vicinity of Murphy, North Carolina. At that time, there were only 8 GPS satellites in orbit, because the DOD had not yet launched all of the planned set of 24 GPS satellites. Consequently, this limited number of satellites in orbit restricted the time when GPS data could be collected to a 3-hour window of observation each day (shown as the hatch period in Figure 11). Because, a GPS receiver requires signals from at least 4 satellites in view (shown in the Nsats graph in Figure 11) that have good satellite geometry (i.e. not orbiting so close to each other as to cause erroneous results). Such cases of poor satellite geometry would be indicated by a high Position Dilution of Precision level (shown as spikes in the PDOP graph in Figure 11). This narrow window of observation was the only drawback of GPS during its formative years (i.e. the late 1980s through early 1990s).

Throughout the history of GPS up to the year 2000, the DOD intentionally degraded the accuracy of GPS signals (timing and satellite positional information) by the process termed "selective availability" to prevent hostile forces from using the system against the U.S. Fortunately, selective availability can be overcome by the process of "differential correction", which involves using two GPS receivers to collect data simultaneously: one receiver (base station) collects data at a known position and the other receiver (rover) collects data at

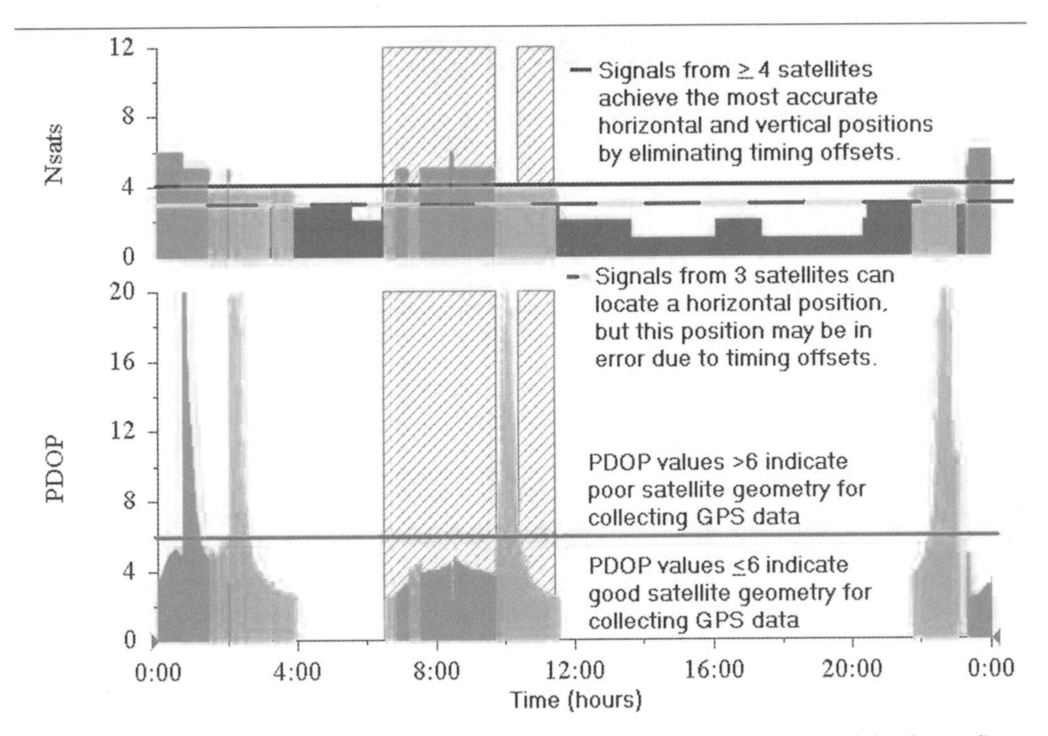

FIGURE 11. *An example of the limited number of hours that a GPS survey could be conducted (hatch period) on a day (time shown on the horizontal axis) in 1990, which was due to having few GPS satellites in orbit. The Nsats graph shows the number of satellites in view (Note: a GPS receiver requires signals from at least 4 satellites). The PDOP graph reports the "Position Dilution of Precision", which is an index of satellite geometry (i.e. how close the satellites are to each other). Lower PDOP values indicate widely spaced satellites that will yield more accurate GPS positions than higher PDOP values (Note: A GPS receiver requires a PDOP value < 6).*

an unknown position. In addition, differential correction also enhances GPS accuracy by reducing atmospheric delay errors.

GPS BASE STATION NETWORK: NCGS realized that it could best assist GPS users by establishing permanent GPS base stations throughout the state that would each continuously collect GPS data at a known position so users could differentially correct their field files. In 1992, NCGS established the NCGS GPS base station network with GPS base stations in Asheville, Raleigh, and Washington. Since then the NCGS GPS base station network

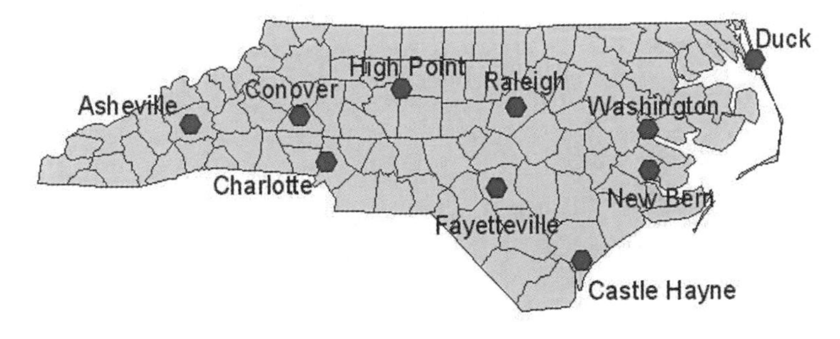

FIGURE 12. *The North Carolina Geodetic Survey GPS base station network in 2002.*

has expanded with federal, municipal and other NCGS operated base stations to include the following additional cities: Castle Hayne, Charlotte, Conover, Duck, Fayetteville, High Point, and New Bern (Figure 12). Moreover, plans are being made to densify this network with 18 additional stations throughout the state.

The Agency's Fourth and Current Chief, Gary W. Thompson

Gary W. Thompson (Figure 13) became the agency's fourth and current chief in 1994. He had previously worked with the United States Forest Service (USFS) as a survey technician in the Uwharrie National Forest and then started at NCGS as a geodetic survey technician during Larry Akers' tenure.

GOALS: Mr. Thompson has dedicated his tenure to four interrelated goals:

- Establishing and maintaining the State Plane Coordinate System
- Resurveying ambiguous and uncertain State and county boundaries
- Expansion of the GPS base station network
- Advancing the use of GPS technology

FIGURE 13. *The agency's fourth and current chief, Gary Thompson (shown back row fourth from the left) with the staff from the Raleigh office. Front row: Roger Barnes, Wayne Brantley, Luretta Jones, Ginger Faircloth, and Bill King. Back row: Bart Alligood, Joe Scott, Steven Kaufman, Gary Thompson, John Garner, and Curt Johnson. NCGS staff not shown include the following: Mark Boothe and James Gay from the Asheville office; Thomas Wolfe from the Mooresville office; Richard Carraway and Loie Priddy from the Morehead City office; Ronald Hall and Billy Lumpkin from the Raleigh office; and Jerome Hollowell and Michael Mobley from the Washington office.*

HARN: In 1995, NCGS utilized GPS to establish the North Carolina High Accuracy Reference Network "HARN", which is a highly accurate and multi-dimensional geodetic control network of monumented stations spaced throughout North Carolina (Figure 14).

This network further establishes and maintains the State Plane Coordinate System, because surveyors establishing a local GPS network can utilize a HARN monument's highly accurate position to enhance the positional accuracy of the local network's respective monuments using vector analysis. In addition, the HARN will supply highly accurate readings of the following:

- Geodetic latitude (angle based on the perpendicular to the ellipsoid)
- Geodetic longitude (angle measured in the XY plane)
- Orthometric height (height above the geoid)
- Ellipsoidal height (height above the ellipsoid)
- Gravity
- Horizontal and vertical crustal motion

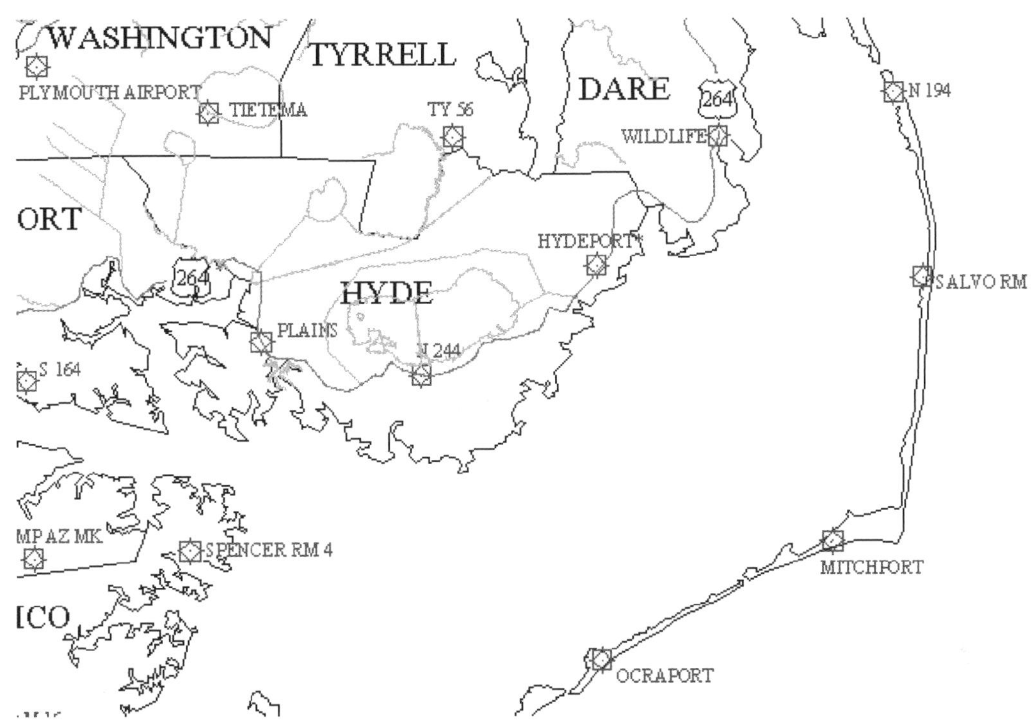

FIGURE 14. *A section of the North Carolina High Accuracy Reference Network (HARN).*
Note: The network encompasses the entire state of North Carolina, but only a section is displayed in this magnified image to emphasize that the network is composed of individual stations.

WEB SITE: In 1997, the agency greatly expanded its ability to disseminate information via our Internet web site (www.ncgs.state.nc.us/) (Figure 15). Users can now access and download such information as monument information from the NCGS database, digital county control maps, GPS base station files for differential correction, and computer software.

North Carolina Geodetic Survey
Division of Land Resources
Department of Environment and Natural Resources

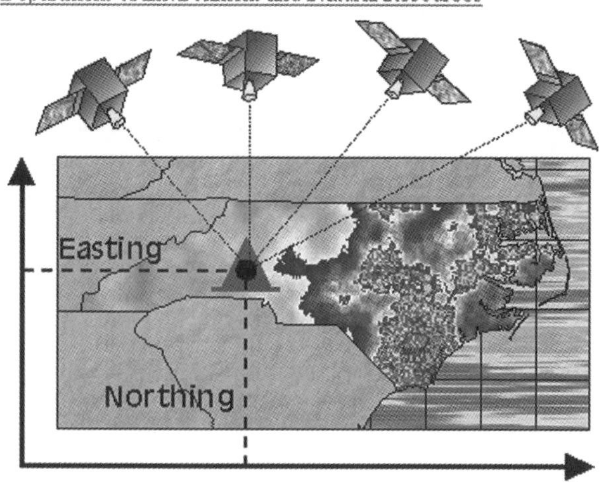

- Mission, Vision and Strategic Goals
- Products and Services
- NCGS Database
- Digital County Maps
- GPS Base Stations
- GPS Projects Map
- HARN Stations Map
- EDM Calibration Baselines
- NCGS FTP Site
- GPS Info Links
- Station Recovery Form NEW

- County & State Boundary Info
- NC Floodplain Mapping Info

National Height Modernization

- NGS Database
- NGS Geodetic Tool Kit
- NGS Software

- ACSM References & Resources
- Federal Geographic Data Committee

FIGURE 15. *The NCGS web site* (www.ncgs.state.nc.us/).

TECHNOLOGY: The agency's surveyors have kept abreast of advances in geodetic technology with the purchase of digital levels and more advanced GPS receivers (Figure 16). Obviously, equipping the agency's survey crews has never been cheap. In the year 2000, digital levels and rods cost $ 15,000 per set and GPS receivers and antennas cost $30,000 per set.

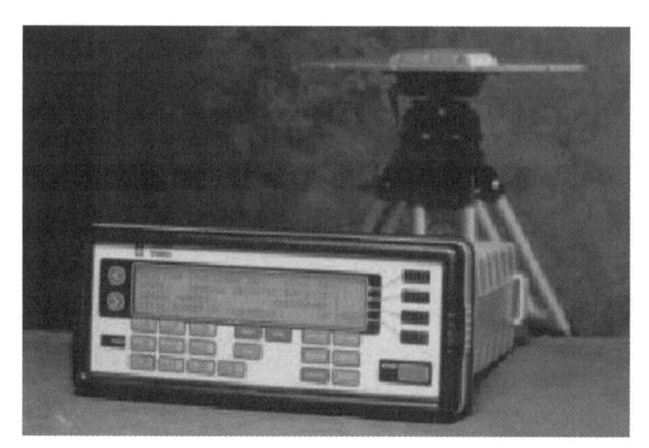

FIGURE 16. *Advanced surveying equipment purchased during the late 1990s. Left image: Zeiss DiNi II digital level, which reads digital invar rods that have UPC type lines as opposed to the traditional numbered lines (Image source: Carl Zeiss, Inc.). Right image: Trimble 4000SSI GPS receiver in the foreground and a tripod mounted, Trimble geodetic antenna with groundplane in the background (Image source: Trimble Navigation Limited).*

STATE AND COUNTY BOUNDARY PROGRAM: In 1999, NCGS started the State and County Boundary program and hired Mr. Rodger Durham as administrator. This program assists the State of North Carolina and North Carolina counties in the resurvey of their ambiguous or uncertain boundaries by contracting private surveyors to recover original boundary monuments and field evidence, perform records research, and refurbish boundaries. The program administrator then presents the resulting information to special county commissioners for boundaries, state boundary commissions, and courts of law. In 2000, Rodger Durham left this program to work for the North Carolina Floodplain Mapping Program and then NCGS hired Mr. Roger Barnes as program administrator in 2001.

The boundary program began its largest project to date with the resurvey of a 27-mile section of the North Carolina/South Carolina State line in the vicinity of Sassafras Mountain (Figure 17). The total length of this border being resurveyed is 54 miles with the State of South Carolina resurveying an adjacent 27-mile section. Both states are contracting this work to private surveying firms in 5-mile subsections.

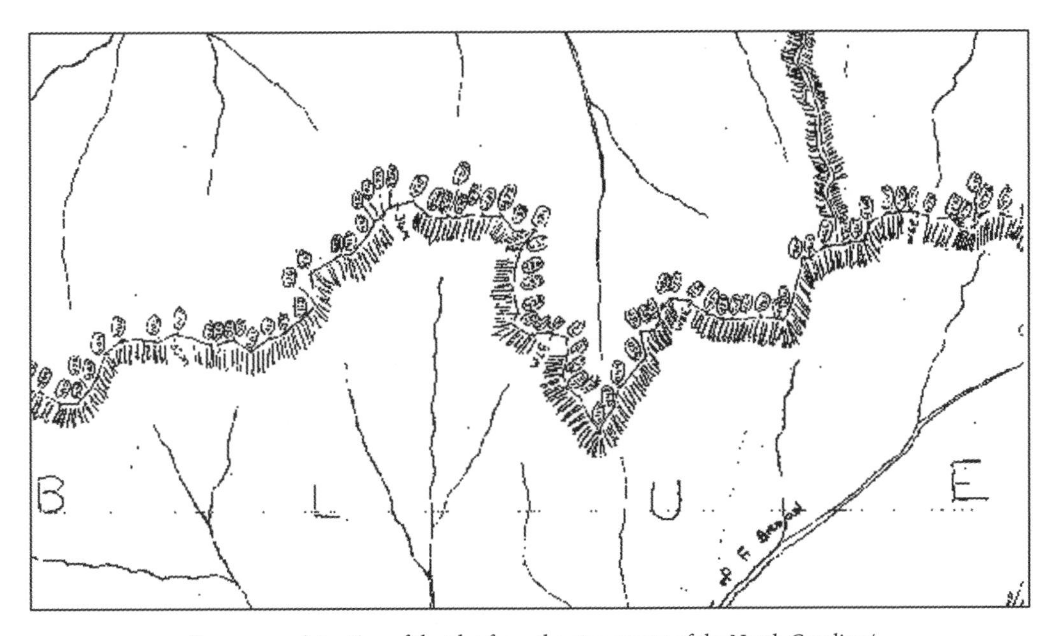

FIGURE 17. *A portion of the plat from the 1815 survey of the North Carolina/ South Carolina State Border near Sassafras Mountain.*

Currently, the resurvey of 40 ambiguous county lines has been requested involving 26 counties. For up-to-date information of the State and County Boundary program, please visit the www.ncgs.state.nc.us/boundary.html web site.

FLOODPLAIN MAPPING PROGRAM: As with people, one test of an agency's merit and expertise is how it takes on a new role. On September 15, 1999, Hurricane Floyd dropped 21 inches of rain upon eastern North Carolina, damaging over 67,000 homes and destroying nearly 8,000 homes. Many of these homes had been built on land that had not been designated as flood prone on the Federal Emergency Management Agency's (FEMA's) Flood Insurance Rate Maps (FIRMs). Furthermore, the subsequent homeowners lacked access to accurate, up-to-date information about their flood risk, because of such major limitations as:

- Out-dated FIRMs with approximately 55% of North Carolina FIRMs being at least 10 years old
- Limited budget for updating these out-dated FIRMs with FEMA funding only one county-wide flood study per year for North Carolina

FIGURE 18. *Hurricane Floyd wrecking devastation on eastern North Carolina and the Atlantic seaboard on September 15, 1999 (Image: Goddard Space Flight Center).*

When the question was asked how these out-dated FIRMS could be updated expeditiously, NCGS responded by teaming with the North Carolina Center for Geographic Information and Analysis (CGIA), the former Office of State Planning (OSPL), the North Carolina Division of Emergency Management (NCEM), and FEMA to devise a solution. What resulted was the creation of the North Carolina Floodplain Mapping Program and a partnership between North Carolina and FEMA through the latter's Cooperating Technical Community partnership initiative.

On September 15, 2000 (one year after Hurricane Floyd), North Carolina became the first Cooperating Technical State (CTS). As a CTS, North Carolina assumed primary ownership and responsibility for the production and maintenance of new, digital FIRMs

(DFIRMs) for all North Carolina counties as part of the National Flood Insurance Program (NFIP). In addition to producing DFIRMS, the Floodplain Mapping Program has:

- Conducted flood hazard scoping with the various North Carolina counties and municipalities
- Collected LIDAR (LIght Detection And Ranging) derived elevation data (Figure 19)
- Performed new hydrology and hydraulics analyses of the floodplains

Although the actual LIDAR mapping work was contracted out to private firms, NCGS performed the quality control (QC) for all privately contracted survey firms conducting QC control work on the LIDAR data (www.ncgs.state.nc.us/floodmap.html).

For up-to-date information on the Floodplain Mapping Program, please visit the www.ncfloodmaps.com/ web site.

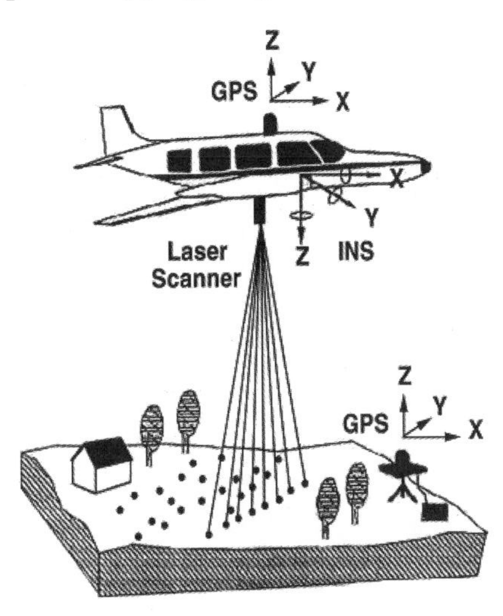

FIGURE 19. *An airplane using LIDAR (LIght Detection And Ranging) technology to map the "bare earth" ground elevation (Image source: Dave Maune – Dewberry & Davis).*

The Electronic Age of Surveying

C. Phil Wagoner, PLS

In the beginning, surveying was the art of using available tools to measure the size and placement of land. This objective has not changed since the days of the ancient rope stretcher of Egypt. Although the tools have changed, the ultimate goal is the same as it was thousands of years ago. Land surveyors have embraced advances in technology more than many other professions.

Those of us who have worked with the more primitive tools and have now embraced the electronic age are still in awe of many of the tools we have today. Personally, I am waiting for the day that a truly useful automated brush cutter comes along. If anyone out there could really invent a Darth Vader light saber, the inventor would be every surveyor's hero.

Once upon a time, not so long ago, a "high tech" surveying business could be started for less than $2,500. Today, that same $2,500 would hardly buy the tools that a couple of rodmen must carry. It is an unfortunate fact that we must spend more to equip a survey crew than some small houses cost. Such is the cost of progress.

A Slow Beginning for the Electronic Age of Surveying

The electronic age of surveying actually began before most of the current surveyors even knew what a surveyor was. The first electronic distance meters were contraptions that few of us used to measure long distances. The unit consisted of a transmitter/receiver that was hauled around on a large truck. A somewhat smaller truck hauled the target repeater. This equipment required a large generator to supply power and some very healthy people to set up the equipment. The control panel had dozens of switches and dials to read and record. In order to determine the distance measured, the numbers that were read from the dials were then compared with numbers in a codebook. This process was comparable to looking up the numbers found under the barcode on grocery items to find out what was in the package.

I have read about these microwave-measuring devices in several different texts, but I do not have a good sense of the accuracy of the measurements, nor the length of time required to make a measurement and decode the data. The real advantage of these devices was that they would measure distances of forty miles or more in any kind of weather. They were said to work in fog, rain, snow, and at night. Considering the fact that they were used extensively to measure the movement of dams, it is safe to assume that the accuracy was within a few

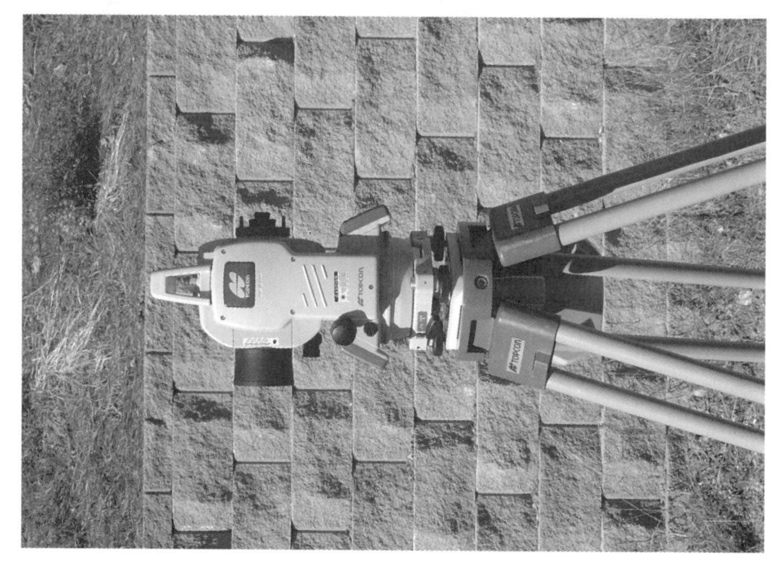

Courtesy Allied Surveying Co., PA—Topcon Hiper and RTK-GPS Unit/Topcon Reflectorless-GPT-3005.

millimeters. Considering that the most advanced electronic devices available at the time, the microwave units consisted of vacuum tubes and crystal oscillators, and the ability to produce such accurate distance measurements was a colossal feat.

The Beginning of the Modern Era

The groundwork for modern surveying equipment was started the day President Kennedy declared that America would put a man on the moon, which was before the end of the 1960s. This declaration and the creation of NASA, gave birth to virtually every electronic device in existence today. In the mid 1950s, Bell Labs invented a gadget called a "transistor," a lightweight, low power substitute for the vacuum tube. Widespread use of transistors did not occur until the mid 1960s. The single driving force behind the use of solid-state electronics was the need for light, rugged circuits to be used in the race to the moon. Every surveyor owes the very existence of our modern equipment to the Cold War, and the need for America to "show up" the Soviet Union.

Where Did the Modern Infrared Electronic Distance Meter Begin?

The modern Electronic Distance Meter (EDM) came into being as the result of the need to measure long distances in a short amount of time. Albert Abraham Michelson successfully measured the speed of light to a very high precision using a rotating mirror and lenses. Michelson had invented the first usable distance meter, but, alas, his devices were never used for that purpose. Just think for a moment; we had an EDM before we had electricity in homes and did not even know it. About 1950, a Swedish company, AGA, developed a device that used incandescent light to measure distances. The device took about two hours to measure a distance, and another two hours to compute the values. This sure beat pulling a tape over long distances. A single device, called an "infrared lasing diode," was developed in the 1960s.

The first widely marketed commercial application of an EDM for surveying was developed by Hewlett-Packard in 1970. Precision International introduced the Beetle the same week as the HP 3800. The Beetle was small, light, and had a relatively short range. The HP 3800-distance meter was carried in a suitcase-size container. The unit was about 18" long, 12" wide, and 8" high. The main housing was set in a "Y" yoke that was mounted on a tribach. The only attachment I ever saw for the HP 3800 was a vertical circle that used a level bubble to measure the slope angle. This EDM required the user to rotate dials similar to an old rotary TV tuner for each digit of the distance. The unit read directly up to 9999.99 feet, and it would shoot every foot in that distance, and more. In about 1973, Hewlett-Packard introduced an improved model, the HP 3805, that had a single button for measurement and a LED display for the distance. The case was the same size, but the era of the analog display was gone forever. The HP 3810 was introduced a few months later and used the same case and basic electronics as the HP 3805, but with a vertical angle sensor built in—horizontal measurement at last! The bell had tolled for the steel tape as the primary measuring tool used by surveyors.

A number of companies began to develop electronic distance meters for land surveying. Between 1975 and 1980, old-line companies such as Keuffel & Esser (K&E), found themselves competing with the new brand names like Beetle, Red-One, and Topcon. During this period, the new lightweight EDM units were mounted on top of, beside, under, and around almost every type of angle measuring equipment that one could imagine. Some of the contraptions that were introduced and sold were as strange looking then as they would be today. Few of us remember when America had forty different companies building automobiles and the big three rose to the top and survived. A similar sequence of events occurred with the electronic distance meter.

The Effect of the Electronic Distance Meter on Land Surveying

The world standardization of units of measure, in 1957, was the beginning of the world technological revolution. The electronic distance meter is the most important event in the history of man as it relates to linear measurement. No other device has had nearly the impact on long-range measurements—measurements of distances exceeding one meter—than the EDM has had. Even GPS is based upon the same fundamental electromagnetic wave propagation theories as the electronic distance meter.

Electronic Theodolites

The theodolite was first introduced by Leonard Digges, in London in 1571, as a "theodolitus." The word "theodolite" was introduced in London in 1720, and described telescopic instruments with horizontal circle and vertical arcs. The "transit theodolite" originated in London in the 1840s. Most surveyors would probably call it a "transit." The double verniers and microscope readers were the big differences between theodolites and transits. The technological advances in measuring angles remained static for the period from the beginning of the twentieth century and the invention of the microchip in the 1960s. Jakob Kern began building theodolites in 1824. Kern continued to build high quality optical instruments until the Kern factory was purchased by Wild in 1988, and closed in 1991. Heinrich Wild began Wild (later Wild-Heerbrugg) in 1921 and developed many fine optical instruments. In the 1930s, Heinrich Wild left his old company and went to work for Kern, from which both he and his son retired.

In 1976, Hewlett-Packard introduced a surveying instrument they dubbed the "HP 3820." The HP 3820 had an EDM built into the telescope and measured angles electronically. The EDM could measure about eight miles, and the angles were read to 0.5 seconds of arc and displayed to one second of arc. The HP 3820 was the last surveying product, excluding software, produced by Hewlett-Packard before it shut down the surveying division about 1983. To my knowledge, the HP 3820 was the first commercially available electronic theodolite and EDM, electronic data collector, and desktop software system to be introduced. The "total station" had been born. (Writer's note: The argument rages about who had the first total station, but I believe a "total station" is a complete system of measurement, data recording and reduction, and the supporting software. The HP 3820 was the earliest product, that I can find, that fits all of the required criteria.)

Several other old line surveying equipment makers such as AGA, Wild, Kern, Leitz, David White, K&E, and Zeiss began to develop and market surveying instruments with electronic angle measurement systems. The first Wild and Kern instruments attached their own brand of EDM to the telescope and routed the distance data through the main body of the instrument. Some companies mounted the EDM on the instrument and measured the angles with a micrometer, while calling the unit a "total station." After a number of mergers and closings, only one old-line company really survived in the total station market—Wild. The Japanese companies, Topcon and Sokkia, emerged as the dominant suppliers of electronic total stations for the average surveyor. Wild and Geodimeter emerged as the high-end leaders of the market. Hewlett-Packard had a timeless design in 1976 with the HP 3820. Nearly every electronic total station built and sold today is made on about the same basic pattern developed by Hewlett-Packard in 1976.

Electronic Data Collectors

Electronic data collectors began to appear in the late 1970s. By 1983, nearly every maker of electronic total stations had their own version of the "best thing since sliced bread." Any discussion of data collectors, and the companies that made them is nearly as diverse as the discussion of breakfast cereals. TDS and SMI eventually emerged as the two most dominant companies for data collectors. I did some programming for Stanley Trent, of SMI, about 1980. Stanley made no bones about the fact that he needed a good product so that he could feed his dozen or so children.

In the simplest form, a data collector is nothing more than an electronic device with a memory bank, that receives data signals from an electronic total station and stores the data for later use. Every data collector performs this basic function. The basic reasoning behind the fact that this type of data storage is so desirable may surprise you. The reason has little to do with the ability to record a large number of point locations in a short time. The primary reason that machine-to-machine transmission of the angle and distance data is so desirable is that we have realized that machines make far fewer mistakes than people do while recording data. The endeavor to eliminate human transcription errors far outweighs any other benefit of the data storage. Computers hardly ever make mistakes, but humans do.

In about 1980, a company in Colorado, called "Omni Electronics," introduced an electronic total station with an onboard data collector. I believe that this was the first affordable total package sold in the United States. The instrument with the data collector sold for a little less than $10,000. The EDM would measure about eight miles and the angular accuracy was the same as a Wild T-2 theodolite—two seconds of arc (I owned a T-2, and my operator's manual stated that the accuracy was two seconds, not the one second touted by the salespeople). The Omni was yellow, had a hexagonal-shaped metal case, weighed about thirty-five pounds, and stored over 1000 shots in the data collector. The Omni was an excellent instrument that performed quite well. It was a monster to carry in rough country. The mining industry in the western states used the Omni extensively.

The Omni was laughed at by many people for its unorthodox appearance, but never for the performance. The control system of the Omni was so unique that it deserves a broader treatment. Unlike the instruments before and after it, the Omni had no buttons on the main unit. The only controls were the power switch and the tangent screws. All control of the instrument was from a small handheld unit. The handheld unit communicated with the main unit by sonic signals. The technology used was very similar to the system used by many cameras of the same era to focus the lens. I developed several computer programs for Omni during its short life. The controller would work from as far as twenty feet from the instrument. I found this to be an advantage when the instrument was set up in a place that was very difficult. I could back away and not risk disturbing the instrument during the shot. The wireless controller basically died with the Omni. Some great ideas do not live a fruitful life.

The evolution of the data collector is by no means a straight line. The early data collectors were custom-made boxes with the software on ROM. The cost varied from about $1,000 to $3,000. The Hewlett-Packard collector for the 3820 cost $8,000. Not much has changed as far as cost. The use of off-the-shelf handheld computers, by the developers of data collector software, has made for a better product. The selection of robust handheld devices by the software vendors has raised the level of confidence of the users.

One of the early pioneers of a really useful field computer was C&G Software Systems. C&G used a modified MC-V to provide a platform for their desktop software. When they included the software that interfaced with the instrument, they produced a product that could be used by both office and field personnel in the same way. C&G may not have been the first to integrate a full-blown field computer with office capabilities, but they produced a product that provided a model for others to follow. The C&G platform is still viable in the market at the beginning of the new millennium. That success is much more than can be said for many of the early data collector suppliers.

Data Collectors and Surveyor's Attitudes

I started using data collectors about twenty-five years ago. During that time, I have had more conversations with surveyors about the benefits and evils of data collectors than I care to remember. Every surveyor has a different opinion about data collectors. Some love them and some hate them. Very few are neutral.

The number of surveyors who refuse to use a data collector seems to shrink each year. The younger generation seems to be much more receptive to the little boxes. The cost has come down so that the purchase of a data collector is not any real obstacle. The fear of losing data seems to have been the primary objection to using collectors. Survey field notes on paper are not as likely to be lost as electronic data. In the last twenty years, I have lost one day of work due to a data collector. I lost the data because of my own stupidity. I was working with a HP 48 in the snow at about five degrees above zero. I let the unit get too cold and started trying to make the unit dump the data before it warmed up. I lost a day of data and had to run the survey over. The HP 48 has not shut down from the cold since then, but if I let it warm up, it works fine. We try to keep the units warm, and we have no trouble. I have talked to very few surveyors who have lost data because of the equipment. Human error is another thing altogether.

During the 1990s, data collectors became a basic part of most survey crew equipment. The newer instruments are being built with PCMCIA Compact Flash memory cards for transporting data. Many of the new instruments have sophisticated software that provides the field crew with a number of tools that were once confined to the office. The future probably holds many newer, smaller, and more powerful tools in the lineage of the data collector.

The Office Personal Computer

For all you "pups" out there—IBM was NOT even a player when surveyors started using computers. Hewlett-Packard was the "King of the Hill" for the first ten years that computers became available to the average surveyor.

About 1969, the Ollivetti Company introduced a computer called the "Programma 101" that used magnetic strips to load programs. It had a series of blinking lights, a numeric keypad, and a thermal printer. I believe that this was the very first desktop computer to be marketed with surveying software. I used one in the early 1970s. It was cumbersome, but it surely did beat a calculator with ten rows of keys that looked like an old cash register. If the computers of today were as tough as the old "101," we could put wheels on them and drive them to work. I once knew a surveyor, who would lose his temper and shove his "101," and the table it was on, across the room. The old "101" would bounce off the wall, and sometimes the floor, but it would keep working. DO NOT try this with your computer at home. He was a trained professional, executing the maneuver on a closed course.

Early in the introduction of the desktop computer to the average surveyor, a few minor players introduced models marketed for surveying. The companies included Ollivetti, Apple, Commodore, Wang, and Monroe. This list is, by no means, complete. My first desktop computer was a Monroe 1765 that used punch cards for programs. The user could write custom programs using the punch card mask and stylus. The machine would perform up to 256 program steps. This was the first desktop computer I ever programmed in the "Dark Ages" of 1972. I could not imagine needing more than 256 program steps to do anything. Was I ever in for a surprise!

Hewlett-Packard entered the desktop computer market for surveying about 1972. The first entry, the HP 9810, was more a market test than anything else. When the HP 9815 came on the market about 1975, Hewlett-Packard entered the surveying market like a bull in a china shop. By 1977, Hewlett-Packard had established a majority of the surveying market for the next seven years.

The HP 9815 was the desktop computer that revolutionized the processing of survey data. The HP 9815 had a tape drive for mass storage. The machine was reasonably fast and could store thousands of points. Traverse adjustments were easy to perform. COGO became a household word among surveyors. The "zizzz-dat-dat" sound of the thermal printer of the HP 9815 became the status symbol of surveyors who had entered the modern age.

Hewlett-Packard introduced a wonderful machine to surveyors about 1980. The marvel was the HP 85. The HP 85 had a video screen that would show graphics, a standard QWERTY keyboard, used a 5-¼" floppy disk, had a tape drive, would drive large format graphic printers and plotters, and could use a modem to communicate with the rest of the world. The BASIC programming language that the HP 85 used was easy to learn. The HP 85, though antiquated by today's standards, was the basic configuration of nearly every successful computer system to follow.

Within a year of introducing the HP 85, Hewlett-Packard introduced the HP 86. The main cosmetic difference between the HP 85 and the HP 86 was the use of a monitor separate from the CPU. The 12" monitor of the HP 86 used the standard 80 column by 25 line text display used by everyone since. The HP 86 was a real leap forward. The "86" supported a 3-½" floppy disk, a 5-¼" floppy disk, and would talk to almost any device one wanted to "wire" to it. There is no doubt in my mind that the HP 86 is still in use in surveying offices today. Mine still works.

The HP 86 system was the last major hardware product introduced for surveyors. Several other models, such as the 9816, 9825, and the 150, never achieved broad acceptance in the surveying world. The division of Hewlett-Packard that produced all of these wonderful toys shut down about 1983. Hewlett-Packard created some wonderful products during the early years of desktop computers.

The IBM Era of Personal Computers

In 1983, IBM introduced its first personal computer. The original IBM-PC was a far cry from what we have today. The first one had an Intel 8086 processor running at 5.44 megahertz. The core memory was a whopping 640 kilobytes. The hard drive would store a tremendous amount of data—10 megabytes. The video monitor had dots as big as raindrops on a windshield. The graphics looked more like crayon sketches than computer drawings. The text would scroll onto the screen at a rate that was not much faster than some competitive typists. The floppy disc drives made noises that sounded like a dying calf in a hailstorm. The world loved it, and the rest is told in the history books.

Some trivia about the first IBM-PC will go well here. The introduction of the IBM-PC in 1983, was one of the finest marketing jobs on the world press and the business world that has ever been pulled off successfully. IBM had watched its sales of typewriters slip downward ever since Apple Computer had introduced a word processor and Tandy Corporation began marketing its own brand of computers at Radio Shack stores. The writing on the wall told IBM that the use of the typewriter was declining. Apple was almost giving the Apple 2e systems to schools, in an effort to build a "familiar base of users" in the children, in hopes that they would purchase Apple computers when they grow up. Wang computers had a strong marketing program to businesses for their word processors and accounting programs. Hewlett-Packard had introduced the HP 3000 mainframe that seriously impacted the IBM market share at a fraction of the cost. The Cray Corporation had introduced their line of super computers that were faster and smarter than anything else was—and may still be the fastest computers in the world.

The marketing influence of IBM is legendary. The introduction of the IBM-PC set in motion the computer revolution and the information age. The basic design has remained unchanged. Many of the programs that were sold for the first PC will still run on the PCs sold today. The investment worldwide in technology, based on the original IBM design, is so large that we are not likely to see any significant change for years to come.

Printers and Plotters

Epson was one of the first major suppliers of printers for personal computers. Epson products first appeared about 1980 and quickly became a standard. The eight-wire print head, tractor feed, multiple font capabilities, and graphics took the computer world by storm. Nearly every dot matrix printer sold was an Epson or was Epson compatible. Any product that was IBM and Epson compatible had some chance of surviving in the market after 1983. Dot matrix printers that failed to be compatible with both IBM and Epson had very little chance of surviving long enough to return the first advertising costs. In the twenty-first century, Epson is still a strong influence in the marketplace.

In 1983, Hewlett-Packard introduced the Laser-Jet printer. A portion of the print technology was bought from Canon Copier Corporation. Overnight, the business world could produce documents that had nearly the same quality as those from a print shop. The cost difference for the laser documents amounted to pennies on the dollar. Hewlett-Packard introduced a product that instantly became a standard, and the Hewlett-Packard market share in laser printers probably reaches over 90%. Once again, a good solid product, with a timeless design, dominates the market.

The first plotter I ever saw was at the North Carolina Surveyor's Convention in about 1974. The unit was built by Wang Computers. The salesman told me that the system sold for something in the neighborhood of $25,000. The plotter was on a big flat table, with a huge pantograph-like arm that held a single pen. The plotter required an area about ten feet square to work. The plotter looked like a tracing table, on a Kern PG-2 stereo plotter, with servo motors. The drawing speed was slow as molasses, but it worked. I was in awe of such a machine!

Hewlett-Packard introduced a plotter, called the HP 9862, about the same time that they entered the surveying market with the HP 9810 desktop computer. Neither unit made any significant impact on the surveying community. The HP 9810 would drive the HP 9862 plotter for simple plots, but the software would not produce anything beyond a working sketch.

In 1978, Hewlett-Packard introduced the HP 9872 plotter. The unit was a flat bed 11"x 17" unit with eight pens. It was fast and would work with the HP 9815. This thing was better than sliced bread.

I must diverge here to tell you a personal story about the first plotter I bought. This may well be one of the more memorable happenings in my life.

I started programming surveying software on an old Monroe 1765 desktop in 1972. I had written programs for a couple of Monroe models, a portable Monroe, and a series of routines for the HP 45 calculator that included such things as intersections, adjustments, and general COGO functions. When I leased my HP 9815 in 1977, I was in "hog heaven." The software that was written by Hewlett-Packard was very good, but I added a couple of dozen programs of my own to make life easier for me. I was hooked on programming.

In the spring of 1978, I received a brochure from Hewlett-Packard showing the HP-9872 plotter. I was fascinated with the possibility of drawing survey maps with a computer. I called my local Hewlett-Packard representative and asked him if Hewlett-Packard had any software for the plotter and surveying. I was told that no plans existed to produce any such product. I convinced my sales representative to order me a set of user and programming manuals for the plotter. I sent him a check, and the books came a couple of weeks later. (This was at a time when computers were sold by the makers, not the local office supply and discount stores.)

By the Fourth of July, I had decided that I could write a program to draw survey maps on my HP 9815 using the HP 9872 plotter. I called my Hewlett-Packard sales representative and asked him to prepare the lease documents for me so I could buy that wonderful plotter. I signed the lease, sent the check for the first and last payments, and mailed the paperwork back to my sales representative. I then settled down to start writing my plotting software, while I waited on the three-month delivery date of my new toy.

Late in July, my phone rang. My local sales representative told me that the local branch manager had declined to let the sale go through, and he was sending my check back. When I inquired why, the sales representative said that the branch manager did not want to sell me a machine that had no Hewlett-Packard software to drive it. I talked to the branch manager about this problem. After relating my plans to write my own software and of the programs I had written before, he was still hesitant. One must realize that the attitudes during that time dictated that hardware and software sales were bundles. Many companies had strict policies against sales of either the hardware or software alone. The next day, I called the Hewlett-Packard corporate office in Palo Alto and had a long conversation with customer service. I received a call from the manager the next day that my order had been put through. I thanked him for his time and tried to reassure both of us that the plotter, without software, would not be a problem. I secretly wondered, for months after that, if he had been correct in resisting the sale and I was embarking on a road with an expensive paperweight.

Hewlett-Packard had a flurry of orders from government agencies for their plotters during July, and my delivery was pushed back to December. I was ecstatic when my plotter came on a big truck a few days before Christmas 1978. About fifteen minutes later, I felt exactly like a dog that had chased down a car after years of trying. Now that I have it, what am I going to do with it?

Most of my early work on the software worked as expected. I plotted my first deed on the plotter on the night of December 25, 1978. My ex-wife is still mad about my going to the office to work on my plotter on Christmas. My new plotter was my Christmas present to me, and I intended to play with it. On that Christmas night, I saw that the end of hand-drafted survey maps was not so far away.

During the first two months of 1979, I refined the software to the point where I could draw a full 11"x 17" map. I had to design a set of pens to draw on mylar with india ink, since no commercial pens were available. I built the first set of wet ink pen bodies in a machine shop in Woodlawn, Virginia, in February 1979. I used the core from my Koh-I-Noor drafting pens in my new pen bodies that would fit the HP 9872 plotter. I started producing finished maps with the plotter in April 1979. The maps were not works of art, but it sure beat drawing maps by hand.

The first week in May, I called my local Hewlett-Packard sales representative and asked him to come to my office to see my new plotter work. He was amazed at what he saw and carried samples of my maps back to show the office manager. On May 12, 1979, I signed the first map drawn by my plotter to be recorded. The map was drawn in pieces, taped together, photographed, and recorded in the Alleghany County, North Carolina, Register of Deeds on May 15, 1979. I believe this to be the first plotter-drawn map to be recorded in this state, maybe in the United States. If anyone can provide me with a certified copy of a plotter-drawn map recorded in any county registrar's office prior to this date, I will then know that I was not the first to do this.

In January of 1981, Hewlett-Packard introduced the famous HP 7580 plotter, the HP 85 computer, and the Volume C software as a unit for surveying. This was the first practical package for the average surveyor marketed by a major computer company. The HP 7580 plotter and its variants became the world standard for high production, high quality plotting devices for surveying, engineering, architecture, and anyone else who needed large format drawings.

During the 1980s, a number of companies such as Calcomp, Tectronix, Cito, Gerber, and Houston-Instruments marketed plotters to surveyors. The early dominance by Hewlett-Packard was never overtaken by any of the competitors. Today, Hewlett-Packard holds a commanding lead over the nearest competitor in the surveying and engineering market. The most significant advance in plotters, since their invention, has been the use of ink-jet technology. A plot that would take hours on a pen plotter can be made in minutes using a plotter with the ink-jet technology. The large format hard copy is finally reaching a level of quality and speed that puts the plotter on par with the laser printer technology that is nearly twenty years old. Given the current advancement rate of the business, I do not think that it is unreasonable to expect to see an E-size drawing that would take a draftsman two weeks to draw and emerge from a plotter in one minute or less.

The number of surveyors who do not use plotters is larger than one might think. Engineers and architects have similar groups. I would encourage those surveyors who are not using plotters to re-examine their reasons for not doing it. Paper documents have much less value than do digital documents. The time spent drawing maps by hand, compared to drawing maps by computer, is significant. I did hand drafting for twelve years before I bought my first plotter. For six of those years, I was drawing survey maps. I could never produce the volume of work by hand that I can using a computer and plotter. The number of drafting mistakes is also significantly reduced by using a computer and plotter. The next decade may well shut out any surveyor who cannot produce a map for digital transmission and recording. The world will move on.

The Evolution of Surveying Software

Computer software for desktop computers providing surveying solutions began to appear on the market about thirty years ago. The first packages were primitive by today's standards. The reduction of slope distance to horizontal, the solution of traverses for closure and the calculation of coordinates, and a number of intersection and curve solutions were the cutting edge in 1970. Most of the software was written by the computer companies and sold as a package of hardware and software. This trend continued until the introduction of the IBM PC in 1983. A few independent software companies tied their products to specific hardware. I tied my software to the HP 85 and HP 86. Pac-Soft and HASP tied their products to the HP 9816. A few packages were sold for the Tandy TRS-80. The Commodore 64 and the Apple 2e had lesser followings. None of the independent software companies ever made a real impact on the industry, because the software written for one type of machine was not transportable to another. Hewlett-Packard used its wealth and marketing network to lock in a majority of the sales of surveying software until 1983. The rise and fall of software companies was nearly a weekly occurrence. Large computer companies do not lend a great deal of help to software companies that are competing with products sold by the hardware manufacturers.

The introduction of the IBM-PC signaled the end of the proprietary operating system. Consequently, software writers were no longer tied to a single hardware manufacturer. Hewlett-Packard lost its stranglehold on the surveying market in the wink of an eye. Every surveying software writer in America was faced with the same problem–make your product IBM compatible or die. Many products died. A fairly large number were so severely wounded that they never fully recovered. A new crop of whiz kids began to emerge from nowhere.

The current leader in computer-aided drafting did not have a grand start. The story goes something like this. A group of programmers, managers, and financiers got together and formed a company called "Autodesk." They did not have a product to sell; some have said that they did not even have a real good idea of what they would sell. The programmers and managers broke into teams and each dreamed up a product to sell. A few months later, the groups came back together to compare each other's work. AutoCAD 1.0 was an instant hit with most of the group. The product was shown to a select group of architects and was an instant hit. The other products developed were trashed, and the rest is history. The open architecture of AutoCAD worked well with the open architecture of the IBM-PC.

During the next ten years, a number of companies introduced surveying software packages. Most relied on their own graphics engines or engines licensed from other firms. Most of these were deeply entrenched in the "also ran" category. One company, DCA Engineering, in the "hot bed" of high tech New Hampshire, decided to build a software package for in-house use. It decided to use the new AutoCAD package as the graphics engine and the AutoLisp language to produce hundreds of micro programs to run inside AutoCAD. I have no idea whether it was an extraordinary stroke of luck, being in the right place at the right time, or divine intervention, but David C. Arnold decided to market his library of surveying and engineering programs for AutoCAD. He chose the simple name of D.C.A. By 1987, D.C.A. was the most popular add-on package in the United States for AutoCAD, surveying, and civil engineering. David C. Arnold was on his way to being a very rich man. In the mid 1990s, D.C.A. changed its name to SoftDesk. Autodesk eventually purchased SoftDesk. About 1995, SoftDesk produced a couple of low cost cad engines for the PC market. One was even a trimmed-down version of the SoftDesk / AutoCAD package that ran without AutoCAD. SoftDesk was too big for Autodesk to kill, but not too big to buy.

Intergraph is a major player in the engineering and architecture market. Intergraph traditionally has been far too expensive for the average surveyor. In the last few years, it has started to make inroads into the desktop market, but it is too early to know if it will have any significant impact on the average surveyor. Intergraph does have a good penetration of the state DOTs.

Not every successful surveying software company hitched a ride on AutoCAD. In the late 1970s, a couple of practicing land surveyors in Atlanta, Georgia, started writing surveying software for their own use on a Tandy TRS-80 computer. One of them was a very good businessman with a keen sense of what was to come. The other was an excellent programmer with a deep understanding of what a surveying software package should do. These two licensed land surveyors were Ed Cowherd and Dean Goodman. They formed a company called C&G Software Systems. C&G was one of the few software companies to make the switch from the proprietary operating systems to the IBM operating system and come out stronger than before. C&G used a graphics engine of their own design and integrated a COGO and drafting package that became very popular. C&G finally embraced the AutoCAD and the Intellicad engine in one of its products. With a good solid product, they competed for years against bigger companies. C&G was purchased by Carlson Software and Dean Goodman continues to provide solid products through Carlson in the increasingly competitive world of software.

One company that produced, and extensively marketed, a surveying software package for the IBM-PC was Surveyors Supply Company. The package was called Surv-a-Soft. A large number of users could be found in the southeast. After the death of Earl Smith, the founder of Surveyors Supply, the company seemed to stress other areas of the business. Surv-a-Soft and the SuperROM for the HP 41 were two significant products produced in North Carolina and sold nationwide. Products come and go, but the basic core of Surveyors Supply's business was always tools and supplies for the surveying community. Sadly, Surveyor's Supply Company closed its doors in 2003 and the great "toy store" is no more.

The potential market for surveying software is huge. If someone writes a program that sells for $100 and sells one to every company in the United States that offers surveying services, that entrepreneur would gross about $5,000,000. The market for surveying software is a serious market, and we can expect to see products in the near future that we cannot even dream of today. Hold on to your seat—this is going to be one unforgettable ride.

Surveying with Satellites

All of us have seen magic shows. The Global Positioning System, or GPS, is as close to a magic show as surveyors have come. The science is solid, but the illusions are nearly "amazing" to those who are not acquainted with the technology.

GPS was not the first satellite-based terrestrial measuring system. During the 1970s, a number of the Transit Navigation Satellites were launched. The only device with which I have had any experience that used the Transit satellites was the Motorola Ranger. The Ranger consisted of a box of electronics about one foot cubed and weighed about forty pounds. It had an antenna that looked like something that a HAM radio operator would use. It was placed at a point and left for about twenty-four hours. The best I remember, there were only four or five Transit satellites operational when I used the Ranger in 1982. The twenty-four hours of observation would yield a latitude, longitude, and elevation accurate to about a meter. Not bad for the day.

The Beginnings of GPS

GPS was planned for many years. The original implementation began in 1983. The United States military needed a land, air, and sea navigation system to replace the Transit system, LORAN, VOR, and all the other earlier radio navigation systems. A space-based system was the most secure and would provide the worldwide coverage that the military needed. Remember, we were in the Cold War with the USSR at this time. Military conflict and national security concerns produce many technological advances that later become staples in the civilian economy.

During its first ten years, GPS was a very fledgling child. The first satellite receivers I ever remember seeing were produced by a company in Maryland called Geohydro. The cost was about $200,000. Needless to say, I never owned one. One of the primary developers of the GPS technology, Clyde Goad, is from Mount Airy, North Carolina, and teaches at Ohio State. During the early days, GPS seemed as far away from a general use product as the space shuttle would have appeared to Chuck Yeager, when he was trying to fly faster than the speed of sound.

Every technology needs a pioneer. John Shipp was the pioneer of the infrared lasing EDM system. Javad Ashjaee was the pioneer of the consumer versions of the GPS receiver. He started a company in California called Javad Positioning Systems, or JPS, which was sold to Topcon in 2001. Both men moved around a lot.

What is GPS?

Simply put, GPS is a constellation of satellites orbiting the earth in several inclined orbits similar to the electrons around the nucleus of an atom. In general, the orbit radius is about 12,000 miles, and the satellites orbit the earth once about every twelve hours. Each satellite has a radio transmitter and a very precise clock on board. Each satellite transmits a unique signal pattern that can be differentiated from all the other satellites. The GPS constellation was declared fully operational in early 1994, when the full twenty-four satellites became simultaneously available.

The technical dynamics of GPS is far too complex to review here, but some of the basic principles can be expressed without losing one in tech talk.

How Does GPS Work

The basic principle of GPS is similar to the principles used in an electronic distance meter. Both light "waves" and radio "waves" travel at the same speed–approximately 300,000,000 meters per second in a vacuum. Both slow down in air, solids, and liquids. Air pressure and the temperature of the air have the greatest effect on the infrared light of an EDM, and the ionosphere has the greatest effect on the GPS radio signals. Other atmospheric conditions affect both, but to a lesser degree. Interestingly enough, the radio signal from the GPS satellites reacts to solid objects more like light than most other EM radiation: the signal bounces off most solid objects rather than penetrate like most radio waves.

The position of each satellite is relative to the latitude and longitude of the earth and the height above the ellipsoid. The position for each moment in time is monitored by the United States Air Force Space Command at Cheyenne Mountain every second of every day. The satellites broadcast an ephemeris, or table of positions, for every second of every day. This is called the "broadcast ephemeris." The position of each satellite is also monitored, and the ephemeris is corrected by observations. This is called the "precise ephemeris" and contains very precise positions of where the satellites are at any given moment of time. The precise ephemeris is used to try to tweak out one or two millimeters in a 100-kilometer line.

Satellite receivers have very precise clocks. The digital signal transmitted from the satellite has a pattern that repeats every thirty-two days. By comparing the template of the pattern received with the model pattern on file, the receiver can determine when the signal left the satellite. Multiply the difference between the time the signal was received and the time it was sent (a small fraction of a second), by the speed of light, and you have the distance from the receiver to the satellite. Repeat this process with three more satellites, and you have the elements of a three-dimensional distance-distance intersection. This example is vastly oversimplified, but it will serve to illustrate that the GPS problem is still a time and distance problem. In reality, very fast computers require several seconds of calculation to solve the problem—perhaps a few billion computations for survey grade positions.

Classifications of GPS Receivers

There are at present three broad categories of civilian GPS receivers. They are:

1. Recreation Grade. Those receivers that are stand-alone units that employ the L1 carrier phase signal and do not store precise data for post processing. Several companies, such as Garmin and Magellan, manufacture and sell these units. The cost usually ranges from about $100 to more than $500. These units are used by almost every segment of the general public for a million different tasks. The positional accuracy of these units varies at any given moment in time, from less than a foot to as much as sixty feet, with selective availability off. The elevation accuracy is generally better than 100 feet in elevation.
2. Mapping Grade—those receivers that have the ability to store precise data for post-processing and are widely used in preparing GIS type data bases. These units generally cost between $2,500 and $7,500. The positional accuracy of the data, after post-processing, is generally within one meter or less.
3. Survey Grade—those units that have the ability to store precise data and post-process that data using differential techniques for positional accuracy of one centimeter or less. The cost ranges from about $5,000 to more than $30,000 each. Survey grade receivers are further broken down into:

    a. Single Frequency GPS—those receivers that receive and process the L1 carrier wave signal. These receivers are generally limited to the measurement of lines of twenty km or less, because of the lack of a method of correcting for the effects of the ionosphere. Lines longer than twenty km have a greater chance of not being measured within the one cm tolerance.
    b. Single Frequency GPS and GLONASS—those receivers that process the United States and Russian satellite data from the L1 signals. These receivers can reliably measure lines somewhat longer than the twenty km limit of strictly L1 GPS receivers, but only when enough Russian satellites are in view. Because these receivers can use more satellites, they are more useful than the single frequency GPS receivers.
    c. Dual Frequency GPS—those receivers that receive and process precise data from all the GPS satellite radio channels available to the civilian user. These units produce positional accuracies within the one cm level. Dual frequency receivers require less time to measure a line than do single frequency receivers, but are no more precise under the twenty km range than are single frequency receivers. Dual frequency can be reliably used to measure lines of hundreds, or even thousands, of km in length. The cost of dual frequency receivers is generally about two to three times that of a single frequency receiver.

d. Dual Frequency GPS and GLONASS—those receivers that use every signal available from all current United States and Russian satellites. Only the Javad (Topcon) receivers have this capability at the time of this writing. Simply put, the more satellites available, the better and faster the measurements.

Methods of Measurement and Relative Accuracy

I really enjoy the advertising literature that some of the GPS marketing people publish. Some of it is funny, but some of it could get a novice hurt. I have owned GPS since early 1994, and I have tried about every crazy thing one could think of with it. I have pushed the limits of what it would do on dozens of occasions. I have learned a lot, and I have spent a lot of money on payroll, experimenting on methods and techniques. Some things work, some things do not. What works now may not work an hour from now, and vise versa. If I only had Jordy LaForge (Star Trek—The Next Generation) and his wonderful visor to tell me where the radio signals were.

Autonomous or Stand Alone positions are a thing of wonder. Stand in the middle of nowhere, with a device that can hide under a hamburger bun, and almost instantly know where you are. Nearly magic. These positions are the ones that the advertising people scare me with. I have a Garmin e-Map handheld that regularly reports instantaneous positions correctly within about twenty feet or less on an average day. I have Ashtech single frequency survey grade that will report instantaneous autonomous positions correctly within about twenty feet or less on an average day. I paid about seventy-five times as much for the Ashtech receiver as I did the Garmin. I have Javad dual frequency GPS—GLONASS that will report an instantaneous, autonomous position within about twenty feet on an average day. I paid about twice as much for the Javad as I did for the Ashtech. If I let the Garmin average positions for an hour or so, then it will report about the same twenty feet or less. Averaging the single frequency, Ashtech for an hour or so gets me down to about ten feet or less. Averaging the dual frequency, Javad for **two minutes** gets me to within about five feet or less. The dual frequency has so much more data to work with that it is not a fair test. For any single, instantaneous position, I would not give a stale biscuit for the difference between a $175 receiver and a $20,000 receiver.

Static Differential GPS is the framework of all GPS measurements. The method is simple. Place one receiver on a point of known latitude, longitude, and altitude, and one or more (preferably a minimum of three in the network) receivers on unknown points. Record satellite observation data for a time, generally from fifteen minutes to several hours, depending on the type of project, and then post-process the observation data. The post-processing software will calculate very precise geodetic directions and distances between the receivers. By applying these delta offset values to the known position, the positions of the unknown points can be determined. All high precision geodetic control networks use the static method. This method can regularly yield precisions of one part per million or better. Static measurements at one ppm should reliably allow you to repeat the location of a dime at about 10.5 miles, time and again. Single frequency receivers require more time to acquire sufficient data to solve the lines than do the dual frequency receivers, but lines of less than twenty km measured with either will be nearly equally as precise if at least an hour of data is used.

Dynamic or kinematic measurements are made while at least one receiver is stationary on a known point and one or more receivers are moving from point to point. True kinematic measurements are made while the roving receiver is in motion. Under very good conditions, these measurements can be quite precise, from one cm to ten cm positional accuracy. This is the method used in airborne GPS control of aerial photography. Use of this method for ground surveys is extremely difficult because the risk of losing lock on the satellites is so great. A variant of the terrestrial form is "stop and go" where the roving receiver is allowed to collect data from a few seconds, to a few minutes, on each point. This method can generate accuracies that can be from one cm to two cm. Very few surveyors use the true kinematic methods.

Real Time Kinematic or RTK is becoming the prevalent method of the private practicing surveyor. RTK is getting close to the "light saber" we have been looking for. In open areas with no close metal buildings, RTK is a joy to watch and use. In an area with sky blockage from trees and buildings, it is as worthless as a truck with four flat tires and a dead battery in the middle of the Rocky Mountains. RTK is by far the most expensive and most complicated measuring system that a surveyor would use in the arena of GPS.

RTK measurements are much different from either autonomous, static, or true kinematic. A receiver is set up on a known point and the known positional data is sent to the base receiver via a handheld device. The base receiver records data from the various satellites and transmits that observation data to the roving receiver over a radio modem data link. The roving receiver then uses the data from the base receiver and the observation data that it recorded, to calculate the position of the rover relative to the base receiver. The position of the rover is then calculated and sent to the handheld computer for display, recording, and use by the operator. Once again, a very simplified explanation of an extremely complex process.

RTK measurements are more likely to be affected by multi-path (reflected signals that follow longer flight paths than do direct signals from the satellite) than are static measurements, since only one moment in time is used to generate the data. RTK in tree cover is especially tough. An inexperienced user of RTK can collect trash data and never know it. The difference in the demands upon the user's skill levels, between gathering reliable measurement data with a modern total station and a data collector and a dual frequency RTK system, is nearly akin to the difference between driving a car and flying a corporate jet. There is very little you learn while driving a car that will help you fly a Lear. The same is true between the total station and the RTK system. GPS measurements are not repeatable; they are just checked with a new one.

RTK is inherently less accurate than static, probably better than true kinematic, and far above the total station. Errors in the positional accuracy of RTK measurements are not cumulative, like they are with a total station. We have found that the positional accuracy of about ninety-five percent of the points located with RTK will be within 0.03 to 0.05 feet of where they would be, if we had used static methods. This error is the same whether we are working ten feet from the base station, or two miles from the base station. About 1 in 100 points will kick out to 0.10 ft. from a static measurement. In wooded areas and when working near woods, I allow the error to climb to about 0.075 ft. radius error ellipse. Before you panic, Second Order, Class 1 geodetic surveys are nowhere near that precise. The positional accuracy of Second Order monuments, when compared to First Order static GPS positions, rarely falls below 0.25 ft. per mile or 20 ppm. We find that the RTK measurements checked between good static First Order positions generally yield an error of less than 10 ppm. Consistent measurement to these tolerances is the result of a great deal of experimentation and the use of **rigid** field procedures. RTK is as dangerous to a novice user, as is a loaded handgun to a four-year-old child. Careless RTK practices will kill an otherwise good survey quicker than anything I know.

GPS of the Future

The hardware will continue to improve. The software will continue to improve. The price will moderate somewhat, but GPS probably will never be cheap. The size and bulk will reduce and the power consumption will reduce. The batteries for my RTK rover weigh more than the receiver. New satellite frequencies are planned for the first decade of the new millennium. The Russians plan to replenish their constellation to a full complement of twenty-four satellites. NOAA plans to install several more CORS stations and other facilities that will transmit real time corrections. We have great things to look forward to in the world of GPS.

The real problem is the satellite signal strength. If the signal could penetrate tree leaf canopy and small branches, GPS would do to the EDM what the EDM did to the steel tape. When the signals from the satellites can reliably penetrate the tree canopy, the total station will be as much a relic as is the transit.

Robotics and Reflectorless

The robotic instruments are truly a thing of wonder! A few years ago, I could never have imagined that a surveying instrument could reliably track a retro prism and allow a person to work alone, with no one running the instrument. The robotic instruments work very similar to RTK GPS, except that they require a line of sight.

I have come to believe that since I am getting old, I have stared at far too many computer screens, squinted at a transit or total station telescope for so long that my eyes are not what they used to be. My robot turns better angles and gets better closures than my eyes can. There is hope for us old blind guys.

The reflectorless EDM is a real joy to use. Until recently, an EDM required a glass retro prism to work. The lasing diode sent out a modulated light beam that reflected off the glass prism. The prism had been used since AGA developed their EDM in the 1950s. Then, along comes an EDM that does not need a retro prism.

Hunters have had laser range finders for years. They have a range of from about 400 meters to about 1000 meters, depending on the model and the reflective quality of the target. Ground hog and prairie dog hunters swear by them. I have used one for years for recon surveys.

A survey quality reflectorless EDM is a quantum leap in measurement technology. The ability to point and shoot at objects, without needing a retro prism at the target, appears to have nearly the same timesaving factor as does the EDM over the tape. The accuracy is now down to about three mm or so, and the range has been extended to about three-quarters of a mile. The EDM has finally grown up and moved away from the retro prism for many applications. The safety factor alone is enormous.

Future Surveying Technology

I have failed as a sage all my life. I do suspect that one day, all property corner monuments will be catalogued using the state grid system and will have some type of electronic locating device for the convenience of the landowner. I think some descendant of GPS will be the standard measuring tool, though it may be remotely operated. The cutting of brush will surely be eliminated, along with exposure to bee stings, poison ivy, crazy neighbors, and intolerable weather conditions. I think that clients who do not want to pay may be with us a while longer.

I will leave the future up to all you young geniuses to figure out after I am gone. All I want to see is warp drive, transporters, and a chance to walk on Mars. Given the slim chance of seeing the previous three, I will just take all the chocolate I find and wish ya'll well. Good luck with all the great toys to come.

Many of the products mentioned in this work were either owned by me or used by me at some time. I would like to thank some of my friends who helped me gather my thoughts and structure the chronology: Fritz Seiker (Hewlett-Packer programmer in early days), John Shipp (EDM designer); Curt Busby and Larry Worley (Hewlett-Packard programmer and marketer); and my wife, who tolerated me during the process. Many other people read, added, and corrected parts of the story, and I thank them all.

For those of you who would like to do further research on the development of surveying instruments, the Smithsonian Institute web site at http://americanhistory2.si.edu/surveying will point you to a wealth of information. For a good treatment of the Kern and Wild instruments, many excellent photos, and their history, you can look at the private web site http://homepage.swissonline.ch/dedual/wild-heerbrugg/toc.htm. where many documents can be found. There are a large number of both private and public internet web sites that have everything from obscure papers to full-blown museums on line. A few hours of browsing will produce a wealth of history on the subject of surveying.

AUTHOR'S NOTE History is, by its very nature, only a snapshot into the truth of things past as seen through the eyes of the writer. I have drawn on many old texts, older friends and acquaintances, and a fading memory of things past, to prepare this writing. I have used many resources to try to write a technically correct paper, but some of the dates and other items are impossible to verify with the resources I have available to me. The events presented here are my observation of those events, and I do not wish to offend anyone with my recollections. Please accept the failings of an aging surveyor and his memories. I hope you enjoy my memories as much as I do.

Permissions

"Land Grants and the North Carolina Surveyor" by Walter G. Robillard, Esq., RLS. Used by permission of the author.

"Compass/Transit Era," "Acknowledgements," "Introduction" by Otis A. Jones. Used by permission of the author.

Joseph Kerner Map and Deed of a 1145 acre tract, September 20, 1830. Used by permission of John G. Wolfe III.

"Wachovia, North Carolina, The First Settlements." Reproduced by permission of GITC America, Inc., The Professional Surveyor Magazine (March 1996) pp. 61, 62

"William Churton (fl. 1749-1767 Part I, Part II." Reproduced by permission of GITC America, Inc. The Professional Surveyor Magazine Part I (July/August 2001/September 2001) pp 78–79, Part II, (September 2001) pp 86–87.

"John Vogler 1783–1881 Silversmith of Old Salem," Reproduced by permission of GITC America, Inc., The Professional Surveyor Magazine (January 2001) pp 69–70

"Surveying on the Outer Banks" by Henry C. Cuningham, PLS. Used by permission of the author.

"Outdoor Hardships Retold by a Surveyor's Son" by Hank Cuningham. Reprinted by permission of Hank Cuningham the author, who published it in The Scotland Neck Commonwealth Newspaper when he was employed by the newspaper, and Joseph R. Holiday, Publisher. .

"Moving a Piece of History, Cape Hatteras Lighthouse." Vicki Speed is a freelance writer based in Dove Canyon, California. Article and graphics reproduced with permission of *Point of Beginning (POB) magazine*, a BNP Media publication, issue dated December 1999, pages 16, 17, 19, 20.

"Redrawing the Line," Lieca N. Brown is editor of *Point of Beginning (POB) magazine*. Bobby Stalls, PLS, of NCDOT contributed valuable historical research to this article. Article and pictures reproduced with permission of *Point of Beginning magazine*, a BNP Media publication, issue date February 2003, pages 34-39

"Surveying in the Coastal Plains" with photograph by John W. Parker, PLS. Used by permission of the author.

"Trying to Remember" by A. J. "Jimmie" Davis, III, PLS. Used by permission of the author.

"Early North Carolina Surveyors" by A. J. "Jimmie" Davis, III, PLS. Used by permission of the author.

"175 Years of Surveying and Engineering, the Ward and Blanchard Family Heritage 1811-1986" by Tom Boney, Sr. Authorized and used by permission of Tom Boney, Jr., and William W. Blanchard, PE-PLS.

"15 Years of Surveying and Engineering, the Ward and Blanchard Family Heritage, 1987-2001" by William W. Blanchard, PE, PLS. Used by permission of the author.

"Surveying in the Piedmont" by Michael J. Evans, Sr., PLS. Used by permission of the author.

"Surveying in the Mountains of Western North Carolina, and "Foreword" by Kenneth T. Mills, PLS. Used by permission of the author.

"Woodrow W. Bedsaul, PLS, Compass-Transit-Electronic Surveyor in North Carolina in the Twentieth Century" compiled by Carolyn M. Huskey. Used by permission of Carolyn M. Huskey and Ann Bedsaul Hawks.

"North Carolina Society of Surveyors, Inc. History Part I, 1939–1956" by Otis A. Jones, PLS. Used by permission of the author.

"North Carolina Society of Surveyors, Inc. History Part II, 1957–2003" by R. Larry Greene, PLS. Used by permission of the author.

"North Carolina Society of Surveyors Institute "A Unique Experience in Continuing Education"—Reprinted by permission of the Professional Engineer—March/April 1993, page 10.

*"North Carolina Board of Examiners for Engineers and Surveyors History 1921–2003" by R. Larry Greene, PLS. Used by permission of the author.

*North Carolina Board of Examiners for Engineers and Surveyors—Permission to use the board minutes, list of board members, 1921–2003 and the contents of the *1960 Manual of Practice* (Blue Book).

"North Carolina Geodetic Survey—The First State Agency—Dedicated to the Coordinate System" by Gary W. Thompson, PLS. Used by permission of the author.

"North Carolina Geodetic Survey 1959–2002" by Curt E. Johnson, NCGS Technical Writer. Used by permission of the author.

"The Electronic Age of Surveying" by C. Phil Wagoner, PLS. Used by permission of the author.

Photographs—various office, field surveying instruments and historical maps contributed by Allied Land Surveying Co., PA, Otis A. Jones Surveying Company, Inc., and NCSS Maps, Inc. Photographs by W. Kevin Davie and Kenneth T. Mills in a joint photo session for ownership by NCSS Maps, Inc. Used by permission.

Western North Carolina photographs for back cover and chapter of book. Contributed by Blue Ridge Land Surveying, Inc. Used by permission.

Photographs—Statue of Abraham Lincoln surveying and other pictures taken by Otis A. Jones. Used by permission of Lincoln's New Salem State Historic Site, Petersburg, Illinois.

Photographs (5)—"Collection of the Wachovia Historical Society". Courtesy of Old Salem, Inc. Used by permission for "Wachovia, North Carolina, The First Settlements," "William Churton, fl. 1749–1767 Parts I and II," and "John Vogler, Silversmith of Old Salem 1783–1881."

Two sketches of compass and transit by Elinor C. Jones. Used by permission.

North Carolina Maps and County Maps. Reproduced by permission of North Carolina Department of Cultural Resources Office of Archives and History, Raleigh, North Carolina.

Information from the "North Carolina Society of Surveyors, Inc. (NCSS) Minutes 1939–2003", and the Tarheel Surveyor. Used by permission.

Verses from the "Faith Partners Bible (KJV)". Used by permission of Liberty University, Lynchburg, Virginia.

Appendix

In Honor of Those Who Brought Us to the Future
NCSS Past Presidents

F. C. Morton, 1939
William S. Ragsdale, 1940
Grady S. Harrell, 1941
Weldon Willis, 1942
Philip R. Inscoe, 1943
R. S. Gillespie, 1944
Meriwether Lewis, 1945
Richard Seawell, 1946
Frank Blanchard, 1947
Grady S. Harrell, 1948
C. B. Fulghum, 1949
Alvin B. Hafer, 1950
J. Chandler Eakes, 1951
Johnie C. Currin, 1952
A. Cory, 1953
B. W. Paschal, 1954
E. P. Fitts, 1955
J. Atwood Whitman, 1956
Moses Farmer, 1957
Gerald H. Ehringer, 1958
W. J. Outlaw, 1959
C. W. Russum, 1960
E. C. Smith, 1961
Gerald H. Ehringer, 1962
Ed Little, 1963
Theodore Rondthaler, 1964
Paul Ward, 1965
Joseph Hardee, 1966
Joseph Hardee 1967
A. J. Davis, 1968
Louis Smith, 1969
Willard Hintz, 1970
Robert E. Wilson, 1971
Hoyt Bradshaw, 1972
Mike Donovan, 1973
Marvin Borum, 1974
Howard Loughlin, 1975
Paul A. Lawson, 1976
Richard M. Biggs, 1977
C. H. (Pat) Blue, 1978
Robert E. Stephenson, 1979
George T. Paris, 1980
Billy M. Duncan, 1981
R. Larry Greene, 1982
Larry W. Akers, 1983
Larry R. Ritter, 1984
Sam T. Marlowe, 1985
Otis A. Jones, 1986
Derward D. Baker, 1987
M. Patricia Hutchinson, 1988
Albert E. Frieze,. 1989
Charles A. Rawls, 1990
Gary W. Thompson, 1991
William R. Coleman, 1992
Charles O. Hampton, Jr., 1993
Johnie C. Garrason, 1994
Webb A. Morgan, 1995
C. Wayne Hyatt, 1996
William C. Owen, 1997
Kenneth T. Mills, 1998
M. Luther Barrow, Jr., 1999
J. Dean Slate, 2000
Richard P. Bennett, 2001
Mark R. Seffels, 2002
Richard M. Benton, 2003
Benjamin C. Brown, 2004

NCSS Institute Graduates 1989–2004

James Adams
Lloyd B. Adams
Gregory B Armentrout
Derwood W. Baker
Jimmy C. Barbour
A. R. Barnes
John L. Barnes
Jimmy E. Bass
Bruce Beavers
Ted M. Benbow
T. R. Bishop
Eliza C. Bishop
H. Stephen Bowers
Timothy Bowes
Richard A. Brandon
Timothy Brothers
Charles R. Brown
Jimmy C. Bunce
Carl D. Bunton
John Capps, Jr.
William R. Capron
William Dennis Campbell, III
Ronald H. Carpenter
John K. Causby
Jody B. Childress
John E. Clay
Kenneth D. Close
William R. Coleman
Dan H. Collier
Eugene L. Conway
James B. Crouch
Richard C. Current
S. Taylor Currin
Charles M. Davis, Jr.
Robert W. Davis
Raymond B. Dawber
William T. Dement, Jr.
Andrew T. Edgemon
Zackery S. Edgemon
Linda D. Edmondson
Jay English
Michael J. Evans, Sr.
Billy F. Felton
Charles J. Ferguson
Robert G. Fields
Matthew Day Foster
Stephen S. Foster
Wesley G. Fox
John T. Furmage
Joseph Thomas Gallagher
Kenneth L. Gallimore
W. Douglas Gamber
Kendall E. Gaskins
Edward M. Gerringer
Michael E. Gizinski
Michael D. Goodfred
Ronald O. Graham
Jay A. Hallman
Charles O. Hampton, Jr.
Ronald Harding
Frank L. Hayes
Philip T. Hedrick
Kevin D. Hefner
Algie D. Hicks
Sylvia B. Higdon
Jeff S. Hiadun
Richard James Homovec
J. Mike Honeycutt
John R. Howard
William C. Howard, Jr.
Rogell E. Hunsucker
Bradley L. Hunter
Tommy R. Hutchens
C. Wayne Hyatt, Jr.
Gene W. Johnson
R. Joel Johnson

Otis A. Jones
John E. Keen
A. Bowman Kelly
James G. Kennedy
Edward L. Kilough
Kristopher M. Kline
Michael M. Lacey
Jerry R. Lackey
Robert J. Lackey
Joseph F. Laird, III
D. Dobbins Lattimore
Patrick C. Lee
Robin L. Lee
John B. Link
Charles S. Logue
George Scott Logue
George C. Love, Jr.
Willie I. Lumpkin, Jr.
Charles D. Mackey
Sam T. Marlowe
Ray Mason
W. Stanton Massengill
Richard A. McCannell, II
William H. McCarthy, Jr.
Walter R. McCracken
Robert B. McHenry, Sr.
Darrell Miller
Peter R. Moran
Eric Paul Morgan
Henry W. Murray
Richard E. Navy
Jimmy Nelson
James J. Nivens
Edward N. Orange
Ronald L. Oxendine
George L. Pace
Jerry A. Parker
Stephen T. Paul
Charles V. Powell
James L. Powell
Kenneth T. Presson
F. Elliott Quinn
Randy Rambeau, Sr.
Linwood L. Rawls
Wyche H. Ray, Jr.
Rudolf E. Rehquate
Walter Reynolds
Norman G. Ribelin
Andrew H. Robinson
Keith A. Shrader
Gaston W. Shelley
David N. Simpson
Wayne T. Sims
J. Dean Slate
Larry Slaughter
Burl H. Smith, IV
E. Steve Smith
James R. Smith, Jr.
David H. Snide
John S. Steele
David K. Stern
Sherrill H. Styers
David E. Summey
Kenneth D. Suttles
Ronald A. Swift
Phillip M. Taylor
Jack C. Thomas
Tony K. Thomas
Gary W. Thompson
Rodney L. Trexler
Johnny D. Varney
W. Anthony Vaughn
C. Phil Wagoner
P. Rex Walker
Leroy Walters, Jr.
Joseph E. Whaley, Jr.
Bennett White, Sr.
Lee O. White
Richard W. Willis
David J. Wilson
Donald P. Wilson
Jonathan Witherspoon
Mark E. Wood

NCSS Surveyor of the Year

Guidelines for election of NCSS Surveyor of the Year

The candidate must:

1. Have been an active Regular, Life, or Fellow Member of NCSS for the past five years.
2. Have a record of outstanding achievement and service to NCSS.
3. Be willing to have his/her name submitted for the National Surveying Excellence Award.

Nominations may be made by:

1. A NCSS Chapter, or
2. A petition signed by ten or more Regular, Life, or Fellow Members of NCSS.

NCSS Surveyor of the Year

1989	Otis A. Jones
1990	Gary W. Thompson
1991	Albert D. Frieze, Jr.
1992	Johnie C. Garrason
1993	C. Wayne Hyatt, Jr.
1994	Richard D. Hodges
1995	Charles O. Hampton
1996	Thomas W. Morgan
1997	Linda E. Edmondson
1998	William C. Owen
1999	C. Phil Wagoner
2000	Thomas W. Morgan
2001	Gary W. Thompson
2002	John T. Furmage
2003	Richard M. Benton
2004	Charles E. Robertson

NSPS Surveying Excellence Award

1986	Larry W. Akers
1993	Johnny C. Garrason
1986	Thomas W. Morgan

North Carolina Society of Surveyors Membership Listing

Honorary Members
- Linda Peace
- Andrew Ritter
- Walter G. Robillard
- Montgomery Speir
- Lacy H. Thornburg
- O. Richard Wright

Fellow/Life Members
- Larry W. Akers
- Ray Anders
- C. H. Blue
- Irwin L. Gentry
- Robert D. Inman
- Otis A. Jones
- A.E. Little (Ed)
- Howard M. Loughlin

Fellow/Regular Members
- Richard M. Biggs
- William R. Coleman
- R. Larry Greeme
- Bobby M. Long
- Larry R. Ritter
- Kenneth D. Suttles
- Gary W. Thompaons
- Donald P. Wilson

Life Members
- William Arrowood
- C. David Averette
- Robert J. Ayers
- Derward W. Baker
- Lewin T. Baker
- Phillip R. Ball
- Martin L. Barrow
- William W. Blanchard
- Marvin L. Borum
- Hoyt S. Bradshaw
- Charles V. Brooks
- Raymond T. Buckner
- William D. Bunce
- J. David Campbell
- Leslie F. Caskey
- Glenn M. Cathey
- Kenneth D. Close
- William Crocker
- Henry C. Cuningham
- Richard C. Current
- A.J. "Jimmie" Davis
- Jerry M. Davis
- T. Frank Davis
- Mack W. Drake
- Billy M. Duncan
- Joseph F. Dunnehoo
- Mont B. Gilmore
- D. Stuart Gooden
- Robert H. Goslee
- Paul D. Grimes
- Charles Hale
- Joseph E. Hardee
- Loren R. Harding
- Algie D. Hicks
- Williard A. Hintz
- Leach M. Johnson
- Thomas W. Joyce
- Robert W. Keefe
- Robert B. Kestler
- W. R. Lambert
- Paul A. Lawson
- Mack M. Lewis
- William C. Lewis

George C. Love
Howard E. McCauley
Reece F. McRorie
G. Jerome Norman
Wilbur J. Page
Felix E. Palmer
Wayne B. Perry
Robert B. Pharr
J. David Plowman
Geo. Sam Rowe
C.W. Russum
Bill E. Sawyer
Roger M. Seitter
Ben L. Smith
Robert E. Stephenson
James E. Stewart
Jack G. Stocks
Melvin P. Sullivan
J. D. Turner
Otties H. Wester
Bennett B. White
S. Elmo Williams
Robert E. Wilson
John R. Yarbrough
Leo J. Zoutewelle

North Carolina Board of Examiners for Engineers and Surveyors

NAME	TERM
Gilbert C. White PE	1921–1930
Charles E. Waddell, PE, RLS	1921–1931
Harry Tucker, PE, RLS	1921–1928
N.S. Mullican, PE, RLS	1921–1941
Park H. Daggett, PE	1921–1929
Carroll L. Mann, PE, RLS	1928–1954
John E. Lear, PE	1929–1948
John L. Becton, PE, RLS	1930–1938
John E. S. Thorpe, PE	1931–1950
Arthur C. Lee, PE	1938–1954
Grady S. Harrell, RLS	1941–1961
Robert B. Rice, PE	1948–1969
H. Dennett Jones, PE	1950–1954
William G. Brown, PE, RLS	1954–1958
Arvin Page, PE	1954–1966
Walter J. Seeley, PE	1954–1958
John E. Watson, PE	1958–1966
Louis E. Wooten, PE	1958–1959
George A. Rawlins, PE	1959–1969
Meriwether Lewis, RLS	1962–1968
Chilton R. Jones, PE	1966–1969
William N. Turner, RLS	1966–1969
Ernest Elsevier, PE, RLS	1967–1969
Alonzo E. Little, RLS	1970–1973
Clarence H. Blue, RLS	1970–1973
Lambeth T. Gibbs, PE, RLS	1970–1973
Robert D. Inman, RLS	1970–1978
Richard H. Moore, PE, RLS	1970–1974
Robert F. Ruffner, PE	1970–1975
William I. Bigger, PE, RLS	1974–1979
Howard E. McCauley,RLS	1974–1979
H. Nelson Sellers, PE, RLS	1975–1978
James R. Burrow, RLS	1975–1981
Larry D. Nixon, PE, RLS	1976–1981
A. L. Henderson, PE	1977–1982
Phillip L. Stanley, PE, RLS	1978–1983
Robert E. Turner, PE, RLS	1978–1985
Howard M. Louglin, RLS	1979–1988
Chappell N. Noble, PE, RLS	1979–1986
George T. Paris, RLS	1981–1985
Charles Y. Proffitt, PE	1981–1985
Marvin Raper, Public	1981–1984
Charles B. Langston, Public	1981–1988
Guy H. Cheek, PE	1982–1986
Ronald H. Carpenter, RLS	1983–1987
Gilbert R. Alligood, PE, RLS	1985–1990
Larry E. Barnett, Public	1985–1989
James N. Poole, PE	1986–1989
Frank L. Turner, Public	1989–1993
William T. Stever, PE, RLS	1989–1993
Geraldine A. Overby, Public	1990–1990
Bobby M. Long, RLS	1986–1995
Dana H. Rucker III, PE, RLS	1986–1995
J. Albert Bass, Jr. PE, RLS	1987–1996
Ray E. Anders, PLS	1988–1997
Helen W. Merritt, Public	1990–1998
R. Larry Greene, PLS	1989–1999
J. Richard Cottingham, PE, PLS	1990–2000
Kenneth D. Suttles, PLS	1996–2001
C. Phil Wagoner, PLS	1998–2001
M. Frank Tyndall, PE	1994–2003
David L. Peeler, PE	1996–2005
George E. Freeman, PE, PLS	1997–2006
Doris M. Rodgers, Public	1998–2004
William C. Owen, PLS	1999–2003
Joseph Monroe, Ph.D., Public	1999–2003
Henry V. Liles, Jr., PE	2000–2004
Johnie C. Garrason, PLS	2001–2005
J. Glenn Haynes, PLS	2001–2007
Caroline M. Guznicak, PE	2003–2008
Gary W. Thompson, PLS	2004–2008

NORTH CAROLINA STATE BOARD OF
REGISTRATION FOR PROFESSIONAL
ENGINEERS AND LAND SURVEYORS

MANUAL OF PRACTICE
FOR
LAND SURVEYING

JULY 1st

1960

RULES AND REGULATIONS TO BE OBSERVED BY REGISTERED ENGINEERS AND REGISTERED LAND SURVEYORS IN THE PRACTICE OF LAND SURVEYING IN NORTH CAROLINA

VOLUME I

Historical Document

NORTH CAROLINA LAND SURVEYING MANUAL

Rules and Regulations to be Observed in The Practice of Land Surveying in North Carolina. Compiled and Adopted by the Board Under the Provisions of Section 16—Chapter 89 of The General Statutes of North Carolina.

MANUAL OF PRACTICE

FOR THE INFORMATION AND GUIDANCE OF THOSE ENGAGED IN THE PRACTICE OF LAND SURVEYING IN NORTH CAROLINA

COMPILED AND ADOPTED BY
NORTH CAROLINA STATE BOARD OF REGISTRATION FOR PROFESSIONAL ENGINEERS AND LAND SURVEYORS

ARVIN PAGE, *Chairman*
The Bahnson Company
1001 S. Marshall Street
Winston-Salem, N. C.

JOHN D. WATSON, *Vice-Chairman*
2003 Carlisle Road
P. O. Box 6267
Greensboro, N. C.

ROBERT B. RICE, *Secretary-Treasurer*
401 Oberlin Road
P. O. Box 5131
Raleigh, N. C.

GEORGE S. RAWLINS
101 Wrenwood Lane
P. O. Box 10336
Charlotte, N. C.

GRADY S. HARRELL
Route 1
Shannon, N. C.

JULY 1, 1960

$2.00 per copy

CONTENTS

		Page
INTRODUCTORY		1
I	GENERAL	2
II	NOMENCLATURE	4
III	DEFINITIONS	5
IV	REQUIREMENTS FOR REGISTRATION	6
V	CLASSIFICATION OF SURVEYS	7
VI	MAPS AND MAPPING	9
VII	LAND DESCRIPTIONS	12
VIII	MONUMENTS AND MARKERS	14
IX	CLASSIFICATION OF LEVELING SURVEYS	15
X	ENGINEERING SURVEYS	16
XI	MAGNETIC DECLINATION	16
XII	INSTRUMENTS AND APPARATUS	17
XIII	REFERENCE BOOKS	18
XIV	APPENDIX	
	A. Typical Surveying Agreement	19
	B. Typical Monuments and Markers	20
	C. Typical Tabulation and Calculation for Area of Closure	21
	D. Typical Boundary Survey Map	22
	E. Typical Topographical Survey Map	23
	F. Typical Subdivision Survey Map	24

STATUTES OF NORTH CAROLINA DEALING WITH LAND SURVEYING

39-32.1	Requirement of Permanent Markers as "Control Corners"
39-32.2	Control Corners fixed at time of recording plat or prior to sale
39-32.3	Recordation of Plat showing Control Corners
39-32.4	Description of land by reference to control corner
81-59	Standard Surveyor's chain; tests
81-60	Using untested chain misdemeanor
81-61	Tests for magnetic variation and for chain
81-62	Magnetic variation to be recorded with survey
81-63	Surveys in another county; data as to variation recorded
81-64	Tests returned to register; records kept
81-65	Meridian monuments protected by county commissioners
81-66	Defacing meridian monuments misdemeanor
89-2(d) (e)	Definitions of land surveyor and land surveying
89-2-II(b) (1) (2)	Minimum Evidence of Qualification requirements—education and experience
89-10	Effect of certification; seals
89-11	Unauthorized practice of land surveying; penalties
89-13	Corporate or partnership practice of land surveying
89-14	Grandfather Clause registration
89-16	Manual of practice for land surveyors
102-1	Name and Description of official survey base
102-2	Physical control
102-3	Use of Name—"North Carolina Co-ordinate System"
102-4	Damaging, defacing, or destroying Monuments
102-5	Limitations of Use
102-6	Legality of Use in descriptions
102-7	Use not compulsory
102-8	Administrative Agency of N. C. Co-ordinate System
102-9	Duties and Powers of the Agency
102-10	Prior work
102-11	Vertical Control
146-31	Warrant for survey issued
146-32	Duplicate warrants
146-33	Surveys according to priority of entry
146-34	Chainbearers sworn
146-35	Survey made and plots prepared
146-36	Plots and warrants sent to Secretary of State
146-37	Special surveyor appointed, if no county surveyor
146-38	Special surveyor, when county surveyor interested
146-39	Record of surveys to be kept
146-40	Former surveys recorded
146-41	What record must show; received as evidence
146-42	Fees for recording
146-43	Penalty for failure to make record
150.9 through 150.34	Legal Procedures for Revocation of Licenses
154-1	Election and term of office of County Surveyor
154-2	Repealed by Session Laws 1951, c. 21
154-3	May appoint deputies
154-4	Power to administer oaths
156-32	Designating County Surveyor as a Chairman of Committee for drainage study
156-39	Commissioners may appoint surveyor to prepare a map for canal drainage
156-69	Nature of the Survey

NORTH CAROLINA LAND SURVEYING MANUAL

Rules and Regulations To Be Observed in The Practice of Land Surveying in North Carolina.

JULY 1, 1960

INTRODUCTORY

Senate Bill Number 64 enacted into Law by the General Assembly during the 1959 Legislature directs that the North Carolina State Board of Registration for Engineers and Land Surveyors shall publish a "Manual of Practice for Land Surveying." This Manual is a set of rules and regulations which establishes definitions, standards, and procedures governing the practice of Land Surveying in North Carolina. The law further stipulates that "the Board shall review said Manual (Manual of Practice for Land Surveying) annually and shall revise same if revisions are deemed advisable or necessary by the Board."

In compliance with the Statute this Board does hereby respectfully submit to the General Assembly of North Carolina, to the property owners in North Carolina, and to the Engineers and Land Surveyors who are engaged in the practice of surveying land boundaries and preparing maps and descriptions the following rules and regulations which are compiled and adopted by the Board and which establish hereby minimum standards to be rigidly observed by those engaged in the practice of Land Surveying in this State.

In preparing this Manual it is anticipated that it will be of considerable value to property owners in North Carolina in engaging the services of qualified personnel to establish corners and boundaries to their respective properties with a degree of accuracy which will stand the test of time. It is further anticipated that this Manual will assist the Clerks of Court and Registers of Deeds in the several counties of North Carolina in receiving and accepting maps for recordation which maps in complying with the rules of this Manual will be accurate and complete in detail.

It is further anticipated that this Manual in establishing and printing standards which are generally accepted by the professions will be of assistance to the Engineers and Land Surveyors in North Carolina insofar as meeting the needs of their clients or satisfying the requirements of the Mapping Law and that property surveyed henceforth can be readily located, be described in a manner such that if a corner or marker is destroyed it can be readily replaced, and mapped in such a manner that it can be readily read and understood.

It is lastly anticipated that this Manual will be of considerable interest and value to other professions most notably the Legal and the Real Estate professions.

In enacting and adopting the rules in this Manual the Board acknowledges its indebtedness to members and committees of the Professional Engineers of North Carolina, the N. C. Section of the American Congress of Surveying and Mapping, and the North Carolina Society of Land Surveyors. The Board acknowledges information it received from individuals representing the Colleges and Universities of North Carolina as well as the State Highway and Public Works Commission. The Board also expresses its appreciation for the conscientious efforts of Mr. William G. Brown, Jr., and Mr. Louis E. Wooten, Sr., former members of the Registration Board, who most unselfishly gave of their time and knowledge in preparing the manuscript.

I—GENERAL

A. An Engineer or Land Surveyor who practices Land Surveying in North Carolina in violation of these rules and regulations, on complaint in writing, sworn-to by the complainant, and submitted to the Board, shall be notified of the complaint, afforded opportunity to be heard before the Board, and on being found guilty shall be subject to the penalties provided by the Statutes under GS 89-9. Under the provisions of GS 89-11 he shall, if deemed guilty of a misdemeanor, be punished by a fine of not less than one hundred dollars ($100.00) or by imprisonment for three (3) months or both at the discretion of the court; or, under the provisions of GS 47-30 he may be punished by a fine of not less than fifty dollars ($50.00) nor more than five hundred dollars ($500.00).

B. In the Board's determination to make certain that this information will reach all individuals who are most influenced by the Statutes and the Rules set forth herein, each Engineer and Land Surveyor registered to practice in North Carolina has been provided by the Board with a copy of this Manual of Practice. A copy has also been sent to State officials, to each Clerk of Court and Register of Deeds in North Carolina, and to those Libraries which have indicated their interest. Copies will also be made available to the Public on written request.

C. The rules set forth in this Manual are rules which have been observed and have been practiced by Engineers and Land Surveyors in their normal day-to-day practice of Land Surveying for many years. ~~There are no new rules listed herein.~~

D. It is a duty of this Registration Board and is a basic requirement of Ethical Standards of the Engineers and Land Surveyors, and GS 89-16 provides the means, to make certain that the State and Public receive some degree of protection in the Surveying of their lands. If the Rules set forth in this Manual are faithfully followed, as a direct result the Public will receive fair and equitable land surveys.

E. The Board ~~solicits~~ will consider new information from Clerks of Court and Registers of Deeds together with clients and land owners throughout the State of North Carolina if and when in their opinion a Surveyor has conducted a survey, prepared a map, prepared a description, or submitted a map for recordation which is not in full compliance with this Manual of Practice. When an Engineer or Land Surveyor obligates himself and contracts to survey a piece of land property in North Carolina by virtue of his registration and the license granted him by this State he accepts the responsibility of making certain that the survey is accurate at least within the limits prescribed herein in the absence of a contract which stipulates otherwise.

F. In a Class A survey and in many Class B surveys, as well as industrial and commercial surveys, it is imperative that the Land Surveyor employ the best possible equipment. This will include a properly adjusted transit and an alloy steel tape of low coefficient of expansion and graduated to 1/100 of a foot.

G. In surveys where the highest order of accuracy is required and the

land slope is excessive distance along the ground and the slope angle shall be measured and the horizontal distance computed.

H. In highest order surveys a spring balance shall be used in all taping. In highest order surveys the transit shall not be permitted to stand in the sun, but shall be protected with some type of covering.

I. In Appendix (D, E, and F) are included typical Maps covering three aspects of Land Surveying and which represent acceptable practice under the rules set forth in this Manual. These Maps can be used as yardsticks by Engineers or Land Surveyors in the preparation of their maps. They may be used by Registers of Deeds and Clerks of Court in evaluating maps submitted to them for recordation. They may be used by property owners throughout the State in determining the level and quality of workmanship to which they are entitled in a Land Survey and under the terms of their agreement with their Surveyor. These maps are necessarily reduced photographically in order to make them available at this time as part of the Manual. An Engineer or Land Surveyor who has never conducted a higher order Land Survey, but who has surveyed many Rural properties, should study these maps carefully in the interest of complying with the Manual and the Law. In addition this study will assist him in preparing himself to conduct surveys of higher order and which his registration under the laws of North Carolina entitle him to execute.

J. A client and the public are entitled to and should have the opportunity of negotiating for a degree of accuracy in a Land Survey which is reasonably commensurate with the value of the land property being surveyed. The accuracy of a boundary survey as defined by GS 47-30 shall be designated on the face of a map in units of one (1) foot per__________feet of perimeter. (For example in a Class "A" survey as 1:10000) computed by latitudes and departures or other equally accurate method.

K. Unless a written agreement has been executed between the property owner or his agent and the Surveyor prior to the land survey and a statement to that effect is included on the face of a Map and designating a tolerance or allowable accuracy of survey desired by the land owner and at variance with those values allowed by the Manual then the values of accuracy and Error of Closure listed in the Manual shall prevail.

L. The proper execution of a survey, the accuracy of land mapping, and all other details of a survey are the direct responsibility of the Registered Engineer or the Registered Land Surveyor whose seal and signature appears on the map. The Clerk of Court and Register of Deeds should and do have the right to make certain that the map in general meets to their satisfaction the requirements of the Mapping Law GS 47-30, as amended by the 1959 General Assembly. However, the fact that a Map is accepted by a Register of Deeds for recordation in no way relieves the Engineer or Land Surveyor whose seal appears upon the drawing of any responsibility.

M. A Map is nominally the possession of the Engineer or Land Surveyor whose Seal appears thereon. It should therefore be professionally and accurately prepared as a permanent record and after reproducible prints or copies have been made for recordation or other purposes it should be carefully preserved along with the Surveyors original field notes, calculations, and work sheets to be produced in evidence if and when required either by the Board or by the Courts.

N. On the Third Thursday in October of each year the Board will schedule and conduct in the State Capitol in Raleigh a hearing for the purpose of gathering information and suggestions from Engineers, Land Surveyors, and other interested parties and preparatory to reviewing, rewriting, or revising this Manual. Suggestions in writing will be received by the Board up to three weeks prior to the hearing.

II—NOMENCLATURE

In preparing maps and in land surveying work in general it is necessary at times to employ abbreviations and symbols. Unless necessary because of space or other limitation abbreviations and symbols are not to be used. However when necessary the following abbreviations and symbols are acceptable and shall be employed in Land Surveying work in North Carolina.

Ac	Acres	Mk	Marker
Ang	Angle	N	North
Ave	Avenue	NCCS	N. C. Control System Mon
Az	Azimuth	P	Perimeter
BM	Bench Mark	PC	Point of Curve
CC	Calculated Course	POC	Point on Curve
CF	Curb Face	POT	Point on Tangent
₵	Center Line	PRC	Point of Reverse Curve
Cos	Cosine	PT	Point of Tangency
CB	Catch Basin	pt	Point
D	Degree of Curve	Pvt	Pavement
DB	Deed Book	R	Radius
Defl Ang	Deflection Angle	RP	Reference Point
Dep	Departure	RR	Railway
DH	Drill Hole	R/W	Right of Way
DMD	Double Meridian Distance	S	South
Δ	Delta Angle	Sin	Sine
E	East	Sq	Square
EC	Error of Closure	St	Street
EIP	Existing Iron Pipe	Sta	Station
El	Elevation	Stk	Stake
L	Length of Curve	T	Tangent of Curve
Lat	Latitude	Tan	Tangent
LC	Long Chord	Tk	Tack
M	Mile	Tr	Tract
MC	Magnetic Course	Tra	Traverse
Mon	Monument	Vert	Vertical
		W	West

III—DEFINITIONS

A. Chapter 89 of the General Statutes of North Carolina defines Land Surveying as: "The surveying of areas for their correct determination and for conveyancing or for the establishment or re-establishment of land boundaries or for the plotting of lands and subdivisions thereof or the determination of elevations and the drawing of descriptions of lands or lines so surveyed." (GS 89-2-(e)).

B. GS 89-16 as rewritten and enacted into law by the 1959 General Assembly instructs the Board in the preparation of this Manual to clarify this definition in such a manner as it will have full technical significance to the Engineer or Land Surveyor in the practice of his profession and in sufficient detail that the public and the property owner can and may make certain that the survey of his lands is reasonably valid and sufficiently accurate to forever safeguard his property.

C. The Board in meeting the requirements of the law and adopting these rules defines Land Surveying in technical terminology as follows. Land Surveying shall comprise the accurate determination and location or relocation of land boundaries, land boundary corners, and objects located on the land. Land Surveying shall comprise the accurate preparation of maps indicating clearly the shapes and areas of tracts of land or tracts of land divided or subdivided and including the accurate and complete locating of existing roads, streets, rights-of-way, and other objects on or adjacent to the land when necessary, all drawn in compliance with the North Carolina Mapping Law (GS 47-30), and the Mapping rules of this Manual. Land Surveying shall comprise the preparation and interpretation of land descriptions for incorporation into deeds, leases, or other documents compiled accurately and detailed with regard to information necessary to locate or relocate land boundaries in terms of deeds or court decisions.

D. Land Surveying does not include Engineering Surveying such as required for the construction of buildings, machinery, railways, highways, airports, utility lines, bridges, and the like although the determination of land boundaries to be used for such engineering projects. the preparation of land maps, and the legal description of the land is Land Surveying. Land Surveying shall include topographical surveying and mapping of lands for the purpose of plotting the accurate location of existing surface and subsurface objects, elevations, and contour lines. The employment of a topographical map for the purpose of locating and designing streets, roads, highways, or for cuts and fills and earth moving or for the location and design of sewer lines, water lines, or other utilities or for similar purposes is Engineering and not Land Surveying. However, the locating and setting of batter boards for housing projects and the like may well be construed to be Land Surveying.

E. GS 89-12 provides that an Engineer is permitted to conduct Land Surveys in North Carolina. A satisfactory land survey requires a great deal of skill, knowledge, and experience. An Engineer is therefore permitted to conduct land surveys **only** within the framework of this Manual.

F. Chapter 89 of the General Statutes of North Carolina provides that Land Surveys in North Carolina shall be conducted by Engineers or Land Surveyors registered and licensed to practice in North Carolina. This Manual is adopted by the Board primarily as a set of rules governing the Surveying of Land. Therefore, when the term "Land Surveyor" or "Surveyor" is employed in this Manual it shall mean either a Registered Engineer or Land Surveyor.

IV—REQUIREMENTS FOR REGISTRATION

A. Under the provisions of GS 89-7 II(b)(1) a citizen who is of good character and over 21 years of age may be registered by the Board to practice Land Surveying as a Registered Land Surveyor in North Carolina on "graduation from a school or college approved by the Board and including the satisfactory completion of a program of study in surveying approved by the Board, a specific record of one or more years of progressive Land Surveying work of a nature and level approved by the Board, and satisfactorily passing such Oral and Written Examination written in the presence of and required by the Board all of which shall determine and indicate that the candidate is competent to practice Land Surveying . . .". The Statute also provides that . . . "if an individual is not a graduate of a school or college but possesses a record of five years or more of Land Surveying work of a nature and level approved by the Board and satisfactorily passes the above Examinations then he too, if found otherwise qualified, may be Registered by the Board to practice Land Surveying in North Carolina."

In either case as part of his application the Board may require an Applicant to, "submit exhibits, drawings, plats, and other tangible evidence of Land Surveying work executed by him and which he personally accomplished or supervised."

B. In evaluating and approving the curriculum or program of study in Surveying of a school or college, approved by the Board, such program of study shall include in addition to basic studies, general studies, and class and field work in land surveying:

1. **Mathematics.** The mathematical program shall include a study of algebra, geometry, trigonometry, and logarithms. In addition to formal disciplines in these studies shall be included ample concomitant studies and drill in the applied mathematics of surveying problems including the closing of surveys, calculation of coordinates, latitudes and departures, and the use of the coordinate systems in the control of surveys.

2. **Science.** The science course shall include a study of heat as it affects metals and other materials used in connection with Land Surveying, a study of the basic fundamentals of electricity and magnetism especially insofar as either would influence surveying equipment and its accuracy, and a study of light and optics in order that an applicant understand and be reasonably familiar with the optical system employed in his transit together with other phenomena involving light and sight as they influence the science of Land Surveying.

3. **Mechanics.** The mechanics program shall include course study in the fundamentals of applied mechanics including those phases of statics and dynamics that might be employed by a Land Surveyor. It will include an intimate study of the mechanisms employed in the transit and their adjustment together with other types of surveying instruments and apparatus which might be used in connection with Land Surveying.

4. **History.** This course of study shall include the history of the principles and the systems of land subdivision used in the United States. Also, it shall include a study of the United States system of public lands surveys.

5. **Drawing.** The drawing course of study shall include instruction and practice or laboratory work in the art of orthographic projection in order that the applicant shall be skilled in the drawing, in accordance with accepted Engineering standards, of neat and legible drawings, maps and plats. The course shall include a study of the fundamentals of descriptive geometry.

6. **Engineering Law.** This course shall include the study of the legal essentials of surveys and resurveys including those involving boundary disputes, defective descriptions, riparian rights, and adverse possession. It shall include also course study involving the legal and judicial functions of a Land Surveyor.

V—CLASSIFICATION OF SURVEYS

A. On the basis of the size and character of the land, boundary surveys for conveyancing, mapping, or describing property shall be classified as follows.

1. **Tracts of Land.** It is usually a parcel of land of some proportion. It may or may not be used for residential or industrial purposes. This usually requires locating old corners and retracing old lines.

2. **Subdivisions.** This is the division of tracts of land into smaller units or individual lots generally for residential purposes. This is usually an original or initial survey. The boundary survey of the entire tract usually requires locating old corners and retracing old lines. However, the design and layout of streets, curbs, gutters, and utilities for a subdivision is Engineering and not Land Surveying.

3. **Individual Lots.** These are usually smaller parcels of land which are generally designed for residential, commercial or industrial purposes. This usually requires locating old corners and retracing old lines.

B. On the basis of the occupancy of the land and the purpose for which the land will be employed all land surveys in North Carolina divide themselves into two general categories. The first category shall be known as Commercial or Industrial Land Surveys and the second category shall be known as General Land Surveys.

1. **Commercial and Industrial Land Surveys (Class AA).** This class of land survey shall apply to any commercial or industrial site or area in North Carolina. It will include sites for Public, State, and Federal buildings. For these surveys the allowable angular error of closure shall not exceed 15 seconds times the square root of the number of angles turned. The linear error of closure shall not exceed one (1) foot per 15000 feet of perimeter of the lot of land—(1:15000).

2. **General Land Surveys.** All other Land Surveys shall be catalogued as General Land Surveys. For the purpose of establishing minimum allowable surveying standards and errors of closure the Board establishes five general classifications of lands in North Carolina from the standpoint of their real value, tax value, or location. On the basis of these classifications the Land Surveyor and his client or the land owner shall at the outset arrive at an equitable agreement concerning the details of the property survey including map and description of the property together with degree of accuracy with which the Land Surveyor will conduct the survey in the field. For lands not specifically covered by the classifications listed in this Manual or for borderline cases the degree of accuracy and error of closure shall be determined and agreed to in writing by the Land Surveyor and his client prior to commencing the survey.

a. **Urban Land Surveys (Class A).** Urban surveys include land properties which lie within town or city limits. These lands are usually the most valuable and justify maximum surveying accuracy. For Class A surveys in North Carolina the allowable angular error of closure shall not exceed 20 seconds times the square root of the number of angles turned. The linear error of closure shall not exceed one (1) foot per 10000 feet of perimeter of the lot of land—(1:10000).

b. **Suburban Land Surveys (Class B).** Suburban surveys include properties surrounding the urban area of a town or city. The lands represented by these surveys is often valuable but more important it is land whose value is by definition rapidly increasing. For Class B surveys in North Carolina the allowable angular error of closure shall not exceed 25 seconds times the square root of the number of angles turned. The linear error of closure shall not exceed one (1) foot per 7500 feet of perimeter of the lot of land—(1:7500).

c. **Rural Land Surveys (Class C).** Rural surveys include properties located in rural areas of North Carolina and generally outside the suburban properties. For Class C surveys in North Carolina the allowable angular error of closure shall not exceed 30 seconds times the square root of the number of angles turned. The linear error of closure shall not exceed one (1) foot per 5000 feet of perimeter of the lot of land—(1:5000).

d. **Farm Land Surveys (Class D).** Farm surveys include properties located throughout the bulk of North Carolina and represents lands which may be cultivated, may provide space for farm houses and buildings, or may be employed as timber lands. For Class D Surveys in North Carolina the angular error of closure shall not exceed 60 seconds times the square root of the number of angles turned. The linear error of closure shall not exceed one (1) foot per 2500 feet of perimeter of the lot of land—(1:2500).

e. **Marginal Land Surveys (Class E).** Each of the previous classifications of land surveys is predicated to some degree upon the value of the land and the purpose for which it is employed. In addition to the thousands of square miles of urban and agricultural lands North Carolina has many square miles of marginal lands whose value at this time is nebulous. For Class E Surveys in North Carolina the allowable angular error of closure shall not exceed 120 seconds times the square root of the number of angles

turned. The linear error of closure shall not exceed one (1) foot per 1000 feet of perimeter of the lot of land—(1:1000).

C. **Error of Linear Closure** shall be computed by latitudes and departures or by equally accurate method.

D. **Survey Agreement.** Prior to any land survey a suitable agreement shall be executed between the property owner or his agent and the Surveyor designating clearly to all parties concerned the type of land being surveyed and the class of survey being called for. If on completing a land survey the angular closure does not fall within the limits for the Class of survey specified then the Surveyor shall return to the field and reconduct such portions of the survey as are necessary until the angular closure is within the prescribed or agreed limits. If the linear error of closure does not fall within the limits for the class of survey specified then the Surveyor shall return to the field and reconduct such portions of the survey as are necessary until the error of closure is within the prescribed or agreed limits.

Appendix A contains typical agreement forms covering land surveying.

VI—MAPS AND MAPPING

A. **A Map** is defined as an accurate graphical representation neatly lettered and properly dimensioned and identified of a property line or boundary on the Earth's surface surveyed and representing a finite piece of land property and including pertinent and important data and information pertaining thereto. Every land survey requires a Map properly and accurately drawn and revealing all of the information developed by and during the survey. The purpose of a Map is manifold. In the first place if it is accurately drawn and includes all details it is a valuable asset or implement of a client and land owner in developing his property, in locating buildings and improvements, in subdividing it, or in transferring or selling it. A function of a Map is to record and preserve officially data discovered or involved in the survey and to reveal configurations and important features of the land property. Certain definite specific rules must be observed in the preparation of a Map including those rules of the Mapping Law GS 47-30 which was enacted into law and became effective January 1, 1960.

B. **The size of a Map** drawing shall be such that all details can be shown clearly.

1. **Land Maps presented to a Register of Deeds.** Maps for recordation shall have an outside marginal size of not more than 21 inches by 30 inches. The exact outside marginal size of a Map which is to be recorded by a Register of Deeds shall be determined by the standards of the County in which the Map is recorded GS 47-30. Certain counties at this time are modifying their rules concerning Map size.

2. **Maps in general.** Maps in general shall be drawn on a sheet no smaller than 11 inches by 17 inches. All Maps shall have a one and one-half inch left margin for binding and a one-half inch border on each of the other sides.

3. **Larger Maps.** If a parcel of land is of such proportions that it cannot be drawn adequately on a 11-inch by 17-inch sheet then it shall be

drawn on a sheet of such larger size as is necessary to indicate clearly all details. If, however, the Map is to be reduced photographically as for recordation then it shall be of suitable proportions such that the linear reduction scale shall be no more than 25 per cent.

4. **Sectionalized.** When Maps of larger properties as large tracts or subdivisions are prepared for recordation the Map is to be sectionalized. Each sectionalized drawing shall be adequately identified with respect to its position in the entire tract, drawn to the same scale, clearly marked with match-lines, and labeled as: (1 of 3), (2 of 3), (3 of 3) . . . . etc. The outside marginal size of each of these drawings shall follow the above rules.

5. **Scale.** In any case the Surveyor shall select a scale and locate his drawing on the sheet so there will be ample space for references, notations, the required title block, and the several certificates required which shall appear on the face of the Map.

C. **Certifications** shall be in accordance with the following rules.

1. **On the Face.** On the face of each Map there shall appear a Certificate acknowledged before an officer authorized to take acknowledgments and executed by the person making the Survey or Map stating the origin and source of all information shown on the Map including Deeds and any recorded data shown thereon. The Certificate shall include a statement of error of closure calculated by latitudes and departures. Any lines on the Map which were not actually surveyed must be clearly indicated on the Map and a statement included in the Certificate revealing the source of information.

2. **The Certificate.** The Certificate shall take the following general form.
I, ________ certify that under my direction and supervision this Map was drawn from (an actual field land survey) or* (deed, description recorded in book____, page ____) or* (book____, page____, etc.) or* (other); that the Error of Closure is calculated by latitudes and departures is 1:______; that the boundaries not surveyed are shown as broken lines plotted from information in book____ page____; that this Map was prepared in accordance with GS 47-30 as amended.
WITNESS my hand and Seal this ____ day of ________ A.D. 19____.

Signature________________
Engineer or Land Surveyor

Registration Number________________

In addition shall appear on the face of the Map submitted for recordation such additional Certificates as are required by the city or town in which the property is located and in which the Map is filed.

D. **Map Tracings** shall be reproducible and drawn on cloth, linen, film, or other and equally suitable material and designed for drafting or drawing purposes. All Maps are to be carefully drawn with India ink or equally permanent and suitable black drawing medium. Erasures shall not be made after the surveyor's seal is affixed to a Map. If a dimension is in error draw a line through it and letter the correct value above or below.

*NOTE: In using this form, insert whichever applies to the particular survey.

E. **The Title Block** or title space of each Map shall contain the property designation, name of owner, location including township, county, and state, the date or dates the survey was conducted, scale of drawing in feet per inch listed in words or figures and a bar-graph, name, address, registration number, and seal of the Surveyor.

F. **Other Information** shall appear on a Map. All Maps shall have neatly, legibly, and accurately located on their face all information concerning the survey. If the Map is to be reduced photographically this shall be taken into consideration in selecting size of lettering and similar details.

1. **North Arrow**—A properly designed North Arrow accurately positioned and designated as (a) magnetic north, (b) true north, or (c) NCCS Grid (see appendix D, E, and F for design of typical North Arrow).

2. **Corners**—A corner is the point of intersection of curved or straight boundary lines. Each corner shall be adequately identified, marked, and labeled.

3. **Property Corner Tie**—At least one corner of the property surveyed shall be designated by course and distance (tie) from a readily discernible reference marker. If a corner is within 2000 feet of a US Coast and Geodetic Station or NC Grid System coordinated monument, then this corner shall be marked with a Monument so designated and shall be accurately tied to this Station or Monument by computed x and y coordinates which shall appear on the Map with a statement identifying this station or Monument and to an accuracy of 1:15000. When such a Monument or Station is not available, the tie shall be made to some pertinent and readily recognizable land mark or identifiable point, physical object, or structure.

4. **Boundary Lines**—Courses and distances of **all** boundary lines and other lines shall be lettered neatly thereupon in feet and hundredths of a foot and degrees, minutes, and seconds.

5. **Adjoining Property and Landmarks**—The names of adjoining property owners or utilities bordering on or crossing the premises, the names of principal adjoining streams, the names and numbers of principal highways, and rights-of-way, easements or other pertinent details shall be indicated, defined, and located on the map if they are visible and cross or form a boundary of the property being surveyed. Control corners, coordinated monuments, and permanent markers or monuments on adjoining property shall be identified and located.

6. **Area**—In preparing a Map if the area of the land is indicated then this area shall be computed by double—meridian—distance or equally accurate means and the method of computation employed by the Surveyor shall be indicated. Designation of area by estimation or copying it from another source is **not** acceptable.

7. **Curves**—Where a boundary includes or is formed by a curved line the actual survey data from the point of curvature of the curve to the point of tangency shall be shown on the face of the Map as standard curve data or as traverse chords around the curve.

8. **Encroachments**—Any and all encroachments on the property being surveyed shall be accurately located and clearly indicated.

9. **Monuments and Markers**—Suitable notation shall be made concerning Monuments and Markers which were found on the property and those which were set by the Surveyor.

G. **Subdivision Maps** shall comply with the above Rules of Mapping.

1. **Streets.** In addition all streets and lots in a Subdivision shall be accurately plotted and labeled.

2. **Dimensions.** Dimension lines shall be used to indicate widths and other dimentions of streets and other data necessary to re-establish them in the field shall be included.

3. **Use of Ditto.** Courses and distances on all lines in a Subdivision shall be shown except when repeated in which case ditto marks may be used.

4. **Adjoining Property.** If an existing Subdivision adjoins the property being surveyed then the name of the subdivision, block number or adjoining lot numbers, and book and page number of recordation shall appear on the Map.

VII—LAND DESCRIPTIONS

A. **Land Description.** A land description is the detailed statement of appropriate information necessary to completely locate, relocate, or define the boundaries of a certain area or tract of land.

1. **Documents.** A Land Description is part of a Land Survey and is used in connection with the preparation of deeds or similar documents.

2. **Complete.** It is the Surveyor's responsibility to make certain that a Description is complete and proper. The fact that some element or object which should be described is not included in the above rule does not justify the Surveyor's omitting it from his Description.

B. **Definitions.** The following definitions and terminology shall be used in land descriptions.

1. **Boundary Line**—Any line bounding an area or dividing separate properties and adequately dimensioned and described. Such lines can be straight, irregular, circular, or spiral.

2. **Beginning**—A well defined readily located and permanent point or monument that is the starting point for a metes and bounds description and also is the final point of such description.

3. **Convey**—The act of transferring title or rights to a property.

4. **Grantor**—A person or party conveying property or rights to a grantee.

5. **Grantee**—A person or party receiving title or rights to a property.

6. **Title**—A written claim or right which constitutes a just and legal cause of exclusive possession.

7. **Metes and Bounds Description**—A description in which the boundary lines starting from a given point are described by listing the direction and distance of the lines forming this boundary and in succession.

8. **Description by Lot Number**—A description which identifies a lot or tract of land by reference to a recorded plat and by Book and Page number together with other pertinent information.

9. **Recorded**—Placed on record in the office of the Register of Deeds for the County in which all or part of the land lies.

10. **Coordinate Description**—A description of lands in which the angle points or other points in the boundary are each referred to grid coordinates on the North Carolina or similar coordinate system.

11. **Grid Coordinates**—Distances measured at right angles to each other in a rectangular system having two base lines at right angles to each other.

C. **Preparing a Description.** In a Land Survey the land description shall be prepared by the Surveyor. The writing of a Deed is the practice of Law and is not the practice of Land Surveying. In certifying a Description the full name and signature of the Surveyor, his registration number and seal, and the date of survey from which the information was procured or the Book and page number of the recorded map or deed if it is used in preparing the description shall appear as part of the document.

D. **Types of Land Descriptions and Their Content.** In describing a lot located in a subdivision by number, the plat or map referred to must be stated along with the name of this subdivision, the Surveyor's name, the date, and the general location of the property. In addition shall be the Book and page number in which the particular lot is recorded.

E. **Metes and Bounds Description.** A Land Description shall include the general location of the tract or lot with sufficient accuracy such that all corners can be located readily and accurately on the ground. The Point of Beginning must be selected such that it can be readily and accurately located from some previously established monument or corner of record and can be readily described. The Description shall include the names of adjoining property owners on all lines and at all points. The Monument or Marker at each corner shall be described. A metes and bounds description shall describe a course around a tract or lot either in a clockwise or counterclockwise direction. The Description shall include the value of error of closure computed by latitudes and departures. All lines adjacent to streets, roads, or other rights-of-way shall be referenced to these and all pertinent distances and curve data shall be listed. All corners falling in roads or other inaccessible locations shall be referenced to nearby and permanent points. Any encroachment such as fences, houses, ponds, cultivated area, etc. and indicated on a map shall be written into the Description. Any adjoining property which encroaches or is encroached upon by the tract Description shall be listed unless this encroachment can be settled by agreement between the owners before writing the Description. All rights-of-way crossing the property shall be described and accurately located with respect to boundaries.

F. **Description by Coordinates.** Chapter 102 of the General Statutes of North Carolina provides that a Surveyor may describe a parcel of land by the coordinate system. In this instance the Description shall include the general location of the tract by county, township, and similar identification. The more exact location is established by the use of the North Carolina State Plane Coordinates. The Description shall include bearings based on grid north, length of each boundary line, and the state plane grid coordinates of each corner and angle point in the boundary line. Other facts and descriptions shall be included as in the metes and bounds descriptions.

VIII—MONUMENTS AND MARKERS

A. **General.** The following are rules to be observed for the design and placing Monuments and Markers,

1. **Agreement.** Every Surveyor in North Carolina who undertakes to survey a parcel of land shall include in his agreement with his client or the property owner provision for installing suitable Monuments and Markers and accurately locating Control Corners

2. **Labeled.** Monuments and Markers so labeled and designated, of adequate design and durability, shall be set in sufficient number, and effectively placed so as not to be easily disturbed. Together with Monuments and Markers already in existence at the site these Monuments and Markers will insure perpetuation of the record and ready re-establishment of any point or line of the survey. Any Monument or Marker set by a Surveyor as a reference point or Control Corner on a property or land line shall be so designated and permanently marked with the date and Registration Number of the Surveyor setting it. Under GS 81-66 it is unlawful to deface a meridian monument.

3. **Inaccessible Point.** Where a corner or important point falls in a right-of-way, in a tree, or in a stream, or on a fence post, boulder, stone, etc., two Monuments or Markers shall be located one on either side of the point in question so that the point may be located accurately on the ground and the map.

B. **Subdivision.** Specific rules are established for subdivisions.

1. **Control Corners.** Whenever any person, firm, or corporation shall divide any parcel of real estate into lots and lay off streets through this real estate development it shall be the duty of the Surveyor to cause two or more Monuments of such development to be designated as "Control Corners" and to place at such control corners Monuments adequately marked as Control Corners and which shall be of such material and affixed to the earth in such manner as to assure a great degree of permanency. (GS 39-32.1). Any lot or lots sold or otherwise transferred and located in a subdivision and described by Metes and Bounds shall be described in a manner to include reference to the location of the lot or lots with respect to the subdivision's Control Corners if such exist. (GS 39-32.4).

2. **Two Monuments.** In surveying subdivisions at least two Monuments designated as Control Corners shall be placed in each block for the control of that block.

3. **Other Points.** Markers shall be set at **all** corners except those located by Monuments. A Marker shall also be set at a point of curve, point of intersection, property line, point of tangency, reference point and tangent unless a Monument has already been placed at these points.

C. **Monument.** A Monument is defined as a column or shaft of stone, concrete, or concrete and metal, employed to designate a fixed point, buried vertically in the earth, designed for maximum permanency, employed by a Surveyor to mark corners, and of a design and composition approved by the State Board of Registration. Basic designs are illustrated in Appendix B.

1. **Plate.** Each Monument shall have imbedded in its top or attached by suitable means a metal plate of noncorrosive material of a design approved by the Board and marked plainly with the point, the Surveyor's Registration Number, the month and year it was installed, and the word "Monument" or "Control Corner."

2. **Setting.** A Monument shall be set at least thirty inches in the ground, at least six inches above the ground exposed, and plainly visible unless impractical because of traffic or similar factors.

3. **Additional Monuments.** At least one Monument shall be located at a corner or in a boundary of every boundary survey. The Surveyor shall employ additional Monuments if and when required.

4. **Large Tracts.** In surveying large tracts or intricate areas additional Monuments above the minimum number and depending on the requirements of the survey shall be installed. As a general rule Monuments shall be so placed in corners and in the perimeter of a parcel of land to be not more than one thousand (1000) feet apart. If a Monument is within two thousand (2000) feet of a station belonging to a US Coast and Geodetic Survey coordinated station or the NC Grid System Coordinated Monument it shall be so coordinated and stated on the Map.

D. **Markers.** In addition to Monuments, at all other survey points in a land survey shall be placed suitable Markers set as nearly permanently as possible and of a design approved by the State Board of Registration and shown in Appendix B.

1. **Plate.** A Marker is defined as a steel or wrought-iron pipe or the equivalent to which is attached permanently a visible metal cap of noncorrosive material of a design approved by the Board and plainly marked with the Surveyor's Registration number, month and year installed, and the word "Marker".

2. **Setting.** Markers shall be set at all corners in a survey except those occupied by Monuments. Markers shall be set at a point of curve, point of intersection, property line, point of tangency, reference point, and tangent unless a Monument has already been set at these points.

3. **Other Points.** Additional Markers shall be placed at other points of importance if and when required.

IX—LEVELING SURVEYS

A. **Leveling.** Surveys involving the control of levels for land areas where a common datum is necessary shall be classified on the basis of accuracy.*

1. **Urban.** Leveling employed for Commercial, Industrial, or Urban Land Surveys shall be executed with a precision or error of closure (Y) not to exceed, in feet:

$$Y = \pm 0.04(M)^{0.5}$$

2. **Other.** Other leveling surveys shall be conducted with a precision or error of closure (Y) not to exceed, in feet:

$$Y = \pm 0.10(M)^{0.5}$$

Where: Y = the discrepancy in vertical measurement in feet
M = the distance from datum reference in miles.

*NOTE: A text covering the detailed procedure for field work in leveling is published by the American Society of Civil Engineers. Manual Number 10 entitled "Technical Procedures for City Surveys"—1957.

B. **Agreement.** In each type of Leveling Survey the Surveyor shall with his client determine and set forth in written agreement prior to the Survey the accuracy with which the Leveling Survey will be conducted and the general procedure to be employed. This information shall appear on the Map.

C. **Precision.** Leveling Surveys and particularly those requiring maximum precision are normally designated as Engineering Surveys.

X—ENGINEERING SURVEYING

A. **Engineer.** A Registered Engineer in North Carolina under the provisions of GS 89-12 may practice Land Surveying. There is no provision, however, whereby a Registered Land Surveyor is permitted to practice Engineering. This is partially justified by the fact that all Engineers are compelled to meet rigid educational requirements and are registered by written examination which examination does include questions and problems in addition to engineering problems; involving the art and science of Land Surveying.

B. **An Engineer shall be qualified.** It is not anticipated that a Registered Engineer will endeavor to practice any aspect of Land Surveying, unless he is adequately qualified through experience and training in addition to his formal education. In any case his work and his practice of Land Surveying is governed by the rules and standards established in the Manuel. A Registered Engineer is compelled by Statute to abide by every detail set forth herein.

C. **Definition.** Engineering Surveying is defined and includes the determination and establishment of roads and street grades; the design of surface drainage and culverts; the design of curbs, gutters, and storm sewers; the design of sanitary sewers; and, control surveys of first order accuracy, geodetic surveys, gravity surveys, photogrametric surveys, cartographic surveys, hydrographic surveys, and aero surveys.

D. It has been ruled by the North Carolina Revenue Department that when an Engineer pays his privilege tax under GS 105-41, Section 109, he is not also liable for an additional privilege tax for his Land Surveying practice. The Revenue Department considers for tax purposes that Land Surveying is a branch or part of Engineering.

XI—MAGNETIC DECLINATION

In tracing old lines, which were originally run with a compass, and preliminary to a Land Survey, it is necessary to know the magnetic declination since the date of the original survey.* Inasmuch as this declination is constantly changing, Tables and Isogonic Charts providing this information shall be used in calculations and may be procured from the Department of Commerce—Coast and Geodetic Survey. (See Reference Books).

*NOTE: Today the compass is not used in new surveys. Unless a land survey can be retraced many years later the survey is of little value. It is therefore necessary that a surveyor possess a good working knowledge of the limitations of and the troubles which arise from attempting to survey properties by the use of the compass. However, many of the old property surveys were conducted with the compass, and today it is often necessary for a surveyor to locate old corners which were set and to resurvey the property according to modern standards. From this it is seen that a surveyor must have a good **knowledge** of compass surveys. Several of the Government publications cover this subject thoroughly. In addition Government publications include valid data on magnetic declination, making the retracing of old lines a much more valid procedure through accurate knowledge of the magnetic compass.

Certain of our Government pamphlets as early as 1890 prohibited the use of a magnetic needle (except for subdividing and meandering and then only in areas which were free from local attractions).

XII—INSTRUMENTS AND APPARATUS

A. **Transit.** Land Surveying in North Carolina shall be conducted in the field with a properly adjusted Transit having a horizontal circle with vernier graduated to one minute or less and as determined by the class of surveying for which it will be used. Transits shall have a telescopic line of sight, a magnifying or erecting power of at least 20 diameters and a verticle circle with vernier graduated to one minute or less. The Transit shall be tested at regular intervals and adjusted to maintain its optimum accuracy.

B. **Tapes.** All tapes shall be of alloy or carbon steel and shall be calibrated or certified as U. S. Bureau of Standards quality with a known coefficient of temperature and tension corrections and graduated in feet and decimal parts of a foot. If a Surveyor employs a spliced tape it is his personal responsibility and he is personally liable for any errors which may enter into his survey as a result thereof.

XIII—REFERENCE BOOKS

An Engineer or Land Surveyor will require texts, handbooks, and publications in his work. Certain of these are literally indispensable and others are necessary for the most accurate calculations required in Class AA and A Surveys. A brief list includes:

TEXTS

Principles and Practice of Land Surveying
Land Surveying Fundamentals
Advanced Land Surveying Fundamentals
Care and Adjustment of Surveying Instruments

HANDBOOKS AND TABLES

Surveying Handbook

Mathematics Handbook of Five Place Natural Trigonometric Functions for Every one (1) Minute from 0° to 90°

Mathematics Handbook of Seven Place Natural Trigonometric Functions for Every ten (10) Seconds from 0° to 90°

GOVERNMENT PUBLICATIONS*

U. S. Coast & Geodetic (Gov't Printing Office) Special Publication No. 166
U. S. Coast & Geodetic (Gov't Printing Office) Special Publication No. 231
U. S. Coast & Geodetic (Gov't Printing Office) Special Publication No. 246
U. S. Coast & Geodetic (Gov't Printing Office) Special Publication No. 272
U. S. Coast & Geodetic (Gov't Printing Office) Special Publication No. 313
U. S. Coast & Geodetic (Gov't Printing Office) Special Publication No. 537
U. S. Coast & Geodetic (Gov't Printing Office) Special Publication No. 663
U. S. Coast & Geodetic (Gov't Printing Office) Special Publication No. 664
U. S. Coast & Geodetic (Gov't Printing Office) Special Publication No. 667
U. S. Coast & Geodetic (Gov't Printing Office) Special Publication No. 718
U. S. Coast & Geodetic (Gov't Printing Office) Special Publication No. 726

*NOTE: These publications may be obtained from the Director, United States Coast and Geodetic Survey, Washington 25, D. C.

There are many Government publications available to the Surveyor and from which he can derive immeasurable benefit in improving his land surveying skill. In addition, certain of these Government pamphlets contain information of long standing, rules which have been tried and tested over a good many years, and techniques which are generally accepted throughout this country. Others of these publications contain information which is not generally available elsewhere. The justification for printing many of these pamphlets stems from the fact that many problems peculiar to land surveying and similar to those which cause difficulty in North Carolina have been encountered, reported, and solved by surveyors throughout the United States for many years.

The restoration of lost corners is an art which is possessed by only a very few of our best surveyors. And yet in many surveys the first step cannot be taken until an "existent corner" is located. An existent corner is defined as one whose position can be identified by verifying the evidence of the monument, or its accessories, by reference to the description contained in the field notes, or where the point can be located by an acceptable supplemental survey record, some physical evidence, or testimony. Even more important in many instances is effort on the part of the surveyor to locate "an obliterated corner." To recover the point of an obliterated corner beyond reasonable doubt requires more than the average insight, knowledge, and skill.

APPENDIX A

TYPICAL SURVEYING AGREEMENT

I, ______________ (Client) of ______________ (Address) do authorize ______________ (Surveyor) to furnish complete surveying services in connection with ______________ (Job) at ______________ (Location) for the following consideration:

A. (Lump-Sum Contract) $________ which will include all necessary work, materials, supervision, and other costs required to complete the Land Survey of the property described herein and in accordance with the Rules of The Manual of Practice of Land Surveying in North Carolina.

OR

B. (Time-Rate Contract) computed at the rate of: $________ per ________ (Unit of Time)

for a ________ man field party. Time to be charged for includes traveling time between ______________ and the Survey Project. All materials including monuments, markers, etc. are to be supplied by the Surveyor on the following negotiated basis:

Subsistance at the rate of ______________

Transportation at the rate of ______________

Drafting, calculations, and other office work shall be paid at the rate of $________ per man-hour. (An established minimum fee shall be so stated in the Agreement if one exists.)

AND

It is agreed this survey shall be conducted as a Class ______ Survey as defined by the Manual of Practice of Land Surveying in North Carolina.

Any omissions or details at variance with the Manual shall be listed:

____

____

______________ Signature Client	______________ Signature Surveyor
______________ Date	______________ Date
______________ Witness	______________ Registration No. Surveyor

APPENDIX B

MONUMENTS AND METAL PLATES

Of a Design and General Nature Approved by the Registration Board

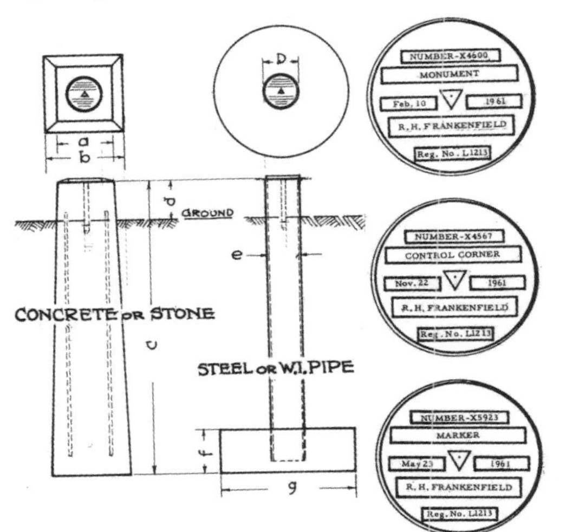

a.	Top dimension	4 in	6 in	8 in
b.	Bottom dimension	6	8	10
c.	Length of Monument or Pipe	36	42	48
c!	Length of Marker	18	24	36
d.	Distance out of ground	4	8	12
e.	Pipe diameter for Monument	1½	2	2½

f. & g. Concrete block or base (if used) to suit requirement of the survey.

D. Diameter of plate to be determined by type of Monument or Marker.

APPENDIX C

Typical Tabulation & Calculation for Area of Closure

CLOSURE AND AREA COMPUTATION SHEET

Property of SMITH & JONES Area 28.00 AC. Date 3-7-59 Job No. B-1728
Location NEAR HIGH POINT, N. C. Closure 1:11,590 Survey By A. W. D. Computation By J. R. MARSHALL

STA.	BEARING	DIST.	COSINE / SINE	LATITUDE N	LATITUDE S	DEPARTURE E	DEPARTURE W	BALANCED LAT.	BALANCED DEP.	D. M. D.	DOUBLE AREA PLUS	DOUBLE AREA MINUS
			.1928074	−1		+6						
	N 78° 53′ E	461.46	.9812366	88.97		452.80		+ 88.96	+ 452.86	517.54	46,040	
			.0482687			+6						
	N 87° 14′ E	496.29	.9988344	23.96		495.71		+ 23.96	+ 495.77	1,466.17	35,129	
			.9937787		+16		−2					
	S 6° 23′ 40″ W	1523.52	.1113726		1514.04		169.68	−1514.20	− 169.66	1,792.28		2,713,870
			.1318239	−1			−10					
	N 82° 25′ 30″ W	796.38	.9912732	104.98			789.43	+ 104.97	− 789.33	833.29	87,470	
			.9987194	−7		+1						
	N 2° 54′ E	762.92	.0505929	761.94		38.60		+ 761.87	+ 38.61	82.57	62,908	
			.1293725				−1					
	N 82° 34′ W	61.11	.9915961	7.91			60.60	+ 7.91	− 60.59	60.59	479	
			.9821872	−2		+1						
	N 10° 49′ 30″ E	242.56	.1878099	238.24		45.56		+ 238.22	+ 45.57	45.57	10,856	
			.9945674	−1								
	N 5° 58′ 30″ E	144.69	.1040945	143.90		15.06		+ 143.89	+ 15.06	106.20	15,281	
			.9813486	−1								
	N 11° 05′ W	147.17	.1922365	144.43			28.29	+ 144.42	− 28.29	92.97	13,427	
	Total Dist.	4636.10		1514.33	1514.04	1047.73	1048.00			Totals	271,590	2,713,870
	Hyp. of Error	0.40			+ 0.29		+ 0.27			Diff.=D. A. Area in S.F.		2,442,280 1,221,140
								Lexington Ave.		Area Between Arc & Tan		− 1,381
										Total S. F. Total Acres		1,219,759 28.002

ERROR OF CLOSURE $= (0.29^2+0.27^2)^{1/2} = (0.1570)^{1/2} = 0.3963$ ft.

Perimeter $= 4636.1$ ft. & Closure $= \frac{4636.1}{0.3963} = 1{:}11{,}590$

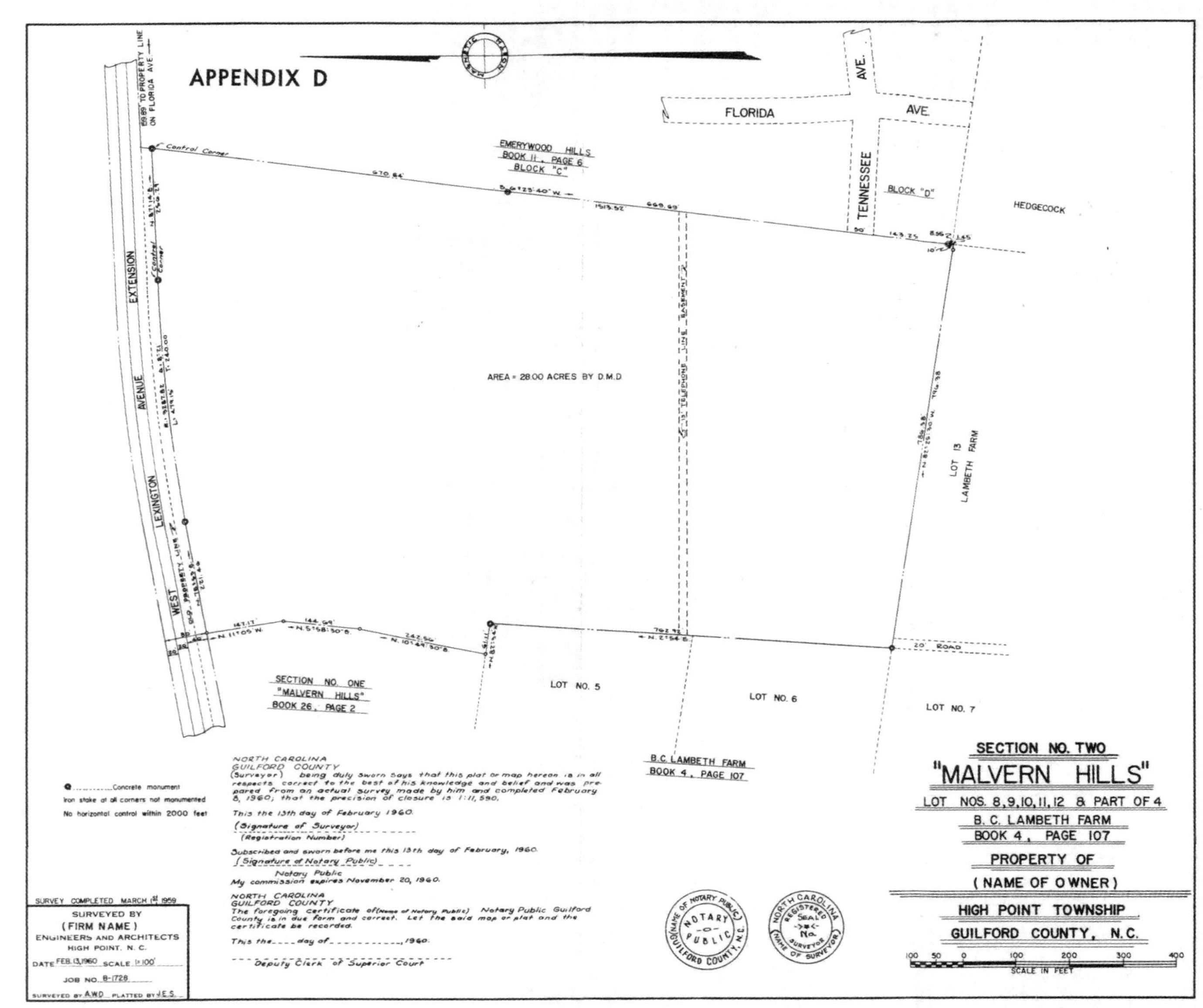

Fold out for Appendix C

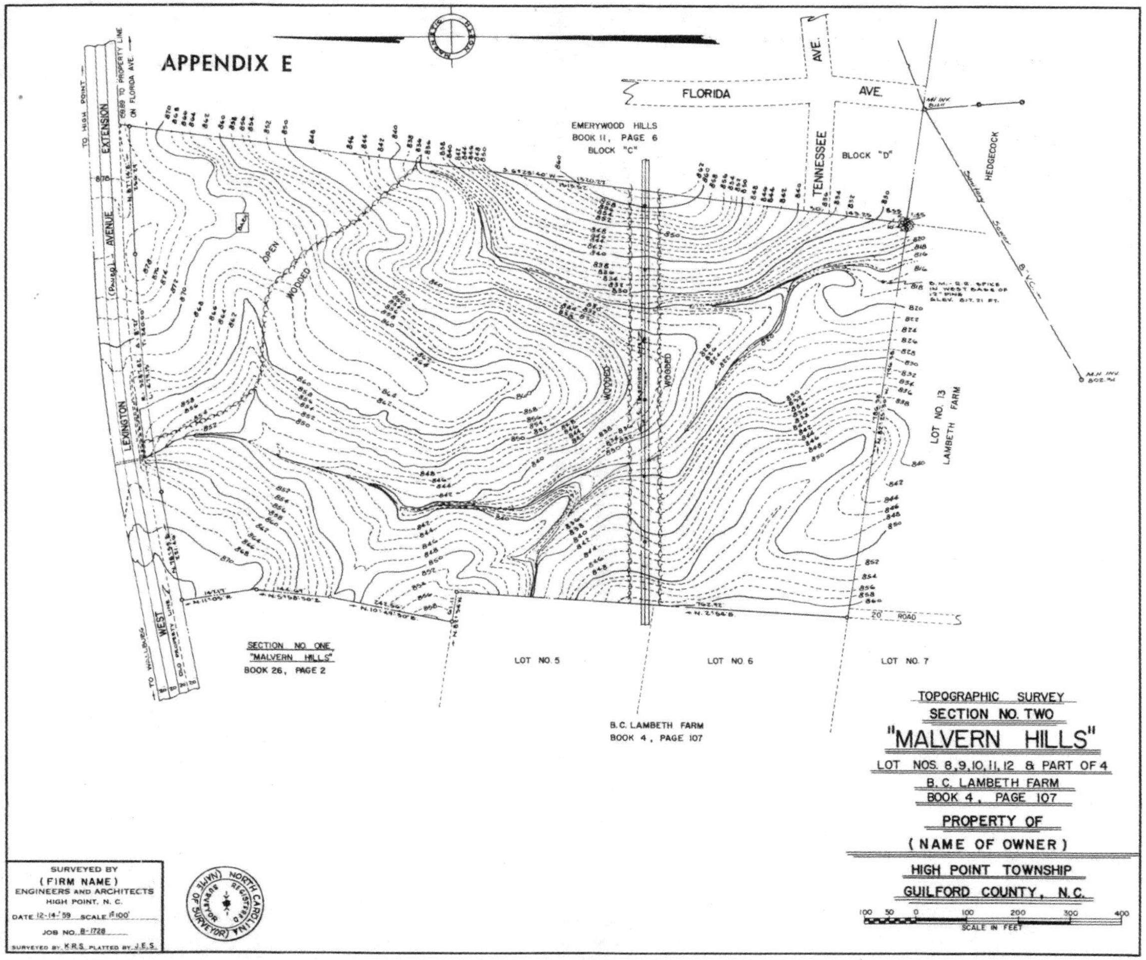
APPENDIX E
FLORIDA
AVE.
AVE.
TENNESSEE
BLOCK "D"
HEDGECOCK
EMERYWOOD HILLS
BOOK 11, PAGE 6
BLOCK "C"
OPEN
WOODED
WOODED
WOODED
LOT NO. 13
LAMBETH FARM
TO HIGH POINT
EXTENSION
(Paved) AVENUE
LEXINGTON
WEST
TO WALLBURG
SECTION NO. ONE
"MALVERN HILLS"
BOOK 26, PAGE 2
LOT NO. 5
LOT NO. 6
LOT NO. 7
20' ROAD
B.C. LAMBETH FARM
BOOK 4, PAGE 107
TOPOGRAPHIC SURVEY
SECTION NO. TWO
"MALVERN HILLS"
LOT NOS. 8,9,10,11,12 & PART OF 4
B.C. LAMBETH FARM
BOOK 4, PAGE 107
PROPERTY OF
(NAME OF OWNER)
HIGH POINT TOWNSHIP
GUILFORD COUNTY, N.C.
SCALE IN FEET
SURVEYED BY
(FIRM NAME)
ENGINEERS AND ARCHITECTS
HIGH POINT, N. C.
DATE 12-14-'59 SCALE 1"=100'
JOB NO. B-1728
SURVEYED BY K.R.S. PLATTED BY J.E.S.
NORTH CAROLINA
REGISTERED SURVEYOR
(NAME OF SURVEYOR)

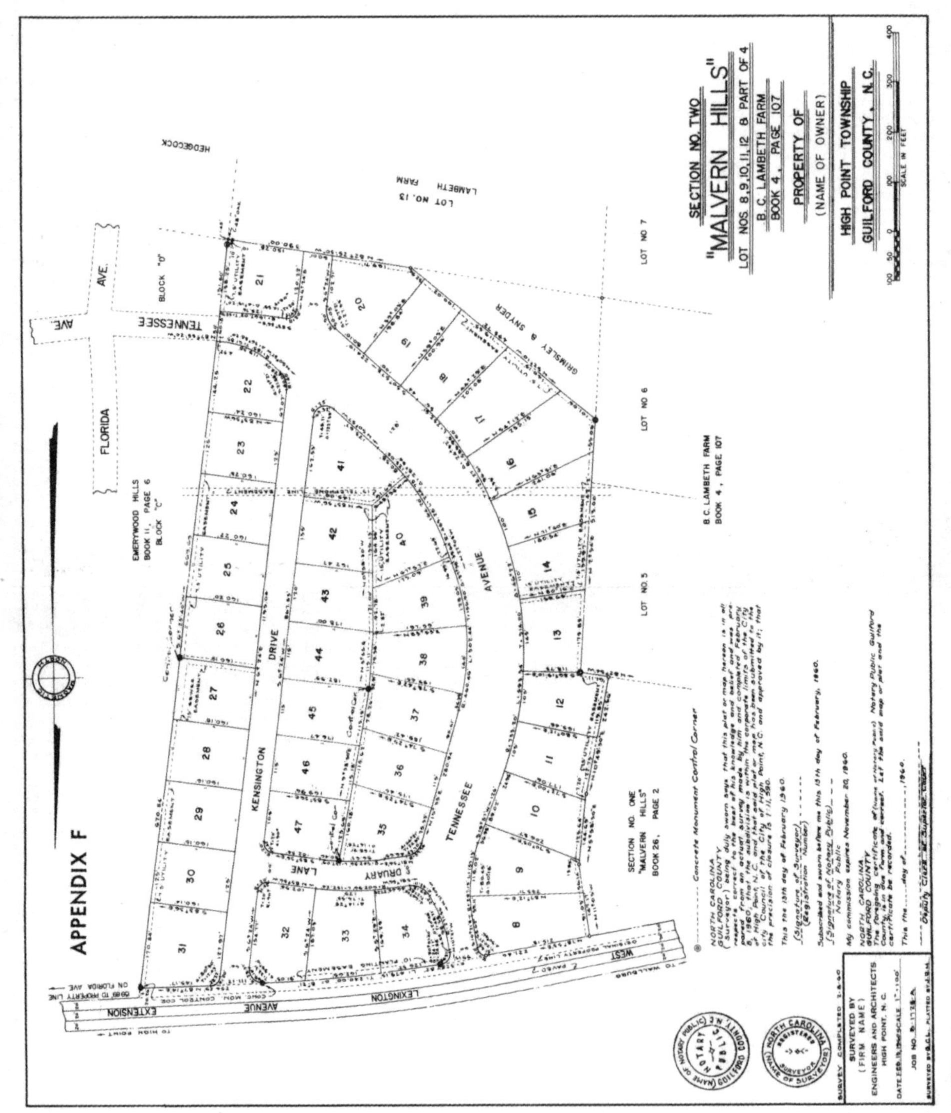

Fold out for Appendix E